FUNDAMENTALS OF
Photographic
Theory

By T. H. JAMES, Ph.D.
GEORGE C. HIGGINS, Ph.D.
Research Laboratories of Eastman Kodak Co.

JOHN WILEY & SONS, INC., NEW YORK
CHAPMAN & HALL, LIMITED, LONDON

Chemistry Lib.

add'l

Preface

THE SCIENCE OF PHOTOGRAPHY can be divided into several separate, though somewhat interdependent, branches, each of which can be assigned to a special field of chemistry or physics. Thus, the preparation of the light-sensitive layer is essentially a colloidal chemical operation. The action of light upon this sensitive layer is a photochemical process involving secondary physical and chemical processes. The method of transforming the light impression into a visible image is chemical in nature. Finally, the problem of evaluating the photographic image in terms of the light which initiated its formation and the light which enables it to be seen is essentially a problem of physics and psychophysics.

The purpose of the present book is to give a general account of the theory of the photographic process, based on the fundamental chemical and physical concepts. A basic knowledge of physics and physical chemistry is presupposed, but a specialist's knowledge in these fields is not required. The historical development of the theory of the photographic process and detailed references to original literature have been avoided for the most part. This procedure, we believe, will permit the general reader to follow the argument with greater economy of space and thought. The reader who desires greater detail on any branch of the subject will find ample material in the general references given at the end of each chapter.

Some omissions require explanation. Only the photographic process which involves the use of silver salts is considered here. This is by far the most important process. The sensitive materials which do not involve the use of silver salts are used only for special purposes, and a satisfactory treatment of the theory involved would require an expenditure of space out of all proportion to their relative importance. No attempt is made to consider the theory of lens design or of camera construction. These are separate subjects. Although they are of considerable importance to the practice of picture making, they do not belong to the science of the photographic process. Finally, the field of color photography is not treated specifically. Much work remains to be done in this field before a satisfactory general theoretical treatment can be given. The omission of an explicit treatment of color photography, however, is less important than it might seem at first glance. Every major color process in use today involves primarily a black-and-white photographic process, and only secondarily a color factor. Latent image formation in color photography is the same as in color-sensitized black-and-white photography, and the primary act of development in both is the reduction of silver halide to silver.

Finally, it is a pleasure to acknowledge the assistance which we have received from our associates. The very existence of the book owes much to the encouragement and advice of Dr. C. E. K. Mees. Others who have read the original manuscript in part or in its entirety and have offered valuable suggestions include: R. Barrows, L. G. S. Brooker, B. H. Carroll, G. T. Eaton, M. L. Huggins, C. E. Ives, E. E. Jelley, L. A. Jones, G. Kornfeld, J. A. Leermakers, L. E. Muehler, C. N. Nelson, F. Perrin, H. D. Russell, J. L. Tupper, R. H. Wagner, J. H. Webb, and H. C. Yutzy.

T. H. J.
G. C. H.

Rochester, N. Y.
November, 1947

Contents

1.

Outline of the Photographic Process. Terminology

The steps normally involved in the making of a photograph are (1) exposure of the sensitive material in a camera or other suitable device, (2) development of the exposed material to give a *negative*, (3) fixing, (4) washing and drying, (5) exposure of a second sensitive material through the negative, and (6) development of this material to give the *positive*, which is then fixed, washed, and dried as before.

The theory of these steps will be considered in some detail in subsequent chapters of this book. It will facilitate the presentation of the theory, however, if these steps are considered briefly at the outset and definitions are given of certain terms commonly used in the literature.

The Light-Sensitive Material (the Emulsion)

The normal sensitive layer consists of a very large number of tiny crystals (*grains*) of silver halide embedded in a layer of gelatin. Figure 1·1 (*a*) shows the appearance under the microscope of some of the grains of a typical photographic material.

The combination of grains and gelatin is often referred to as the *photographic emulsion*, or simply the *emulsion*. It is not a true emulsion, but the terminology is firmly fixed in the photographic literature, and no useful purpose can be served by trying to change it here. In this book, where it is clear that the sensitive photographic layer is being referred to, the simple term emulsion will be used.

The silver halide most commonly employed is the bromide, with or without the addition of small amounts of iodide. Some slow photographic emulsions, however, contain only silver chloride, and some contain a mixture of chloride and bromide.

The emulsion is coated on some suitable support before it is used to "take a picture." If a photographic film is desired, the

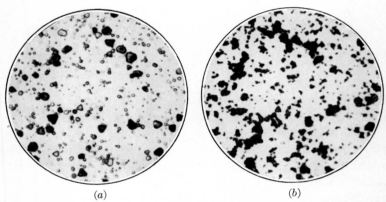

(a)   (b)

FIG. 1·1   Photomicrographs of undeveloped and developed grains. Magnification 1125×.   (a) Undeveloped grains of a typical photographic emulsion. (b) The same grains after exposure and development.   (Loveland.)

support is a sheet of cellulose nitrate or acetate. If photographic paper is wanted, the support is a sheet of suitably sized paper. If photographic plates are desired, the emulsion is coated on glass. Other supports may be used for special purposes.

The Latent Image

Any light that produces a photographic effect must be absorbed by the sensitive material. In ordinary practice the photographic effect is not revealed by any visible change in the appearance of the emulsion, unless the exposure to light has been excessive. The exposed emulsion, however, contains an invisible *latent image* of the light pattern which can be translated readily into a visible silver image by the action of a *developing agent*.

Development

Development is possible because certain agents react with the exposed silver halide in preference to the unexposed, reducing the former to metallic silver in a substantially shorter time. Thus, the developing agent is simply a reducing agent which differentially attacks the exposed grains first. The developing agent is used in a solution containing certain other ingredients which facilitate or mediate the reaction. The complete solution often is referred to simply as the developer.

When the developed image is examined under the microscope it is seen to consist of tiny particles of metallic silver, as shown in Fig. 1·1 (*b*). This figure represents the same portion of the emulsion as that shown in Fig. 1·1 (*a*), except that now the grains have been exposed and developed. For the most part, each silver particle corresponds to the development of a single silver halide grain, although it is apparent that in some places two or more grains are closely aggregated.

Fog

If the development process is continued for a sufficiently long time, all the silver halide, unexposed as well as exposed, will be converted to silver. Even during normal development, some unexposed grains may be reduced, some silver may be deposited rather uniformly over the emulsion, or both may occur. This unselective, and generally undesirable, action constitutes the formation of photographic *fog*, and the silver formed is often referred to as *fog silver*.

Fixing

After development, the unreduced silver halide is dissolved out in a *fixing bath*. The principal ingredient of this solution is a thiosulfate, usually sodium thiosulfate ("hypo") or ammonium thiosulfate.

The Negative and the Positive

Exposure and development of the usual photographic sensitive material yield a photographic *negative*, in which the light and shadow values of the photographed object are reversed. In order to obtain a *positive*, another sensitive material (usually having different characteristics from the first) is exposed through the negative, developed, fixed, washed, and dried as before.

Density

The photographic effectiveness of light is measured by the image which can be developed. The developed image, in turn, can be evaluated in terms of its ability to block the passage of light. The most direct measure is either the *transmittance* or the *opacity*. The former is defined by the ratio I_t/I_o, where I_t is the intensity of the transmitted light and I_o that of the incident light. Thus, the transmittance gives the fraction of the incident light transmitted through the material. Opacity is simply the reciprocal of the transmittance, that is, I_o/I_t.

For most purposes, it is preferable to use the common logarithm of the opacity as a means of evaluating the developed image. The logarithm of the opacity is termed the *optical density*, photographic density, or simply the *density* of the developed image. (For a more complete definition of density, see Chapter 10.) The use of density, which was introduced by the founders of photographic sensitometry, Hurter and Driffield, is dictated partly by the convenience of the logarithmic scale, but also by the relationship which exists under certain conditions between the density and the mass of developed silver per unit area. This relationship can be seen from the following considerations.

If a layer of developed silver particles in a transparent support is placed in front of a light source, it will reduce the intensity of the transmitted light to $1/m$ the value of the incident light. If a second, identical layer of silver particles is placed against the first, the intensity of the transmitted light falls to $(1/m)^2$ because the second layer blocks the passage of the same *fraction* of the light incident upon it as does the first layer. If n layers are used, the intensity falls to $(1/m)^n$.

If a developed photographic emulsion containing n grains of uniform size per unit volume is sliced into n layers in such a way that each layer contains only one grain, in effect n superposed layers will have to be dealt with. A single grain absorbs or prevents the passage of the fraction b of the incident light. The intensity of light transmitted by each layer, then, is given by $1 - b$ of the light incident upon that particular layer, and the intensity transmitted by all n layers is $(1 - b)^n$. Since b is very small, the quantity $(1 - b)^n$ can be replaced to a good approximation by the quantity e^{-nb}. The opacity, therefore, is equal to e^{nb}, and the density is given by

$$D = nb \cdot \log_{10}e = 0.434nb$$

Thus, when the size of the individual silver particles is approximately uniform, the density is approximately equal to the number of such particles per unit volume.

The Characteristic (H & D) Curve

When the intensity and the quality of the light to which the emulsion is exposed are kept constant, the photographic effect (developed density) increases with increasing time of exposure,

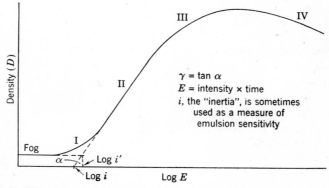

Fig. 1·2   The characteristic curve of the photographic emulsion. I, the toe region; II, the straight portion; III, the shoulder; IV, the region of solarization.

up to a certain limit. Conversely, if the time and quality are kept constant, the photographic effect increases with the intensity of the exposing light, again up to a limit. The relationship between the density and the amount of exposure is commonly represented by the *characteristic curve* which is also known as the H & D curve because it was first employed by Hurter and Driffield. This curve is obtained by plotting the density against the common logarithm of the exposure, where exposure E is determined by the product It of the light intensity I and the time of action t. Figure 1·2 shows the typical form of the characteristic curve.

The characteristic curve may be divided, somewhat arbitrarily, into four regions: a toe (I), a straight portion (II), a shoulder (III), and a region of solarization (IV). The toe portion is sometimes termed the region of underexposure, although the upper part of it can be quite useful for photographic purposes. The straight portion is a region of linear increase of density with log E. This portion is quite extensive in some curves, but may be small or almost non-existent in others. The shoulder is the region of overexposure, where an increase in exposure produces only a relatively slight increase in density. The curve bends away from the straight line and toward the exposure axis, eventually becoming parallel to it. Beyond the shoulder lies the region of solarization, where an increase in exposure actually results in a decrease in developed density.

The density obtained by a standardized development of a given photographic material, however, is not uniquely determined by the value of E; it usually depends to some extent upon the individual values of I and t. If E is obtained by high-intensity light acting for a short time, or by low-intensity light acting for a long time, the result usually will not be the same as that produced by light of moderate intensity acting for an intermediate time, even though the product It is identical in every case. This phenomenon is termed *reciprocity law failure*. Because of it, a characteristic curve obtained by plotting densities corresponding to constant light intensity and varying exposure time will not, in general, coincide with one obtained by plotting densities corresponding to varying light intensity and constant exposure time.

Gamma (γ)

In the region of the straight portion of the characteristic curve where the change in density is proportional to the change in the logarithm of the exposure, the density is given by the relation

$$D = \gamma(\log E - \log i) \qquad (1 \cdot 1)$$

In this equation, log i is the point where the extrapolated straight line cuts the log E axis (see Fig. 1·2) and γ is the proportionality factor, that is, the slope of the straight line. Numerically, the value of γ is equal to the tangent of the angle α.

The value of log i is sometimes taken as a measure of the *sensitivity* of the photographic emulsion. If the fog is appreciable, suitable fog corrections are applied, or the log E value corresponding to a density on the straight line equal to the fog density is used instead of log i itself. This point is represented as log i' in Fig. 1·2. The actual sensitivity values in this system are expressed in terms of $1/i$ (or $1/i'$) or some multiple thereof, and the value of the sensitivity will increase numerically as i diminishes. In Chapter 11 a more elaborate and, for many purposes, more useful method of determining sensitivity will be discussed. Knowledge of the characteristic curve, however, is essential to that method as well as to the simpler one given here.

The characteristic curve depends upon both the nature of the photographic emulsion and the development process. Different

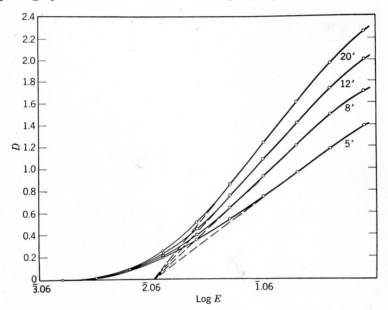

Fig. 1·3 A family of characteristic curves, showing variations with development times.

emulsions may vary greatly in the form and position of their characteristic curves. The time and temperature of development, the composition of the developing solution, and the way in which development is carried out likewise play important parts in determining the shape and position of the curve. Figure 1·3 shows a series of characteristic curves obtained by varying the time of development and keeping all the other factors constant. It will be noted that gamma increases with the time of development. For this reason, gamma is sometimes referred to as the development factor.

2.

The Photographic Emulsion

The two principal ingredients of the photographic emulsion are gelatin and silver halide. Neither has a serious competitor for general use. Materials such as collodion and albumin have been used in place of gelatin (and indeed were its predecessors) but they are far less satisfactory for most purposes. Certain synthetic polymers can be used but are, for the most part, still in the experimental stage. Some materials other than the silver halides are sensitive to light, but none has the wide range of usefulness possessed by the latter.

Gelatin

The medium in which the silver halide particles are embedded must satisfy a number of rather exacting requirements. The medium must keep the silver halide grains well dispersed to eliminate, in so far as possible, clumping of the grains and consequent granularity of the photographic image. It must be relatively stable to insure a reasonable degree of permanence to both the undeveloped and the processed emulsion. It must not impart undesirable photographic characteristics to the emulsion. It must be such that the processing solutions can penetrate it rapidly and without serious detriment to its strength or permanence after the processing operations are completed. Finally, large quantities of it must be available in fairly uniform quality. Gelatin satisfies these requirements quite well. In addition, certain properties of gelatin make it possible to prepare emulsions with it which have a greater sensitivity to light than emulsions prepared with any other dispersing medium.

Gelatin is not a sharply defined chemical individual. Its properties, particularly its photographic properties, depend upon its origin and upon its previous history. Vastly different results can be obtained by the use of gelatins which differ only very slightly in their chemical constitution. Photographic gelatin is generally made from selected clippings of calf hide, ear, and cheek. Pigskin is used for some preparations, and important quantities are made from bone. The raw materials must be carefully selected, and they must be free from bacterial decomposition.

Gelatin belongs to the protein group of natural products. The molecules are made up of amino acid residues, joined end to end to form chains, the joint being made between the acidic group of one amino acid and the basic group of the neighboring one. This kind of joint is known as the *peptide bond,* and the chain is called a polypeptide chain. The gelatin chain is characterized by the repeating grouping

$$-N-\underset{\underset{R}{|}}{\overset{\overset{R'}{|}}{C}}-\underset{\underset{O}{\|}}{\overset{\overset{H}{|}}{C}}-$$

as in the following typical segment which contains three such groupings:

$$-N-\underset{\underset{CH_3}{|}}{\overset{\overset{H}{|}}{C}}----\underset{\underset{O}{\|}}{C}--N-\underset{\underset{H}{|}}{\overset{\overset{H}{|}}{C}}-\underset{\underset{O}{\|}}{\overset{\overset{H}{|}}{C}}--N\overset{CH_2-CH_2-CH_2}{\overset{|}{\rule{0pt}{0pt}}}----\underset{\underset{H}{|}}{C}-\underset{\underset{O}{\|}}{C}-$$

The chain length is large, but not constant even in a specific sample of gelatin. Thus, in one typical gelatin used in the manufacture of photographic emulsions, the average chain length lay in the region of 350 to 500 units, but fractions obtained therefrom appeared to have average chain lengths as low as 250 units and others as high as 800. Chain lengths of over 1000 to 1500 units have been reported for some gelatin preparations. The molecular weights are roughly 100 times the number of units making up the chain.

The gelatin molecules contain both $-NH_2$ and $-COOH$ groups on the ends and side chains. Thus gelatin, just like its constituent amino acids, possesses both acidic and basic properties; that is, it is amphoteric. When it is in solution or surrounded by an aqueous medium containing a high concentration of hydrogen ions, the amino groups add hydrogen ions to form $-NH_3{}^+$ groups, and the molecule as a whole acquires a positive charge. When the hydrogen ion concentration is sufficiently low, the $-COOH$ groups ionize to $-COO^-$, and the molecule as a whole acquires a negative charge. At some particular intermediate hydrogen ion concentration, the gelatin molecules will have no net charge. This concentration defines the *isoelectric point* of the gelatin. The electrical behavior of the gelatin with respect to changes in pH (pH is the common logarithm of the reciprocal of the hydrogen ion concentration, that is, $1/\log_{10} [H^+]$ or simply $-\log_{10} [H^+]$) may be symbolized roughly by the process

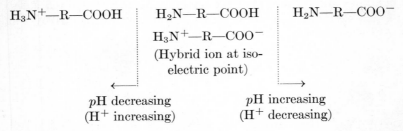

$$H_3N^+ - R - COOH \quad\bigg|\quad H_2N - R - COOH \quad\bigg|\quad H_2N - R - COO^-$$

$$H_3N^+ - R - COO^-$$
(Hybrid ion at iso-
electric point)

$$\longleftarrow$$

pH decreasing pH increasing
(H^+ increasing)   (H^+ decreasing)

Many of the physical properties of gelatin, such as solubility, osmotic pressure, and degree of swelling vary with the pH and have their minimum values at the isoelectric point. The isoelectric points of most gelatins used in photographic work lie in the pH range of 4.7 to 5.2. Some acid-process gelatins, however, have isoelectric points at a pH of 8.0 or above. ~~Basic ?~~

"Dry" gelatin, stored at room temperature and in an atmosphere which is not perfectly dry, contains some water in equilibrium with the air. The greater the relative humidity, the greater is the amount of water. When the gelatin is placed in cold water, it takes up additional water and may swell to several times its original bulk. The amount of liquid taken up depends upon the pH and the salt content of the water. Swelling is a minimum at the isoelectric point in the absence of salt or in the presence of small amounts thereof. Neutral salt depresses the swelling on both sides of the isoelectric point, but may actually produce some increase in swelling at the isoelectric point.

The swollen gelatin is soft, flexible, and easily scratched or torn. If it is placed in a cold solution containing molecules of fairly small size, such as those of the developing agents, the dissolved molecules easily penetrate the swollen gelatin. This is an important property, since the developing agent must penetrate to the silver halide grains before development can occur. At about 40° C or above, the gelatin itself will pass into aqueous solution. However, by suitable hardening, gelatin layers can be obtained which still retain porosity to the developing agent and the salts of the developing bath, but dissolve in water only at considerably higher temperatures.

A sufficiently concentrated solution of gelatin will set into a rigid jelly upon standing at ordinary room temperature or slightly below. Precise figures on the concentration, temperature, and time of setting can be given only for specific gelatins, as the quantities vary somewhat with the origin and history of the gelatin and with the pH and composition of the solution. The strength and rigidity of the jelly depend upon concentration, temperature, and other factors.

By suitable treatment, a gelatin layer can be "hardened" to increase its softening and "melting" temperature and to decrease its tendency to "swell" in the presence of water. Such treatment is of value in the manufacture of photographic emulsions, as the hardening helps to protect the finished product against softening or sticking at high temperatures and humidities. Hardening agents also are usually added to the fixing bath (see Chapter 8) as a safeguard against damage of the wet film during the fixing, washing, and drying operations.

Gelatin layers can be hardened by the action of certain inorganic agents, particularly salts of chromium and aluminum. The mechanism of this type of hardening will be considered in Chapter 8. Certain organic agents, particularly formaldehyde, are also of value.

Formaldehyde reacts with the amino group of an amino acid, tying up that group and permitting direct titration of the carboxyl group. The reaction follows the general pattern

$$R\!-\!NH_2 + HCHO \rightarrow R\!-\!N\!\!=\!\!CH_2 + H_2O$$

and

$$\begin{matrix} R\!-\!NH_2 \\ {} \\ R\!-\!NH_2 \end{matrix} + HCHO \rightarrow \begin{matrix} R\!-\!NH \\ \diagdown \\ \diagup \\ R\!-\!NH \end{matrix}\!\!CH_2 + H_2O$$

A reaction of the second kind may easily lead to considerable hardening in gelatin. One molecule of formaldehyde, by reacting with a free amino group of each of two polypeptide chains, may "weld" these chains together by forming a methylene cross-linkage between them. In successive reactions, a three-dimensional network of polypeptide chains held together by cross-linkages may be built up. Although this may be an oversimplified picture of what actually happens in the hardening of gelatin by formaldehyde, it undoubtedly represents an important aspect of the hardening process.

The Silver Halide

The silver halide is the light-sensitive material of the photographic emulsion. It is present in the form of fine crystals (grains), and it usually makes up 30 to 40 per cent of the total weight of the emulsion. In emulsions of low sensitivity, such as those used in making photographic papers, the silver salt may be the chloride, a solid solution of chloride and bromide, or practically pure bromide. The sensitivity generally increases in the order given. Chlorobromide and pure bromide emulsions are used also in making very slow plates, such as lantern slides. The silver halide crystals in all emulsions of high sensitivity, as well as in some of the less sensitive ones, are essentially silver bromide containing small amounts (seldom exceeding 5 mole per cent) of iodide. Pure silver iodide emulsions are of no commercial importance and of much less scientific interest than those composed of chloride or bromide.

Silver chloride and bromide crystals are made up of positively charged silver ions and the corresponding negatively charged halide ions, arranged in a symmetrical structure. No one halide ion is the sole property of any one silver ion. Each ion is surrounded in space by six ions of the other kind.

X-ray analysis has shown that silver bromide and silver chloride have cubic structures of the same type as sodium chloride. The structure is illustrated in Fig. 2·1. The distance between an ion and its nearest neighbor is 2.88×10^{-8} cm for silver bromide and 2.77×10^{-8} cm for silver chloride. Pure silver iodide crystallizes in either of two structures, both of which are different from that of silver bromide, but the small amounts of iodide used in making the more sensitive silver bromide emulsions dissolve in the bromide without changing its crystal arrangement. The only observed change is a small increase in the average spacing of the ions.

The observed crystal *faces* of the photographic grains are generally octahedral * even though the lattice structure is cubic. Emulsions containing grains that present cubic faces have been prepared but are not common. The relationship between the octahedral and cubic faces is illustrated in Fig. 2·2. The three sides of the cube show a checkerboard-like array of alternate silver and bromide ions. These make up normal cubic faces.

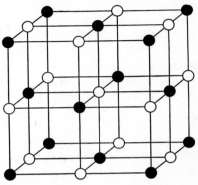

FIG. 2·1. Structure of the silver bromide and silver chloride crystals.

If a corner of the cube is cut off as indicated, a face is obtained which is made up entirely of silver ions. This is an octahedral face (shaded area). Just beneath it and parallel to it lies another octahedral face composed of bromide ions only, then another of silver ions only, and so on. In this direction, the crystal is formed by adding alternate *layers* of silver and bromide ions.

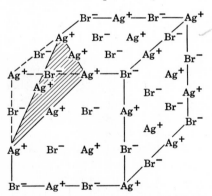

FIG. 2·2   Octahedral and cubic faces of a silver bromide crystal.

During the formation of the crystal, the relative rates of growth normal to the possible faces determine whether the crystal will present octahedral or cubic (or some other) faces. If the crystal grows by adding ion layers much more rapidly to the octahedral faces than to the cubic, the crystal as a

* This terminology originates from the fact that, if the crystal presented only octahedral faces of *equal* area, the outward crystal shape would be that of a regular octahedron. The crystal shapes actually observed in the photographic emulsion can be derived from a regular octahedron by a differential growth or extension of certain faces.

whole will develop *cubic* faces. If the reverse is true, the crystal will develop *octahedral* faces. Under certain conditions, both types of faces may develop. The relative growth is sometimes determined by the presence of impurities in the solution from which the crystal separates. Thus, sodium chloride crystallizing from pure water solution develops cubic faces. On the other hand, sodium chloride crystallizing from a solution containing a small addition of urea develops octahedral faces, probably because the urea, being more strongly adsorbed to the octahedral faces, stabilizes them relative to the cubic and forces the crystal to grow by addition of ions to the cubic faces. In the growth of the photographic grains, gelatin enters as a factor influencing face development. Gelatin, apparently, is more strongly adsorbed to the octahedral face, which it stabilizes in relation to the cubic.

The tiny silver halide crystals, which are the "grains" of the photographic emulsion, may vary considerably in outward appearance. The commonest shapes are flat tablets, either triangular or hexagonal in outline. These tablets are oriented predominantly with their flat planes at angles of less than 45° to the plane of the support on which the emulsion is coated and dried. Thus, evaluation of data obtained for one emulsion coated on glass showed that 90.5 per cent of the grains had inclinations between zero and 45°, whereas only 9.5 per cent had inclinations of greater than 45°. Some emulsions contain long, needle-shaped crystals in addition to the triangular and hexagonal ones; other emulsions contain grains of almost spherical shape, although high magnification usually reveals well-defined crystal faces.

The size of the grains in the photographic emulsion varies through a wide range, from several microns in diameter to below the limits of visibility under the optical microscope. It is not difficult to grow triangular grains which are as large as 20 μ on a side, although the largest grains in practical emulsions seldom exceed about 5 μ. At the opposite extreme, the grains of the Lippmann emulsion are so small that they are not visible through the optical microscope but are revealed only by the electron microscope. Some of them are only 10 to 15 mμ in diameter, and the majority lie between 20 and 40 mμ. Ordinary commercial emulsions cover a fairly wide range of grain sizes between these two extremes.

It is important to consider the grains as individuals in a photographic emulsion because *the grains act as individuals in the photo-*

graphic process. Each grain is a unit for latent image formation; each is a unit for development. In the normal exposure region, the number of developable grains increases with increasing exposure.

Reference to Fig. 1·1 shows that a single emulsion may exhibit a rather wide range of grain sizes. This variation in size is of considerable practical importance, and much study has been accorded it. The variation is usually represented in terms of a size-frequency curve which records data obtained by an actual

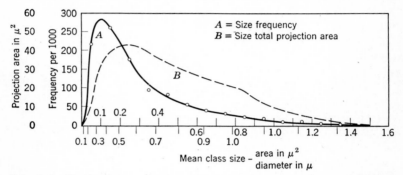

Fig. 2·3 Size-frequency distribution of grains in a typical photographic emulsion.

microscopic examination of the grain population. A sample of the emulsion is coated on a microscope slide and the *projection area* (often termed projective area) of each grain within a suitable area of the slide is determined. (The projection area of the grain gives the effective area which the grain presents as a target to a beam of parallel light impinging upon it.) The grains are then divided into size classes, each of approximately constant projection area, and the number of grains in each class is plotted against the area. Curve *A* of Fig. 2·3 shows a typical result. Some special emulsions have size-frequency curves of the symmetrical Gaussian form, but the badly skewed form shown in the illustration is much more common.

For purposes of correlation with the photographic characteristics of an emulsion, it is more convenient to use the total projection area of all the grains of each size group instead of simply the size distribution. This integral projection area is a measure of the relative importance of each size in contributing to the total area which the silver halide presents to the impinging light. In Fig. 2·3, curve *B* represents the total area as a function of size. The ordinate values used to construct this curve are obtained simply by multiplying each ordinate value of curve *A* by its corresponding abscissa value ($Y = xy$).

If the total projection area of *all the classes* is divided by the total number of grains, a value for the average area, $\bar{a}$, is obtained. This value is given in Table 2·1 for a number of commercial emulsions, together with the total number of grains per cubic centimeter of emulsion.

TABLE 2·1

AVERAGE GRAIN SIZES AND NUMBERS FOR CERTAIN REPRESENTATIVE COMMERCIAL EMULSIONS

	$\bar{a}$ in μ^2	Number
Motion-picture positive	0.31	117.85×10^9
Fine-grain roll film	0.49	52.35
Portrait film	0.61	25.66
High-speed roll film	0.93	22.61
X-ray film	2.30	6.32

The larger grains in a given emulsion absorb more light during a given uniform exposure and are, on the average, more sensitive than the smaller ones; that is, they become developable at a lower exposure. On this basis alone, it may be expected that an emulsion containing a wide range of grain sizes will contain grains of a corresponding range of sensitivities. Such an emulsion should have a much greater range of light response (*latitude*) than an emulsion containing only a small range of grain sizes. This is generally so in practice. Size, however, is by no means the only factor governing sensitivity. There can be no doubt that grains of equal size taken from emulsions of different preparation can vary considerably in inherent sensitivity. Important factors leading to such differences will be considered later in this chapter. It is not even certain that grains of equal size taken from a single preparation have identical inherent sensitivities. Toy[1] found, for example, that geometrically identical grains taken from an ordinary emulsion had a distribution of sensitivity similar to that of the emulsion as a whole, except that the range was narrower. This, however, does not necessarily imply a variation in inherent sensitivity. In Chapter 3 it will be shown that, because of the quantum structure of light, this result may be obtained even though the *inherent* sensitivities of the grains are equal. The measured variation of sensitivity of the grains may be caused simply by a variation in the amount of light absorbed by the individual grains.

Preparation of the Emulsion

A great deal of secrecy surrounds the actual practice of commercial emulsion making. The following discussion, therefore, will be confined to general principles and to some of the methods employed and results obtained in the preparation of relatively simple emulsions.

The preparation of the silver halide emulsion involves a series of steps, generally including all or most of the following:

1. The silver halide is precipitated in a dilute gelatin solution.

2. The precipitate is allowed to *ripen*. During this period, the silver halide grains attain approximately their ultimate size and form. In practice, a certain amount of overlapping between precipitation and ripening is almost inevitable. The extent of the overlapping will depend primarily upon the conditions of precipitation.

3. When ripening has reached the desired stage, enough additional gelatin is introduced into the solution to allow the latter to set to a firm gel upon cooling and standing. This is the gelation stage.

4. The washing operation follows the gelation stage. The set emulsion is shredded into small pieces, which are then washed to free the emulsion from soluble salts.

5. Subsequently, the washed emulsion is melted, fresh gelatin is usually added, and the emulsion is kept for some time at a carefully controlled temperature. This is the important *after-ripening period*. Various ingredients may be added before the after-ripening or just before step 6.

6. The emulsion is finally coated on the support.

The steps in emulsion making may be illustrated by a practical example. Two solutions are prepared which have the composition:

Bromide Solution		Silver Solution	
KBr	165 grams	AgNO$_3$	200 grams
Gelatin	65 grams	Water	2000 ml
Water	1700 ml	Temperature	72° C
Temperature	70° C		

The bromide solution is stirred mechanically while the silver nitrate solution is added through a calibrated nozzle. The emulsion is allowed to ripen for 20 minutes at 70° C; then it is cooled quickly to 45° C. Two hundred fifty grams of gelatin is added, and the whole stirred for 20 minutes at 45° C in order to dissolve this gelatin. The mixture is then allowed to gel by standing overnight in a cold room, after which it is shredded, washed, and then remelted at 42° C. The total weight is then made up to 6.3 kg by the addition of water and 100 grams of gelatin. The emulsion is allowed to after-ripen for 30 minutes at a temperature of 60° C and is then coated on the support. The procedure used throughout is fairly typical of the preparation of one common type of photographic emulsion (the so-called "boiled" emulsion).

The Precipitation Stage

When a solution of silver nitrate is added to a solution of some readily soluble halide, such as potassium bromide, the very slightly soluble silver halide is formed and separates out. The reaction is a simple double decomposition, exemplified by the equation

$$AgNO_3 + KBr \rightarrow AgBr + KNO_3 \qquad (2 \cdot 1)$$

If the initial solutions are sufficiently dilute and one of the reactants is in slight excess, the silver halide can separate out in the colloidal form even though no gelatin is present. Such particles are extremely small and may remain in suspension for a considerable period of time. The particles are electrically charged as a result of having adsorbed some of the excess ion at the particle surface. For example, if the potassium bromide is in excess, the silver bromide surface has adsorbed bromide ions and the particles are negatively charged. This charge is an important factor in keeping the particles suspended in the solution when protective colloids are absent.

In the preparation of photographic emulsions, it is necessary to use relatively concentrated solutions of silver nitrate and either alkali or ammonium halide. A protective colloid must then be used to prevent the silver halide particles from coalescing into a curdy mass. One of the functions, but by no means the sole function, of the gelatin in the preparation of the emulsion is to supply such protection. The gelatin forms an adsorbed layer which serves as a virtual cushion around each particle and prevents or greatly inhibits coalescence. The gelatin, however, does not prevent adsorption of the halide ions.

The method of mixing the component solutions is important. If the silver nitrate solution is simply dumped into a rapidly stirred bromide solution, the resulting mixture at first is highly supersaturated with respect to silver bromide. Almost immediately, a very large number of solid silver bromide nuclei are formed. These grow quickly as more silver bromide crystallizes

TABLE 2·2

RELATION OF GRAIN SIZE AND NUMBER TO TIME OF PRECIPITATION [2]

Time of Precipitation	$\bar{a}$ in μ^2	Number of Grains per Cubic Centimeter	Thickness in Microns
0′ 32″	0.14	3.74×10^9	11.1×10^2
4′ 20″	0.50	0.89	13.1
10′ 10″	0.66	0.37	....
19′ 51″	1.43	0.22	17.8
41′ 23″	2.30	0.10	24.0
63′ 16″	3.45	0.06	27.3
95′ 12″	5.44	0.04	28.4

out upon them, and the process goes forward until the separation of the solid is complete. If, at the other extreme, the silver nitrate solution is added very slowly, silver bromide nuclei are formed by the first few drops to enter the bromide solution, but they are fewer in number. As more silver nitrate is added, most of the silver bromide formed from it crystallizes out on the nuclei already present, rather than forming new nuclei. The net result is an emulsion containing a smaller number of grains but of much larger average grain size.

Table 2·2 illustrates the effect of time of precipitation upon the average area $\bar{a}$ and thickness of the grains and upon the number of grains per unit volume of a relatively simple emulsion. This emulsion was prepared according to the procedure and formula given previously, and the time of precipitation was varied by changing the size of the nozzle. A plot of the time of precipitation against the average grain size gives a reasonably straight line. The rate of stirring during precipitation may be of importance also, but data on this point are not available.

It will be noted (page 18) that only a portion of the total gelatin of the finished emulsion is present during the mixing operation. In general, the presence of larger quantities of gelatin during the precipitation results in smaller grain size. In the preparation of some emulsions of very fine grain, gelatin is added to both the silver and the halide solutions before mixing. Figure 2·4 illustrates the dependence of grain size upon the amount of gelatin

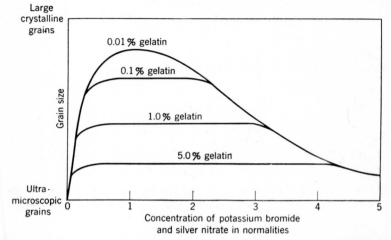

FIG. 2·4   Curves illustrating the dependence of grain size upon the concentrations of gelatin and silver nitrate and potassium bromide present during the precipitation. (Trivelli and Sheppard.)

present during precipitation. It will be noted that the results also depend upon the concentrations of the silver nitrate and the potassium bromide.

All high-speed emulsions contain some iodide. This is present, usually as potassium iodide, during the precipitation stage. The amount of iodide generally does not exceed 5 mole per cent of the total halide, but this small quantity produces a marked increase in the emulsion speed. The relation of speed to iodide content is not simple, in so far as the available data reveal, but the speed passes through a maximum at a concentration of less than 5 per cent, and further increases in iodide content lead to a loss of speed.

The iodide in a finished emulsion is distributed throughout nearly all the grains. Sheppard and Trivelli, in an extensive investigation, failed to find pure silver iodide crystals in an iodobromide emulsion. Renwick, Sease, and Baldsiefen prepared emulsions in which the iodide was added in the form of coarse silver iodide particles; they obtained results which were practically identical with those obtained by adding the same amount of iodide in the form of the soluble potassium salt. However, Renwick and Sease made the observation that the larger grains of an emulsion which they examined contained a higher percentage of iodide than the smaller grains. The distribution ranged from 4.3 to 1.8 per cent, the average for the entire emulsion being 3.2 per cent.

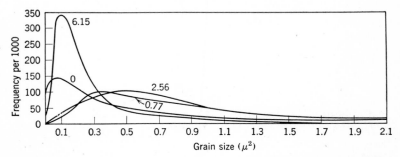

FIG. 2·5 Influence of iodide upon the size-frequency distribution of the grains in a simple photographic emulsion. The figures on the curves give the iodide content in mole per cent. (Trivelli and Smith.)

Iodide exerts some influence on the formation of the grains, as the size-frequency curves in Fig. 2·5 show. The emulsions were prepared according to the formula and procedure given on page 17, except that varying amounts of potassium iodide were present during the precipitation. The emulsions of the series contained (1) no iodide, (2) 0.77 mole per cent, (3) 2.56 per cent, and (4) 6.15 per cent. These amounts of iodide produced a change in the outward form of the crystals. The pure silver bromide grains had the form of flat tablets. With increasing iodide concentration, the average thickness became greater, and the average projection area became smaller. The changes, however, did not show simple relations to the iodide concentrations.

The Ripening Stage

In the second or ripening stage of emulsion making, the grains attain approximately their final size and form. After the initial precipitation is complete, an increase in the size of some crystals can take place only at the expense of other crystals, which then tend to disappear. This phenomenon is well known to the analytical chemist. Precipitates of calcium oxalate and barium sulfate, for example, are commonly allowed to ripen before they are filtered.

The increase in particle size can take place in two principal ways. One is a coalescence of two or more individuals, which clump together and may undergo local recrystallization to form a more or less well-unified single crystal. The second way involves the so-called Ostwald ripening; it appears to be much the more important for the preparation of the photographic emulsion.

In Ostwald ripening, the larger grains grow at the expense of the smaller ones because of a difference in solubility. The basis for this difference is found in energy considerations. If a large crystal is reduced to a powder, energy will be spent in tearing apart the original structure. This energy is stored at the broken surface where the ions are only partly surrounded by compensating partners. The small particles will have a greater surface energy per unit mass than the larger ones. Suppose, now, that the powdered substance is placed in contact with a liquid which can dissolve it, even though slightly, and the liquid is in contact with large crystals of the substance. The small particles will dissolve and deposit out on the large particles because the process involves a decrease in the surface energy.

The rate of ripening is determined by several factors. The rate of solution of the small particles will depend upon the amount of available surface. The smaller the particles are originally, the greater will be the rate of ripening because the greater will be the exposed surface. As the grains grow larger and fewer, the rate of subsequent ripening becomes smaller. Gelatin, being strongly adsorbed to the silver bromide surface, decreases the rate of solution and consequently the rate of Ostwald ripening. Relatively small amounts of other materials which are strongly adsorbed to the grain, such as certain dyes, also greatly decrease the ripening rate. Normally, however, dyes are not present in the emulsion at this stage of its preparation. Mild silver halide solvents, when present, increase the ripening rate. In the preparation of the so-called boiled emulsion (page 18) the large excess of bromide acts as a mild solvent and accelerates ripening.

The idea that excess bromide ions can increase the solubility of silver bromide may seem a violation of the solubility product principle, but it is not. The concentration of silver ions in solution actually does decrease with increasing bromide ion concentration, as required by the solubility product principle. The total solubility of the silver bromide, however, shows a more complicated behavior. At very low bromide ion concentrations, the total solubility of silver bromide decreases with increasing bromide ion concentration, but a minimum solubility is reached at about 0.0002 M Br^-. The solubility increases at higher bromide ion concentrations, becomes equal to that in pure water when the bromide ion concentration reaches about 0.05 M at 25° C, and continues to increase with further increases in bromide ion concentration. The basis for this behavior lies in the formation of soluble complex ions, such as $AgBr_2^-$ and $AgBr_3^=$. At low bromide concentrations, the complexes are not formed to a significant degree, and the solubility decreases because of the solubility product effect. At higher concentrations, the formation of complex ions becomes sufficient to offset the effect of depressing the silver ion concentration. In practical emulsion making, the usual excess of bromide generally lies well within the range where the complexes become important in accelerating the ripening process.

Increased solubility can also be obtained by adding ammonia, either during the precipitation of the silver halide or afterwards. The following formula, which gives an emulsion of motion picture negative quality, illustrates the "ammonia" type.

Bromide Solution		Silver Solution	
KBr	200 grams	AgNO₃	250 grams
KI	5 grams	Water	750 ml
Gelatin	125 grams		
Water	1750 ml		

Prior to the precipitation of the silver halide, ammonia is added to the silver nitrate until the precipitate first formed (silver oxide) just redissolves. This requires more than 2 moles of ammonia for each mole of silver nitrate, and the precipitate dissolves by way of formation of the soluble complex $Ag(NH_3)_2^+$. The resulting ammoniacal silver solution is added to the bromide solution at 50° C. The emulsion is maintained at approximately this temperature for 30 minutes. Then 250 grams of gelatin in 1250 ml water at 50° C is added. The emulsion is digested for a second period of 15 minutes, and then the container is placed in ice water to allow the emulsion to set. Suitable washing and finishing are carried out as described previously.

From the available data, it appears that excess bromide in all concentrations produces a decrease in the solubility of silver bromide in ammoniacal solution. The solubility in the presence of ammonia is still greater than in its absence, however, and the ammonia causes a net acceleration of the ripening process.

A change not connected with an increase in size also may occur during the ripening process. Pure precipitates of silver halide, thrown down in the absence of gelatin, pass through a period of rather rapid "aging" during which the amount of free surface decreases rapidly and the crystals become more and more perfect in structure. This particular process does not involve Ostwald ripening since it bears little relation to the solubility of the salt in the surrounding solution. The decrease in free surface probably is accomplished by a movement of ions along and through an essentially solid surface. It is not known, however, to what extent such a process operates during the ripening of a photographic emulsion.

Washing

At the conclusion of the ripening period, the emulsion contains soluble alkali or ammonium nitrate, excess soluble halide, and, in the ammonia process, excess ammonia. If the emulsion is coated on an impervious support, such as cellulose nitrate or glass, the alkali nitrate will tend to crystallize out when the emulsion is dried and may adversely affect its physical properties. Ammonia remaining in the emulsion will cause excessive fog. A large excess of soluble halide will decrease considerably the sensitivity of the finished emulsion. In practice, therefore, emulsions which are to be coated on impervious supports are generally washed to completely remove ammonia (if present) and to eliminate or greatly reduce nitrates and soluble halides. The emulsions coated on paper supports, however, are often coated without washing, since they usually do not contain ammonia, and the salts present penetrate the paper and do not crystallize out on the emulsion surface.

In preparation for the washing operation, the gelled emulsion is shredded into noodles. These noodles are washed for several hours in a suitable apparatus. The progress of washing can be followed by analytical tests, and the washing itself is usually carried to an empirically determined end point. It is possible to wash an emulsion until the silver ion is actually in excess of the bromide, because silver ion combines with gelatin to form what is loosely termed silver gelatinate. At the equivalence point of pure silver bromide, where the silver ion concentration is approximately 10^{-6}, 1 gram of gelatin is in equilibrium with approximately 1 mg of silver ion in a neutral solution. A gelatin-silver bromide emulsion of average composition can be washed until about 0.4 per cent of the total silver is in combination with gelatin instead of with bromide.

In practice, washing usually is continued only until the excess bromide has been reduced to about the amount desired for the after-ripening and finishing. If washing is carried beyond this point for special reasons, more bromide is added at the conclusion of the washing. The halide should be in some excess in the finished emulsion.

After-Ripening (Finishing)

The emulsion is melted for the after-ripening process, and the final addition of gelatin is made as required. At times, special gelatin rich in sensitizing material (see subsequent discussion) is added at this point. During the after-ripening, which may last an hour or more, the temperature is maintained at a constant value, around 50° C or slightly above. Little or no change occurs in the size of the grains or in their general form. The important change is in sensitivity. The after-ripening is essentially a process of formation of *sensitivity centers.*

It was recognized early that emulsions which absorb approximately the same amount of light may differ widely in their photographic sensitivity. Moreover, batches of gelatin which were very similar in their usual physical and chemical properties sometimes would differ enormously in their photographic properties, as measured by the sensitivity of emulsions prepared from them. Much of the early mystery surrounding this matter was removed by one of the classic investigations in photographic theory.

Sheppard and his collaborators [3] showed that the sensitivity of an emulsion was dependent upon the presence in the gelatin of traces of certain sulfur-bearing compounds related to mustard oil. These substances, of which allyl thiocarbamide is an example, are termed *chemical sensitizers*, and they contain the grouping

$$S{=}C\Big\langle{\,}^{NH-}_{N=}$$

One part in a million can produce a detectable change in speed, and probably not more than 1 part in 50,000 is responsible for the sensitivity of the fastest emulsions. As the amount of sensitizer increases, the emulsion fog increases, and the light sensitivity may even pass through a maximum. These factors limit the ultimate speed attainable by after-ripening.

Chemical sensitizing is obtained only under conditions which bring about a reaction to form silver sulfide. The reaction itself may be the following for allyl thiocarbamide:

$$S{=}C\Big\langle{\,}^{NH_2}_{NHC_3H_5} + 2Ag^+ \rightarrow Ag_2S + 2H^+ + N{\equiv}C{-}NHC_3H_5$$

The preliminary stage apparently is an adsorption of the sensitizer by the silver bromide surface. This process is greatly impeded by the presence of excess bromide; therefore, other things being equal, adsorption takes place to a much greater extent after washing than before.

There is evidence that the reaction of the silver bromide and the adsorbed sensitizer is autocatalytic in nature. The reaction starts at certain points on the grain surface, and the silver sulfide that is initially formed catalyzes the subsequent reaction. Thus, nuclei of silver sulfide form around the sites where the reaction started. These nuclei constitute the sensitivity centers, or at least are an important component of those centers. If the after-ripening is continued for too long a time, the nuclei become too large, and the grains become spontaneously developable, giving rise to emulsion fog.

The rate of after-ripening depends upon the temperature and the alkalinity. In common with most chemical reactions, the rate of formation of silver sulfide increases with temperature. Because the reaction also is favored by a high pH, ammonia emulsions may undergo considerable sensitizing during the initial ripening period, even though considerable excess bromide is present. For this reason, ammonia emulsions are seldom mixed and ripened above 50° C, whereas temperatures of 70° to 80° C are commonly used in the neutral process. The effect of iodide is especially noticeable during the after-ripening. Neutral emulsions with

4 or 5 mole per cent silver iodide can undergo extraordinary changes in effective speed during this period.

Metallic silver may play some part in the formation of sensitivity centers. Commercial emulsions commonly contain some free silver which is formed during the preparation of the emulsion, probably by reduction of silver ions by gelatin or some impurity contained in the gelatin. However, evidence is lacking that silver alone can produce sensitizing comparable in extent to that produced by silver sulfide.

Final Additions before Coating

The changes in swelling that the gelatin will undergo during development, fixing, and washing result in considerable mechanical stress on the gelatin. The ability of gelatin to resist stress can be increased by the addition of certain hardening agents before the emulsion is coated. Chrome alum, in a proportion of about 1 gram per 100 grams of gelatin, can be used for this purpose, and other hardening agents, formaldehyde for example, are available. Excessive hardening, however, can lead to retarded development and loss in sensitivity.

The excess bromide ion and hydrogen ion concentrations are important to the properties of the finished emulsion. In addition to the irreversible effects on chemical sensitizing, discussed in the preceding section, each has a certain reversible effect upon the sensitivity of the finished product. Increase in excess bromide results in a decrease in sensitivity, other things being equal. The sensitivity of the emulsion may likewise be altered by changing the hydrogen ion concentration, provided that it is changed before the final coating. Thus, Rawling [4] found that the sensitivity of an experimental emulsion was two to five times as great at pH 8.5 as at pH 5.0.

The spectral sensitivity of the photographic emulsion can be greatly extended by the addition of suitable dyes called optical sensitizers (see Chapter 12). When these are added, as in the preparation of orthochromatic and panchromatic materials,† the

† Orthochromatic materials are sensitized in the green; therefore the spectral sensitivity range covers green, blue, and violet, and extends for a short distance into the ultraviolet. Panchromatic materials, on the other hand, are sensitized to all visible colors from 400 to 650 mμ. The spectral sensitivity of silver bromide emulsions which have not been optically sensitized is negligible at wave lengths greater than about 490 mμ.

addition is usually made toward the end of the emulsion-manufacturing process. The amount of dye used is extremely small. The dye must be adsorbed to the silver bromide surface before it can sensitize, and the maximum effect is usually reached before the entire surface of the grains has been covered.

The list of known sensitizing dyes is large, and the sensitization can be adjusted to suit the particular requirements within a rather wide range. In addition to the familiar orthochromatic and panchromatic materials, some commercial emulsions are specially sensitized in a particular region, according to the use to which they are put. It is possible, for example, to sensitize emulsions far into the infrared—to about 1300 mμ.

Other special additions, such as of preservatives and antifoggants, are frequently made just before coating. The patent literature on this subject is quite large, but the additions actually made to commercial emulsions usually are not specifically designated.

Coating

The finished emulsion is coated upon some suitable supporting material. The support in ordinary photographic film is a cellulose nitrate or acetate plastic. Glass is the support for photographic plates and paper for the photographic papers. Other materials, such as wood and metal, can be coated with the emulsion for special purposes.

The composition of the finished photographic material varies considerably according to the purpose for which it is intended. Definite figures on silver halide content, gelatin, emulsion thickness, and so on can be given only for specific emulsions. Typical emulsions for negative film contain about 60 parts by weight of dry gelatin to 40 parts of silver halide. The coating thickness is about 0.02 mm, with approximately 1.5 mg of silver halide per square centimeter. The finished film contains some moisture (about 10 per cent of the total weight of gelatin), excess halide, and small amounts of various impurities and additions, as discussed previously. Positive emulsions are usually thinner and contain a somewhat smaller percentage of silver halide.

Notes on Some Special Emulsions

X-ray emulsions are essentially silver bromide emulsions. Numerous possible substitutes, such as silver tungstate, have been tested in the hope of obtaining more complete absorption of the x-rays, but silver bromide has proved superior. In order to obtain as effective absorption as possible, these emulsions are coated considerably thicker than normal, and coatings are frequently made on both sides of the supporting film.

High-contrast emulsions are obtained by rapid mixing of the component silver and bromide solutions, followed by a minimum of ripening. An example of such an emulsion, which brings out one extreme in emulsifying conditions, is patterned after a formula originally published by Eder. The silver nitrate is merely wetted with water, then dissolved in ammonia. This very concentrated solution is literally "flopped" into the bromide solution. An instantaneous precipitation of tiny grains of relatively uniform size results. The bulk gelatin is added immediately, no ripening time being allowed. In general, rapid mixing, low excess bromide or other silver halide solvent, and a very short ripening time (or none at all) are used in the preparation of the high-contrast emulsions. Gelatin may also be used in both the silver and the bromide solutions.

The emulsions used in coating photographic papers are of the slow, relatively fine-grain type. They may contain silver chloride alone, a solid solution of chloride and bromide, or almost pure silver bromide. In general, speed increases in the order given. The details of preparation of these emulsions are largely matters of practical consideration and will not be entered into here. The same theoretical considerations apply to these emulsions as to the higher speed negative materials.

The so-called print-out emulsions represent a rather different type. The sensitive material in these emulsions is silver chloride or some organic silver salt, such as the citrate, tartrate, or oxalate, or more commonly a mixture of silver chloride and some organic salt. Unlike the normal emulsions, the silver ion in print-out emulsions is usually in excess. These emulsions are not developed, the image silver being formed directly by exposure to intense light.

REFERENCES

General

Mees, *The Theory of the Photographic Process*, Macmillan, New York, 1942, Chapters 1, 2, 3.

Baker, *Photographic Emulsion Technique*, American Photographic Publ. Co., Boston, 1941.

Carroll, "Preparation of Photographic Emulsions," *J. Chem. Education,* **8,** 2341–2367 (1931).

Specific
1. Toy, *Phot. J.*, **61,** 417 (1921).
2. Trivelli and Smith, *Phot. J.*, **80,** 285 (1940).
3. Sheppard, *Phot. J.*, **65,** 380 (1925).
4. Rawling and Glassett, *Phot. J.*, **66,** 495 (1926).

3.

Formation of the Latent Image

The latent image, strictly speaking, is known only by its activity, not by its substance. It has been detected with certainty only by development. Accordingly, arguments concerning its nature and mechanism of formation must be based, for the present at least, on indirect evidence.

The theory of the latent image can be divided into two essentially separate branches. The first deals with the statistical relation between the developable density and the amount of exposure. This branch is essentially the theory of the origin of the characteristic curve. The second deals with the actual mechanism of latent image formation in the individual silver halide grains.

Origin of the Characteristic Curve

The characteristic curve is obtained by plotting the developed density against the logarithm of the exposure (Chapter 1). The variation in density along the curve is caused primarily by a variation in the *number of grains* developed per unit area. At any particular exposure below that represented by the maximum point on the curve, only a fraction of the total number of grains will develop. This fraction increases with the amount of exposure.

Numerous attempts have been made to formulate quantitatively the relation between exposure and the number of developed grains. Some of these attempts, which have been purely empirical, have little significance and will not be treated here. The more important theoretical formulations are based upon one or the other of two substantially different viewpoints. In the first,[1] it is assumed that the grains of equal projection area in any given emulsion are all of approximately the same inherent sensitivity, or that the grains can be regarded as belonging to a very small number of equal-sensitivity classes, usually not exceeding two or three. · In the second, it is assumed that the individual grains vary widely in sensitivity, and therefore the number of incident quanta required to make a grain developable differs considerably from grain to grain.

If the grains are all of approximately the same inherent sensitivity, the change in number of developable grains with change in exposure can be explained only by the random distribution in the incidence or absorption of light quanta hitting the emulsion. The number of times a grain is hit during a given exposure varies from grain to grain, according to the laws of probability. Conversely, the number of grains hit by a fixed number of quanta (say 1, 2, or 3) is controlled by probability.

Suppose that the grains under consideration are of equal size, that N is the number of grains in a given area, and that the grains are arranged in a single layer, that is, none of the grains is shielding any other from the light. The layer is now exposed uniformly to light. Although the exposure is uniform from the macroscopic viewpoint, the quanta actually strike the emulsion in a random distribution with respect to areas as small as those presented by photographic grains. If the total number of quanta striking the grains is s, the probability that any one grain will be struck by at least one quantum will be $1 - e^{-s/N}$. This is also the *fractional* number of grains struck by at least one quantum. If one quantum is sufficient to make a grain developable, the total number of developable grains will be given by the equation

$$k = N(1 - e^{-s/N}) \qquad (3 \cdot 1)$$

If one quantum is not sufficient but two are, k can be calculated by multiplying the term $e^{-s/N}$ in equation 3·1 by the factor $1 + (s/N)$. If three are required, the exponential term should be multiplied by the factor $\{1 + (s/N) + (1/2!)(s/N)^2\}$, and so on.

Various elaborations of the preceding formulation have been made to allow for the failure of the grains to utilize effectively (for latent image formation) all the quanta striking them, and to take into account the fact that the grains in a normal photographic emulsion lie in multilayers instead of a single layer. The characteristic curve can be represented rather well by such formulations. A significant feature of them is that they invariably make a small number of quanta, usually one to three, sufficient to make a grain developable.

The second method [2] of formulating the relation between the amount of exposure and the number of developable grains assumes that the inherent sensitivities of the individual grains vary widely. The distribution of sensitivities is treated as a statistical problem. With the aid of certain assumptions concerning the probable distribution of sensitivity, Webb has succeeded in "deriving" the characteristic curves of several commercial emulsions on this basis. In his treatment, the number of incident quanta required per grain ranges from a very few for the most sensitive grains to several hundred for the least sensitive ones. The random distribution of quantum hits (or absorption) still must be considered when the number of quanta per grain is small, but may be ignored when it is large. The function giving the distribution of individual sensitivities is determined empirically from the photographic data.

The transfer from number of developed grains per unit area to optical density is sometimes made merely by multiplication by a suitable factor; that is, it is assumed that $D = A(k/N)$, where A is a constant. This procedure must not be followed indiscriminately, however. In some cases, the relation holds to a good approximation over a large section of the characteristic curve; in others the error is considerable even over a much smaller segment. It is doubtful that the relation ever holds over the entire course of the curve. The validity or lack of validity over a more restricted portion depends upon both the nature of the emulsion and the development process. Development can be particularly influential when the process is incomplete. This subject will be treated further in Chapter 7.

Absorption of Light by Silver Halides

The absorption spectra of the silver halides in the absence of gelatin exhibit maxima in the ultraviolet, but long absorption "tails" extend well into the visible region. The absorption of light in the region of the maximum for each halide probably corresponds to absorption by the tightly bound ions in the body of the crystal. The absorption in the tail region, on the other hand, probably is caused by ions which are not held in a perfect crystal array.

The maximum photographic sensitivity does not correspond to the maximum absorption by the gelatin-free silver halide, since other factors enter to limit the sensitivity. One of these is the absorption by the gelatin, which begins in the violet and increases with decreasing wave length until at 200 mμ it is so strong that practically none of the incident radiation reaches the silver halide grains. Other factors, less well understood, also enter.

Photographically, the absorption of light in the tail region is of primary interest. It depends markedly upon the history and preparation of the salt. Furthermore, the absorption is sensitive to any impurities which may be present. Even the addition of small amounts of iodide to silver bromide, for example, increases the absorption of light in the green and green-yellow region of the spectrum. This increase cannot be accounted for simply by the absorption of the iodide ions themselves, but it may be attributed to a change in the binding energies of some of the bromide ions, probably surface ones. Effects such as these are particularly pronounced for the photographic grains because of their relatively large surface areas.

Nature of the Latent Image

A heavy exposure of silver bromide or silver chloride to photographically active light produces free silver and halogen. There is no evidence that any intermediate chemical substance, such as the sub-halide suggested at one time, is formed by the action of the light. The general reaction can be represented by the equations

$$Br^- + h\nu \rightarrow Br + \epsilon \qquad (3 \cdot 2)$$

and

$$Ag^+ + \epsilon \rightarrow Ag \qquad (3 \cdot 3)$$

where $h\nu$ is a quantum of radiation and ϵ is an electron.

Because analytical methods are not sufficiently refined to detect silver or halogen in grains which have been given only a normal photographic exposure, direct identification of the latent image with one of the photolytic products has not been achieved. However, several factors point to silver as the latent image material.

For one thing, the chemical reactions of the latent image and of silver are approximately the same. Thus, the latent image is destroyed by strong oxidizing agents, such as chromic acid, potassium persulfate, and free halogen. These agents readily oxidize silver. The parallel between the destruction of the latent image and the oxidation of free silver is not quite complete quantitatively, but the differences are such as might be expected if the latent image were intimately associated with the silver halide and hence partially protected by the latter.

Furthermore, the silver halide can be dissolved out of an exposed emulsion without destroying the latent image. The latter can still be developed by a special treatment (physical development) which will be discussed in Chapter 5. Silver nuclei, prepared by the condensation of silver vapor on glass, can be developed in the same way.

Again, in the region where exposure is great enough to produce analytically determinable amounts of silver, a direct proportion has been established[3] between the silver liberated at 20° C and the number of quanta absorbed, provided effective methods are used to remove the halogen liberated. When the data are extrapolated to lower exposures, the straight line passes through the origin. From this it may be deduced that silver is formed in the latent image region. To be sure, the argument is based on an extrapolation, but there are no experimental facts that suggest that the extrapolation is not valid. All in all, the experimental evidence strongly supports the belief that the latent image material is essentially silver.

The photolytic formation of silver is accompanied by the formation of free halogen. If the halogen is not removed, it can recombine with the silver in a "dark" reaction. In experiments on the relation between silver formed and light absorbed, such as those just mentioned, recombination is prevented by the use of a halogen acceptor which reacts with the halogen. In the presence of such an acceptor, one silver atom is formed for every quantum of light absorbed; in its absence, the quantum yield falls well below unity.

Latent Image Nuclei and Development Centers

The photolytic silver produced by a heavy exposure appears in the form of discrete particles[4] which are shown quite clearly by electron microscope photographs. Figure 3·1 reproduces an electron micrograph of nuclei formed by the action of ultraviolet light upon a silver bromide grain. Except for the indicated size of the particles, this actual photograph bears a striking resemblance to the theoretical picture of the latent image nuclei which Svedberg, Sheppard, and others had previously constructed from considerations of photographic phenomena.

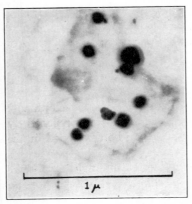

Apart from the electron micrographs, our knowledge of the discrete nature of the latent image is dependent upon development studies. Development of exposed grains starts at discrete points on the grain surface. These *development centers* presumably coincide with the latent image centers which can be reached by the developer.

Fig. 3·1 Electron micrograph of photolytic silver particles formed by action of ultraviolet light on a silver bromide grain. (Hall and Schoen.)

Svedberg counted the development centers on a large number of partially developed grains and found that the centers were distributed in accord with Poisson's law of chance. This law states that the probability $P(n)$ for the occurrence of n centers in a silver bromide grain is

$$P(n) = \frac{\bar{n}^n \cdot e^{-\bar{n}}}{n!} \qquad (3.4)$$

where $\bar{n}$ is the *average number* of centers per grain, taken over all grains.

Concentration Speck Hypothesis

Some connection evidently exists between the silver sulfide nuclei and the latent image nuclei. The great increase in photographic sensitivity produced by the sulfide is well established. However, the sulfide nuclei themselves do not act as the absorbing centers for the light. As evidence, the *spectral* distribution of the photographic sensitivity of the emulsion is not significantly changed when the sulfide nuclei are destroyed by vigorous treatment with chromic acid. The spectral sensitivity is that of the silver bromide, not of the silver sulfide. Moreover, the sulfide nuclei do not affect either the number of quanta absorbed or the number of silver atoms formed per quantum.

From the preceding and other considerations, Sheppard, Trivelli, and Loveland [5] concluded that the function of the silver sulfide nuclei was to bring about a change in the distribution of the silver atoms formed by the light action. Specifically, they suggested that the sulfide nuclei serve as concentration centers for the photolytic silver. The light can be absorbed over the entire area of the grain, or at least over a considerable part of the entire area, but the silver atoms are formed only at discrete points adjacent to the pre-existing nuclei. The grain becomes developable when some particular nucleus has acquired a sufficient number of silver atoms.

The concentration-center rôle of the sensitivity specks has been retained in the more recent hypotheses of latent image formation. The application of quantum mechanics, however, has produced a more specific mechanism for the concentration of silver atoms at the specks. This mechanism is based upon the facts and theory to be discussed in the following sections.

Photoconductivity and Its Relation to Latent Image Formation

The electrical conductivity of silver bromide or silver chloride, as measured by the current carried when a potential is applied across a crystal of the material, is very low when the crystal is kept in the dark. At room temperature it is of the order of 10^{-8} ohm^{-1} cm^{-1} for silver bromide. The conductivity is greatly increased when the crystal is allowed to absorb light in the region of the absorption tail described in an earlier section of this chapter. The increase in conductivity induced by light is termed *photoconductivity*. Under constant illumination, the photocurrent increases at first as the applied potential is increased and then approaches a maximum. The effect, for a relatively pure crystal, is illustrated by curve 1 of Fig. 3·2.

A certain parallel exists between photoconductivity and photographic sensitivity.[6] The long wave length thresholds of the two are the same within the rather wide limits of experimental error. Both increase with decreasing wave length until maxima are reached. The photoconductivity maximum measured in large crystals of a given halide occurs at longer wave lengths than the maximum in photographic sensitivity of the same halide in an emulsion, but the available evidence indicates that the photoconductivity maximum shifts to shorter wave lengths for thinner crystals. The agreement between the photoconductivity of very thin crystals and the photographic sensitivity of single-layer emulsions is satisfactory in so far as indicated by the rather limited experimental data, and measurements [7] of photoconductivity made on actual photographic emulsions confirm the parallel trends of the two phenomena. Accordingly, it may be anticipated that knowledge of the mechanism of photoconductance is directly applicable to the formulation of the mechanism of latent image formation.

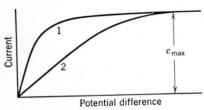

FIG. 3·2 Current-voltage curves for photoconductance in (1) pure silver bromide and in (2) silver bromide containing colloidal silver.

The photocurrent is carried by electrons moving through the crystal, and it is found that the maximum conductance is directly proportional to the light intensity. Thus, an increase in the number of quanta absorbed per unit time produces a corresponding increase in the number of photoelectrons, which carry the current.

The contribution made by each electron to the total current depends not only upon the charge of the electron, which is constant, but also upon the fractional distance which it travels between the electrodes. Above a certain applied potential the electrons are pulled all the way from their point of origin to the positive electrode. At lower potentials some of the electrons apparently are caught in some manner before they reach the electrode, and therefore a smaller current flows through the crystal.

Investigation of the photocurrent below the saturation point has shown that it can vary with the purity of the crystal. Thus, silver halide crystals which contain colloidal particles of silver require higher electric fields for saturation. The effect is illustrated by curve 2 of Fig. 3·2. The conclusion may be drawn that the colloidal silver specks act as traps for the electrons, thereby

cutting down the average distance traveled by each. H
deBoer [8] cites experiments in which a silver chloride crys
nucleated with silver by a strong preliminary exposure to
This crystal showed increased photoconductivity. Further investigation of this result seems desirable.

The results of photoconductivity studies are best interpreted
in terms of the quantum mechanics model of crystal structure.
This treatment brings out clearly the similarity between photoconductance and normal *metallic* conductance. In a metallic
crystal, the electric current is carried by the movement of electrons through the crystal. These electrons occupy an energy
band, termed the *conductance band*,* which is only partially filled
with electrons. If the metal atoms have an uneven number of
valence electrons, these are not enough to fill completely the
uppermost occupied energy band. Such electrons can move with
considerable freedom through the crystal. On the other hand, if
the number of valence electrons is even and hence sufficient to fill
the upper band, a second band overlaps the uppermost filled band,
and electrons from the filled band can move into and through the
second band with considerable freedom.

In a crystal of silver bromide, unlike a metallic crystal, the
conductance band normally is completely empty and is separated
from the highest filled band by a relatively large energy gap. In
this case, an electron cannot acquire from thermal sources alone
the energy required for it to pass into the empty conductance
band. The electron can obtain the energy, however, from the
absorption of a light quantum of suitable wave length. A photoelectron, thus liberated from a bromide ion, can pass through the
crystal with a freedom comparable to that of a conductance electron in a metal crystal.

Very little activation energy is necessary to allow an electron in
the conductance band to move about in the crystal. As proof,
photoconductivity is not materially reduced by a drop in temperature until the temperature reaches about 20° K. It is estimated
that the velocity of the electrons at room temperature is of the
order of 10^7 cm per sec.

The trapping action of colloidal silver, mentioned in connection
with the experiments on photoconductivity, is explained in the
following way. The tiny silver particles in the crystal introduce

* See Appendix and references cited at end of chapter.

regions of localized energy levels corresponding to their own conductance bands. Because the band for silver is below that of the silver halide, an electron passing from the halide to the silver suffers a drop in energy (Fig. 3·3). The electron can be ejected from the silver speck only by an expenditure of energy. In the absence of an adequate source, the electron remains trapped.

Webb [9] applied the preceding theory directly to the problem of latent image formation and proposed the following mechanism. The absorption of a quantum of light by the silver halide grain is followed by the transfer of an electron to the conductance band.

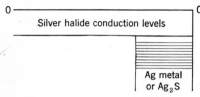

The photoelectron can move freely through the crystal for relatively large distances, so long as it does not enter a region of impurity or fault in the crystal. It becomes trapped, however, when it encounters a sensitivity speck of silver sulfide or silver.

FIG. 3·3 Electron levels in silver halide and silver or silver sulfide (highly schematic).

Thus, an electron can be trapped in an entirely different part of the crystal from that where the quantum of light was absorbed. The latent image, in this hypothesis, is identified with electrons trapped at the sensitivity specks.

A number of photographic effects might be explained in this way. All the virtues claimed for the concentration speck hypothesis might be transferred directly to the new mechanism. However, some notable gaps between fact and theory remain. It might be assumed that the trapped electrons neutralize silver ions adjacent to the sensitivity specks, thus forming latent image silver, but no specific mechanism was given for this process. The dependence of photographic sensitivity upon the temperature of exposure cannot be explained on the basis of photoconductance. For example, the sensitivity at liquid air temperature is only a small fraction of that at 20° C, whereas the photoconductivity shows little change between the two temperatures. Likewise, a great change in the character of the reciprocity law failure occurs as the temperature decreases (Chapter 4), and this change has no parallel in photoconductance phenomena. Moreover, certain other facts, such as the dependence of sensitivity and reciprocity failure upon the concentration of free silver ions, do not find a ready explanation. The removal of some of these difficulties has resulted from an extension of the theory of Gurney and Mott; however, before their contribution to latent image theory is discussed, another diversion to the subject of electrical conductivity is necessary.

Electrical Conductivity of Silver Halides in the Dark

An electric current is conducted through a solid by either the movement of electrons, the movement of ions, or a combination of the two. Examples of the conductance by electrons have

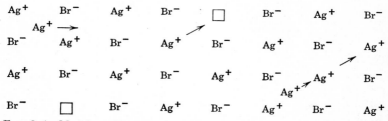

FIG. 3·4   Model to illustrate electrolytic conductivity in silver bromide, according to J. Frenkel. (Webb.)

already been discussed. The conductance in most metal halides, such as potassium and silver bromide, is entirely ionic when these materials are kept in the dark. Under the same conditions, oxides and sulfides of metals may exhibit both electronic and ionic conductance.

The small but real conductivity of silver halide crystals in the dark is possible because certain silver ions within the crystal are relatively mobile. The first satisfactory explanation of how silver ions could move through the crystal was given by Frenkel and later worked out more fully by others. According to the Frenkel mechanism, at any temperature T a certain percentage of silver ions in the crystal are displaced from their regular positions. These ions move into intermediate, or interstitial, positions. The concentration of such interstitial ions depends markedly upon temperature. At room temperature, it is of the order of 10^{-6} for silver bromide and 10^{-8} for silver chloride. The current is conducted, first, by these ions moving to other interstitial positions and, second, by silver ions moving from their normal crystal positions into those left vacant when the interstitial ions were formed. The process is illustrated in Fig. 3·4. The conductivity depends upon both the number of ions and their mobility. The halide ions take no part in the conductivity because the energies of formation and of migration of interstitial halide ions are much greater than the corresponding energies for the silver ions.

The dark conductivity of silver bromide and silver chloride depends markedly upon temperature, as the curves in Fig. 3·5

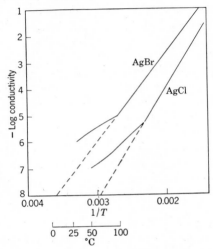

FIG. 3·5 Dependence upon temperature of the dark conductivity (electrolytic) of silver bromide and silver chloride.

show. The conductivity can be represented approximately by the equation

$$\Gamma = Ae^{-E/kT} + A'e^{-E'/kT} \qquad (3\cdot5)$$

where A and A' are constants and E and E' are energy terms. The position of the break in the curve and the conductivity at lower temperatures depend upon the history of the silver halide sample.

The dark conductivity of silver bromide is increased markedly by the addition of small amounts of iodide. The conductivity passes through a maximum at around 3 per cent iodide, where it is about 100 times that of the pure bromide at room temperature. The position of this maximum corresponds reasonably well with the position of the maximum photographic sensitivity, although it is not certain that the connection between the two is as simple as might be implied from the parallel.

The Gurney-Mott Hypothesis

The Gurney-Mott hypothesis [10] divides latent image formation into two parts: (1) a primary, electronic process associated with photoconductance, and (2) a secondary, ionic process involving the migration of interstitial silver ions. The primary process is essentially the same as that postulated in Webb's treatment. The photoelectrons, moving through the crystal with thermal energy, are trapped by the sensitivity specks. The electrostatic potential thus created brings the secondary process into play. Interstitial silver ions are attracted to the negatively charged specks and migrate toward them. At the specks, the ions are neutralized by the electrons, forming silver atoms. Thus, silver nuclei are built up at the sensitivity specks by the alternate process of trapping electrons and neutralizing them with interstitial silver ions.

Experiments at low temperatures offer an excellent means of testing the Gurney-Mott hypothesis. At liquid air temperature, for example, the migration of interstitial ions is negligible. Thus, the ionic process becomes distinctly separated from the electronic, and this separation should be readily evident in the photographic effect. Several tests of this point have been made. The following [11] is an example.

The characteristic curves *A* and *B* shown in the upper left-hand quadrant of Fig. 3·6 represent continuous exposures made at room temperature and at liquid air temperature, respectively. The curves in the other three quadrants represent two series of interrupted exposures, both made at liquid air temperatures. In the *A* series, the emulsion was warmed up to room temperature during the dark periods intervening between exposures and then returned to liquid air temperature. In the *B* series, the emulsion was maintained at the low temperature during the dark periods. A comparison of the several *B* curves shows that no effect is produced by interruption of the exposures made at liquid air temperature, provided that temperature is maintained during the dark periods. The *A* curves, on the other hand, show that the warming-up periods greatly increase the photographic effect. Moreover, the effect is enhanced by an increase in the number of warming-up periods, and as the number increases, the density approaches that obtained by giving the emulsion the same total exposure at 20° C.

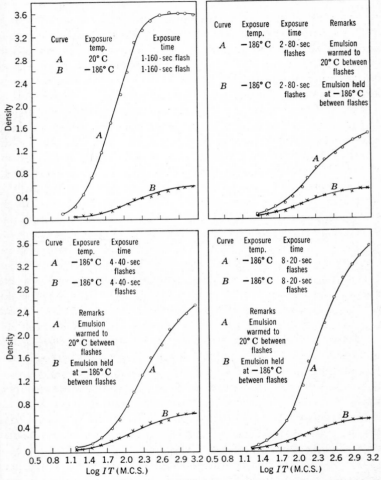

FIG. 3·6 Curves illustrating effect of interrupted exposures at liquid air temperature with warm-up periods between exposures. (Webb.)

According to the Gurney-Mott hypothesis, the electrons should be formed and trapped at liquid air temperatures almost as readily as at room temperature. However, when one electron is trapped but not neutralized at a given speck, the approach of a second is hindered by the electrostatic repulsion. If an interstitial silver ion can move to the speck and neutralize it before a second electron approaches, the latter will be captured. Otherwise, the second electron will probably go elsewhere, either to another trap or to a bromine atom. Thus, the rate at which a speck will collect silver depends upon the frequency with which both electrons and ions approach the speck. At liquid air temperature, the charged specks can be neutralized only at an extremely low rate; hence exposure at this temperature is very inefficient. Intermediate warming-up periods, on the other hand, permit the silver ions to move rapidly and to neutralize the charged specks, which can then trap additional electrons during the next exposure. Thus, the greater the number of warming-up periods, the faster the specks can build up by the addition of silver atoms. The experimental facts are just what would be expected on the basis of the Gurney-Mott picture. The observed initial sensitivity of the emulsion probably results largely from the warming up required before the emulsion can be developed.

Fate of the Halogen

The fate of the halogen liberated by the action of light is not clearly defined in the Gurney-Mott hypothesis, but no real difficulty arises on that account. If the light is absorbed at or very near the grain surface, the halogen atoms have ready access to the gelatin, which acts as a halogen acceptor. If the halogen is formed in the body of the crystal, it still can escape to the surface. The mobility in this case probably is not a matter of mass transport, but rather of electronic replacement. An electron simply jumps to the atom from a neighboring halide ion, and thus the atom and the ion effectively change places in the crystal. This process is repeated along a chain so that the atom eventually reaches the surface, where it is taken up by the gelatin.

Conceivably, the halogen atoms could migrate to a latent image center and cause rehalogenation of silver, or they could capture photoelectrons and revert to halide ions. Either process would mean, effectively, a loss in speed over that which would be obtained if it were prevented. The normal silver chloride or bromide emulsion contains several potential halogen acceptors, that is, substances which can react with halogen and thus prevent it from attacking photolytic silver or capturing photoelectrons. Gelatin and water can both act in this capacity, and may be involved jointly. A suggested [12] reaction for bromine (probably over-simplified) is

$$Br_2 + H_2O \rightleftharpoons HOBr + HBr$$

$$OBr^- + Gelatin \rightleftharpoons Gel.Br + OH^-$$

where Gel.Br symbolizes an as yet unidentified bromination product of gelatin. Chlorine could react in a like manner, and either halogen could react in the atomic state by some other mechanism. Indeed, reaction of the halogen in the atomic state appears to be more probable than reaction in the molecular state, since the halogen atoms emerge from the crystal as individuals. The sensitizing dye, if present, and the silver sulfide of the sensitivity specks are other possible halogen acceptors.

The halogen acceptor or acceptors already present in emulsions of high sensitivity appear to be quite adequate over the normal exposure range (prior to solarization). No increase in sensitivity is obtained by addition of active halogen acceptors as auxiliaries to such emulsions. However, the addition of auxiliary halogen acceptors to some slow, fine-grain emulsions can result in an increase in sensitivity. It may be assumed that rehalogenation in such emulsions is a (detrimental) factor of importance in determining the sensitivity of the emulsion. Moreover, rehalogenation apparently plays a part in some of the photographic effects discussed in the following chapter.

* * * * *

The Gurney-Mott hypothesis of latent image formation has been rather widely accepted because of its ability to correlate existing data and to predict new effects (cf. Chapter 4). The mechanism of latent image formation should not be considered a closed chapter of photographic theory, however. Recent suggestions by Huggins [13] † and others suffice to show that other possible explanations remain to be explored more thoroughly.

† Huggins suggests that the important step in latent image formation is a shift from the normal cubic, or B-1, structure of the silver bromide to a tetrahedral (B-3 or B-4) structure. This shift, occurring in the region of the sensitivity centers, is promoted and stabilized by the presence of photoelectrons. For more details, see references at end of chapter, particularly Sheppard's paper.

Appendix to Chapter 3

Electron Conductance from the Viewpoint of the Band Structure of Crystals

It will be useful first to consider the structure of silver. The individual silver atom is composed of a positively charged nucleus and a group of external electrons. Each electron in the normal isolated atom occupies a discrete energy level and is characterized by a set of quantum numbers. One can think of the atom as having been constructed stepwise, as if electrons were added one by one to fill each energy level, the process starting with the lowest and continuing until the excess positive charge of the nucleus was neutralized. According to the Pauli exclusion principle, each energy level can be occupied by only two electrons, which are mutually equivalent in every way except that they are of opposite "spin." The silver atom, however, contains an odd number of electrons, and so the last occupied level contains only one electron. This outer electron is the valence electron. When it is lost, a silver ion is formed.

When silver atoms are arranged in an orderly fashion to form a crystal of silver metal, the situation is modified. Each atom is now influenced by the energy field of its neighbors. The electrons in the lower levels are not materially affected, and for the present they may be considered still to be simply members of closed atomic shells. The valence electrons, however, are markedly influenced, and are best considered to belong to the crystal as a whole. The energy levels of these electrons are crowded closely together into a quasi-continuous *band*, or zone, of the crystal.

The number of electrons which can be assigned to an energy band of this kind is equal to the sum of the electrons which might be assigned to the valence energy level of all the units making up the array. In the silver crystal, therefore, the band is only half full, and the electrons can move through the crystal with considerable ease. For this reason, the band is termed the conductance band.

The situation is not materially different for *metals* which contain an even number of electrons per atom. In magnesium, for example, there is just the right number of valence electrons to fill the energy band, but a second, higher band overlaps the first.

The electrons occupying the top levels of the lower band can easily pass into the lower levels of the upper band. For this reason, magnesium shows "metallic" conduction.

The silver bromide crystal presents quite a different picture. It is similar to magnesium in that the number of electrons is *even.* There is, however, a fundamental difference. The valence electrons completely fill the lower band (associated with the bromide ions). The upper band, associated with the silver ions, is completely empty and is separated from the lower one by an energy gap much too large to be bridged by mere thermal energy. This corresponds to the chemist's picture of the halogen atom taking an electron away from the metal atom in the act of forming a compound.

There can be no normal conductivity by the electrons in the bromide ion band. If an electron passes in one direction, the Pauli principle requires that another electron must pass simultaneously in the reverse direction, so that no net transfer of electricity is effected. The conductance band remains completely empty unless electrons can acquire the necessary energy for transfer. When the crystal is illuminated by light in the proper spectral region, however, this energy becomes available, and photoelectrons appear in the conductance band.

REFERENCES

General

Mees, *The Theory of the Photographic Process*, Macmillan, New York, 1942, Chapters 4, 5.

Mott and Gurney, *Electronic Processes in Ionic Crystals*, The Clarendon Press, Oxford, 1940.

Webb, "Theory of Photographic Latent Image Formation," *J. Applied Phys.*, **11**, 18–34 (1940).

Berg, "The Physical Chemistry of Latent Image Formation," in *Annual Reports on the Progress of Chemistry for 1942*, Chemical Society, London, 1943.

James and Kornfeld, "Reduction of Silver Halides and the Mechanism of Photographic Development," *Chem. Revs.*, **30**, 1–32 (1942).

Quantum Mechanics of Crystals

Seitz, *Modern Theory of Solids*, McGraw-Hill, New York, 1940.

Mott and Gurney, *Electronic Processes in Ionic Crystals*, The Clarendon Press, Oxford, 1940.

Seitz, *The Physics of Metals*, McGraw-Hill, New York, 1943, Chapter 17 (non-mathematical).

Specific

1. Silberstein and Trivelli, *J. Optical Soc. Am.*, **28**, 441 (1938); **35**, 93 (1945).
2. Webb, *ibid.*, **29**, 314 (1939).
3. Meidinger, *Physik. Z.*, **44**, 1 (1943).
4. Hall and Schoen, *J. Optical Soc. Am.*, **31**, 281 (1941).
5. Sheppard, Trivelli, and Loveland, *J. Franklin Inst.*, **200**, 51 (1925); Sheppard, *Phot. J.*, **65**, 380 (1925).
6. Toy, *Nature*, 120, 441 (1927); Toy and Harrison, *Proc. Roy. Soc. London*, **A127**, 613 (1930).
7. West and Carroll, *J. Chem. Phys.*, **15**, 529 (1947).
8. deBoer, *Electron Emission and Adsorption Phenomena*, Cambridge Press, 1935, p. 300.
9. Webb, *J. Optical Soc. Am.*, **26**, 367 (1936).
10. Gurney and Mott, *Proc. Roy. Soc. London*, **A164**, 151 (1938).
11. Webb and Evans, *J. Optical Soc. Am.*, **23**, 249 (1938).
12. Slater-Price, *Phot. J.*, **71**, 59 (1931).
13. Huggins, *J. Chem. Phys.*, **11**, 412 (1943).

4.

Reciprocity Law Failure and Other Exposure Effects

The electron traps that are capable of participation in the formation of a latent image may be distributed throughout the entire grain. Usually, the most effective traps are located at the grain surface, but those situated in the interior of the grain may, and often do, play a part in determining the photographic effect of a given exposure.

Distribution of the Latent Image

The existence of a latent image in the interior of exposed grains was indicated by the work of Kogelmann in 1894. It is easily demonstrated. Developing solutions that do not contain silver halide solvents act as normal developers toward grains that contain latent image nuclei on the surface. If, however, the external image is destroyed by proper treatment of the grain with an oxidizing agent such as chromic acid, the grain will not develop in the solvent-free solution, or at best it will develop only upon prolonged treatment in that solution. The internal latent image centers do not promote development because the developing solution does not have access to them. If, now, the grains are treated with a mild silver halide solvent, some of these centers will be uncovered. The grains in which internal latent image is thus made accessible to the developing solution will then develop normally.

A quantitative method for determining the distribution of the latent image between surface and interior is still lacking. Semi-quantitative determinations [1,2] show that the distribution may vary with both the conditions of exposure and the nature of the emulsion. The development centers produced by very low exposures of low or moderate intensity are found almost entirely on the surface of the grain in the commercial emulsions thus far examined. More and more centers form in the interior as the exposure increases. A predominant formation of internal centers can be obtained with a very intense exposure of short duration, or even with a normal exposure of certain specially prepared emulsions. Some well-known photographic phenomena such as reciprocity law failure and the Clayden effect (see subsequent sections of this chapter) involve changes in the distribution of the latent image.

Reciprocity Law Failure

The reciprocity law of Bunsen and Roscoe states that the amount of a photochemical reaction is dependent simply upon the actual light energy absorbed and not upon the rate of absorption. According to this law, the total amount of reaction for light of a given wave length is specified by the product of the light intensity I and the time or irradiation t. This law applies to any primary photochemical reaction. It likewise is valid for the formation of *photolytic silver* in the silver bromide emulsion at room temperature, provided rebromination is prevented. However, *it does not hold* for the photographic effect which is measured by the developed density.

Schwarzchild suggested that the photographic effect is determined by the product It^p instead of simply It, where p is a constant having a value of approximately 0.8. However, Schwarzchild's relation holds over only a limited range in practice. Some data are fitted over a rather wide range by a simple catenary equation, but no formula of really general validity is known.

The failure of the reciprocity law is usually represented graphically as follows: The total exposure It required to produce a fixed density is determined for various values of I and t. Log It is then plotted against log I. If the reciprocity law held, this plot would give a horizontal straight line. The actual curve often is characterized by a minimum which corresponds to an optimum intensity. This is the intensity level at which the smallest amount of light energy is required to produce a given photographic effect. The curve rises at intensity values above and below the optimum.

Figure 4·1 shows several experimental curves. The parallel straight lines running at a 45° angle to the coordinates are lines of constant exposure time. These are drawn merely to aid in the interpretation of the reciprocity failure plots.

The reciprocity failure varies greatly with the nature of the emulsion. However, there appears to be no general rule by which the failure can be related to other attributes of the emulsion, such

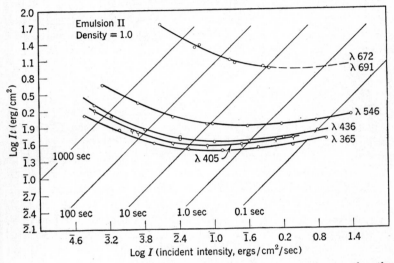

FIG. 4·1 Conventional reciprocity law failure plots for various wave lengths of exposing light. (Webb.)

as speed, grain size, or color sensitivity. The maximum efficiency usually occurs at an intensity value that produces a medium density (for example, 1.0) in 0.1 to 10 seconds.

The variation of reciprocity failure with the wave length of the exposing light follows a rather simple pattern. If the reciprocity failure curves for different wave lengths are plotted as in Fig. 4·1, they have the same general shape but are displaced parallel to each other along the 45° constant-time lines. The displacement can be represented more simply by plotting log It against log t (instead of against log I) whereupon the curves become displaced vertically from one another (Fig. 4·2). Thus, the relative amounts of exposure required to produce a given density at two different wave lengths remains constant with changing time of exposure.

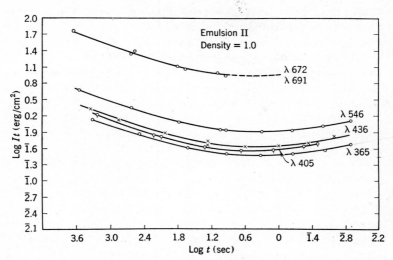

FIG. 4·2 Reciprocity law failure plots on a log t − log It basis. (Webb.)

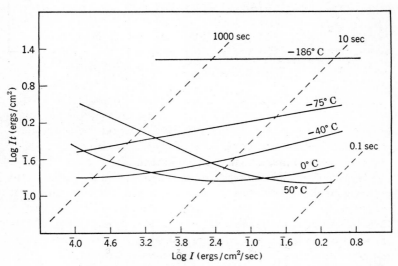

FIG. 4·3 Dependence of reciprocity law failure upon temperature. (Webb.)

In this sense, the spectral sensitivity of an emulsion is independent of the time of exposure.

The reciprocity failure shows a marked variation with the temperature of exposure.[3] A series of curves representing temperatures of 50° to −186° C is reproduced in Fig. 4·3. At high intensities, the log It value for a given log I is greater the lower the temperature. At low intensities, the log It value at first decreases, passes through a minimum, then increases with decreasing temperature. At a sufficiently low temperature, the reciprocity curve becomes parallel to the log I axis; that is, reciprocity failure disappears (cf. curve for −186°). This temperature behavior suggests that two separate effects having different temperature dependencies are at work. One predominates at high intensities, the other at low. Each can be associated with a step in the Gurney-Mott mechanism.

The Gurney-Mott formulation attributes the high-intensity failure to the sluggishness of the migration of interstitial silver ions. Electrons are being liberated at a high rate. The probability of capturing an electron by a given speck, however, will be decreased by the presence of an already captured electron which has not been neutralized because no silver ion has migrated to it. An electron approaching such a charged speck may be repelled and forced to go elsewhere. Thus, the rate of migration of the silver ions limits the rate at which a given sensitivity center can grow.

Many of the rejected electrons are later trapped in the interior of the grain and there form latent image centers. No high-intensity failure of the reciprocity law has been detected for a purely internal latent image.

At very low temperatures, the ionic mobility becomes insignificant. The electronic process alone takes place during the exposure period, and the secondary ionic process occurs only after the emulsion has been warmed up for development. Under these conditions, there should be no effect of intensity level over a wide range, because the rate of charging the sensitivity specks would be immaterial. This prediction of the Gurney-Mott hypothesis was confirmed by subsequent experiment.

The low-intensity failure is diminished by a decrease in temperature (Fig. 4·3). This fact led to the suggestion that the low-intensity failure arises from a thermal disintegration of the latent image. This disintegration is supposed to occur by way of the thermal ejection of an electron from the speck, followed by the diffusing away of a silver ion. The low intensity requires exposures which are of long enough duration to allow time for such disintegration. It is assumed that the tendency is greatest in the initial stages of formation of a nucleus. In the later stages of growth, the nuclei are relatively stable.

The preceding interpretation of low-intensity reciprocity failure is supported by experiments in which exposures of two widely different intensities were made consecutively on the same emulsion. In an experiment by Webb and Evans,[4] the one intensity used corresponded approximately to the value for greatest photographic efficiency, the other to $\frac{1}{1000}$ of that value. The low-intensity exposure by itself was quite inefficient in producing a latent image, but its efficiency was greatly increased when it was preceded by an exposure made at the optimum intensity. When the latter exposure was long enough, the subsequent low-intensity exposure became just as efficient as the optimum. In other words, the reciprocity failure disappeared.

The experiments just described can be explained on the basis that the preliminary exposure at optimum intensity produces a developable latent image in some of the grains and a latent sub-image which is not developable in others. This sub-image might consist simply of specks large enough to be reasonably stable but not large enough to constitute development centers. Such centers, however, can be efficiently built up to development centers by a subsequent low-intensity exposure.

If the spontaneously developable fog grains were ignored, the grains of an exposed emulsion might be classified as follows:

All grains $\begin{cases} \text{developable grains} & \begin{cases} \text{full-image grains} \end{cases} \\ \text{undevelopable grains} & \begin{cases} \text{sub-image grains} \\ \text{grains unaffected by exposure} \end{cases} \end{cases}$

The result of the primary exposure to light of optimum intensity in the experiment just described can be illustrated schematically [5] as in Fig. 4·4 (a) in which the grains are represented as triangles, full-image (developable) specks as black squares on the grains, and sub-image specks as black semicircles. Four * of the twelve

* These figures are, of course, arbitrary, and are intended merely to illustrate the general idea rather than to give quantitative data.

grains represented have full-image specks and are developable. Four more have sub-image specks and are not developable, but can be made developable by a subsequent low-intensity exposure which will efficiently convert the sub-image specks into full

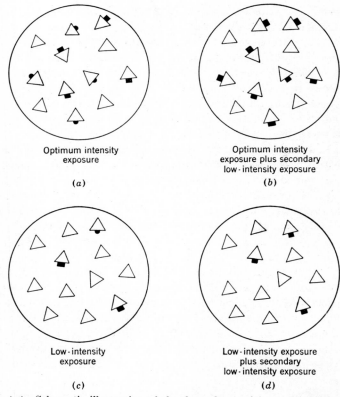

Fig. 4·4 Schematic illustration of the dependence of formation of developable latent image and latent sub-image upon the intensity of the exposing light and the manner of exposure. (After Burton and Berg.)

specks, Fig. 4·4 (*b*). On the other hand, a primary exposure of equal energy but low intensity produces the situation illustrated in Fig. 4·4 (*c*). Only two grains have full-image specks, and only one has a sub-image speck. Most of the exposure has been wasted. A secondary exposure to low-intensity light will be much less efficient here than in the preceding example, since only one-fourth as many stable sub-image specks exist which can be converted into full-image specks, Fig. 4·4 (*d*).

The secondary low-intensity exposure technique has a practical application in latent image intensification. If an underexposed picture is taken at moderate intensity, a second uniform exposure to light of low intensity will often materially improve the picture obtained on subsequent development. The low-intensity exposure builds up at least part of the sub-image to a developable latent image. If the secondary exposure is not continued too long, little fog is produced on the parts of the emulsion unaffected by the original exposure, since the reciprocity failure of the low-intensity exposure is at its full value in those areas. There is, of course, a limit to the amount of secondary exposure that will lead to beneficial results, and this limit depends upon the emulsion.

An alternative explanation of low-intensity reciprocity failure attributes it, at least in part, to rebromination. This explanation can account qualitatively for the temperature dependence and for the dependence of the extent of the reciprocity failure upon the procedure followed in making the photographic emulsion. A final choice between the two explanations has not been made.

Intermittency Effect

An exposure given in a number of discrete installments may lead to the same developable density as a continuous exposure involving equal total energy. More often, however, the intermittent exposure gives a density that is greater or less than that obtained by the continuous exposure. This *intermittency effect* is closely associated with the reciprocity law failure [6] of the emulsion. Its magnitude for a given emulsion depends primarily upon the intensity levels of exposure and the rate of interruption.

The effect of an intermittent exposure lies between the effects produced by two continuous exposures, one of intensity equal to that of the light used in the intermittent exposure, the other of intensity equal to the average over both light and dark periods. For example, if an intermittent exposure is given to light of intensity I and the light and dark periods are of equal duration, the density obtained after a total time t (over both light and dark periods) will lie between the density produced by a continuous exposure of intensity I and duration $\frac{1}{2} t$ and the density produced by a continuous exposure of intensity $\frac{1}{2}I$ and duration t. It may, of course, equal the density produced by one of these extremes.

A continuous exposure and an intermittent exposure of the same *average* intensity become equal in their effects when the frequency of flash exceeds a certain critical value which varies with the intensity level. This equivalence of the two exposures above the critical frequency has been explained on the basis of the quantum structure of light and the haphazard distribution of the quantum hits upon the photographic grains. The normal "continuous" exposure of a grain is really an intermittent exposure from the quantum-hit viewpoint. When the frequency of flash in the intermittency effect experiments becomes great enough, the time-distribution of hits upon each grain becomes essentially the same as for a continuous exposure of the same average intensity. The two exposures then become practically identical in so far as their reciprocity failures are concerned. An abnormally high frequency of flash is not required, since the rate of incidence of quanta on a single photographic grain is moderate even in an exposure of relatively high intensity.

The Clayden Effect

If a photographic emulsion is given first a very short exposure to light of very high intensity and then a second exposure to light of moderate intensity, the two do not add in a simple fashion. The very high-intensity exposure effectively desensitizes the emulsion toward the second exposure. If the first exposure has affected only a part of the emulsion and the second exposure is uniform over all of the emulsion, the image of the first often appears reversed when the film is developed; that is, a positive instead of a negative is formed. This phenomenon is known as the *Clayden effect*. It has been observed frequently in the photography of lightning flashes, where it gives rise to the so-called black lightning.

The Clayden effect is easily explained on the basis of the Gurney-Mott picture. In the initial high-intensity exposure, electrons are liberated much more rapidly than they can be neutralized at the surface traps. Accordingly, most of the electrons go to the interior of the grain and form internal latent image or sub-image nuclei. These internal image nuclei act as effective electron traps and compete with the surface sensitivity centers for the electrons liberated during the secondary exposure. The competitive action of the internal centers may become so successful that less total surface image is formed by the two exposures together than would have been formed by the moderate-intensity exposure alone. The secondary exposure in this way leads to a greater developable density in the regions which have not been touched by the primary exposure.

Solarization

For many photographic materials, the curve representing developable density as a function of exposure passes through a maximum. If the exposure is increased beyond that which produces the maximum density, a decrease in developable density will occur (Fig. 1-1). This effect is known as *solarization*. From the standpoint of the individual grains, solarization means that the increased exposure is actually destroying the developable state which had been induced in some of the grains by the earlier part of the exposure.

Different emulsions vary greatly in the extent to which they exhibit solarization. The solarization curves of some emulsions even pass through a minimum, and a second stage is reached where increase in exposure again produces an increase in density. Many commercial emulsions exhibit enough solarization to be of some practical significance, but really large effects are obtained only with special emulsions. In certain silver iodide emulsions, solarization becomes evident when only about 20 per cent of the grains have been made developable.

Experiment has shown that the amount of solarization is markedly dependent upon the character of the development. Solarization is most readily obtained when the developing solution contains no solvent for silver bromide, and, conversely, strong solvents such as thiosulfate remove solarization completely. The mild solvent action of sodium sulfite, which is a normal constituent of most practical developers, is sufficient to remove much of the solarization *provided development is prolonged*. With short times of development, solarization can still be obtained even in the presence of considerable amounts of sulfite.

Solarization is decreased, and sometimes eliminated, when halogen acceptors are present during exposure. This fact strongly suggests that solarization is in some way connected with a rehalogenation of the latent image.   In the conventional silver bromide emulsion, for example, it is probable that, as long as the exposure is small, the bromine formed is adequately removed by reacting with the gelatin at the grain surface, and rebromination does not occur to any significant extent.   When the exposure is large, however, the amount of bromine is too great to be effectively removed by the gelatin in the surface layer, and some of the bromine attacks the latent image.   When a latent image nucleus becomes coated over by a surface layer of silver bromide, its effectiveness in promoting development is seriously impaired or completely destroyed; the silver nucleus remaining beneath this coating may still be large, but the developer no longer has ready access to it.   In pure silver iodide emulsions, the gelatin does not adequately prevent reiodination even at low exposures, and auxiliary iodine acceptors must be added before the maximum photographic effect can be obtained even in the normal exposure range.

The rehalogenation hypothesis of solarization accounts for the previously mentioned dependence upon the developer.   In the absence of a silver halide solvent, the latent image centers are insulated from the developer by the silver bromide sheath, and no development occurs.   In the presence of a mild solvent, contact occurs only after the solvent has had time to dissolve off the protecting layer of silver bromide, and this process may take considerably more than the normal development time.   A stronger solvent, such as sodium thiosulfate, rapidly removes the silver bromide layer and allows the unbrominated parts of the latent image nuclei to function once more as development centers.   The thiosulfate also can uncover internal latent image centers which have not been affected by the bromine.   There is no solarization of the internal latent image.

As already mentioned, the solarization curve sometimes passes through a minimum, and a second stage is reached where increase in exposure produces an increase in density.   The results of experiments on latent image distribution have suggested an explanation for this second reversal.   Debot [7] obtained a definite second reversal on normal development of the emulsions he used in his investigation.   However, the density obtained by development of the surface image alone continued to decrease with increasing exposure in the solarization region, whereas the density obtained by development of the internal image (after destruction of the surface image) continued to increase with increasing exposure in this region and thus showed no solarization. Addition of the two curves (representing surface and internal image densities) produced a curve which showed initial solarization followed by a second reversal at the higher exposures. The shape of this com-

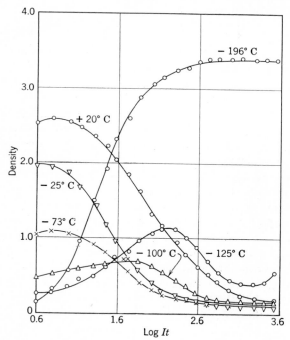

FIG. 4·5   Dependence of solarization upon temperature of exposure. (Webb and Evans.)

posite curve corresponded closely to that of the curve representing normal development of the exposed emulsion.

Solarization shows a significant dependence upon temperature. Figure 4·5 gives a set of curves [8] obtained over a temperature range of 20° to −196° C. The first effect as the temperature decreases is a drop of the maximum density value. After the temperature drops below −73° C, this maximum shifts toward the higher exposure values. Below −100° C, the curve continues to shift and begins to rise again, thereby showing a decrease in solarization. At −196° C, no solarization at all occurs.

The initial increase in solarization with decrease in temperature may be explained on the basis of a progressive loss in the efficiency of gelatin as a halogen acceptor. Such a loss in efficiency would occur if the rate of reaction of halogen with gelatin decreased more rapidly than the rate of reaction with silver. Experiments with other halogen acceptors tend to confirm this explanation.

The absence of solarization at $-196°$ C evidently requires another explanation. The maximum density at this temperature is even greater than at $20°$ C; and practically all the grains are developable. The exposure required to produce the maximum density, however, is about a hundredfold greater than that required at $20°$ C. As already indicated, silver probably is not formed at all at the low temperature. Some electrons are simply trapped at the surface specks, charging them to maximum capacity, and electrons subsequently liberated go to shallow traps in the interior of the grain. The bromine meanwhile has more time to combine with the gelatin or to diffuse away. When the emulsion is warmed, the silver ion migration can come into play, and silver ions neutralize the charge of the sensitivity specks. The electrons in the shallow internal traps are released by thermal energy and contribute to the further building up of the nuclei on the surface into development centers. Alternatively, it might be supposed that bromination is simply too slow to be effective at $-196°$ C and that the bromine diffuses away from the grain surface without reacting with either silver or gelatin.

Several other explanations of solarization have been given in the literature, but none is in sufficient agreement with experimental results to warrant consideration here.

Herschel Effect

If an emulsion which has not been dye-sensitized to red or infrared is exposed to blue light, a latent image will be formed in the normal way. If the emulsion is subsequently exposed to red or infrared radiation before it is developed, some of the effect of the original exposure will be erased. Thus, the long wave length radiation is capable of destroying to some extent the latent image formed by the blue light. This phenomenon is known as the *Herschel effect*. It is not subject to reciprocity law failure so far as is known.

The Herschel effect can be produced by radiation over a rather wide range of wave lengths. Figure 4·6 shows [9] the spectral sensitivity of the effect in a silver bromide emulsion. Curves *A, B, C,* and *D* correspond to increasing exposure to radiation of long wave length subsequent to the uniform blue-light exposure. The maximum effect is observed in the region of 730 to 750 mμ.

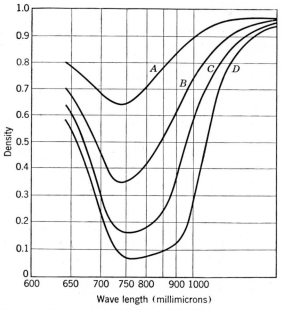

Fɪɢ. 4·6   Spectral distribution of the Herschel effect. *A, B, C,* and *D* correspond to different amounts of exposure, increasing in that order. (Bartelt and Klug.)

The spectral sensitivity of the Herschel effect apparently corresponds to the absorption spectrum of the latent image. Although the latter has not been measured for a normally exposed photographic emulsion, Hilsch and Pohl [10] have made the corresponding measurements on exposed, macroscopic crystals of silver bromide. They observed that intense irradiation of a silver bromide crystal in the blue or near-ultraviolet region induces an absorption band which has its maximum at about 700 mμ. This is the absorption band of the photoproduct, and it is the cause of the discoloration which irradiation produces in the crystal. Its properties are strikingly suggestive of the Herschel effect. The measured width of the band agrees well with the observed spectral distribution of the Herschel effect in the silver bromide emulsion, and the band can be bleached out by continued exposure to radiation which it absorbs. A reasonable assumption, therefore, is that the Herschel effect itself is associated with the absorption of radiation by the latent image centers.

The Herschel effect can be treated as a photoelectric effect. The absorption of a quantum of radiation by latent image silver results in the ejection of an electron into the surrounding silver halide. This leaves at the speck an unneutralized silver ion that subsequently moves away, leaving the size of the silver speck diminished by one silver atom. The process may be repeated until the speck becomes too small to act as a development center.

In support of the preceding explanation, Webb and Evans have shown that no Herschel effect is obtained when the primary (blue light) exposure is made at room temperature and the secondary (long wave length) exposure is made at $-186°$ C. At the latter temperature, the silver ions cannot move away from the latent image centers. If, however, the primary exposure is made at $-186°$ C, so that the latent image consists only of trapped electrons, the secondary exposure to long wave length radiation produces a Herschel effect at the low temperature. The trapped electrons apparently are set free by the secondary exposure and do not participate in, or are less effective in, the subsequent formation of silver at the sensitivity specks after the emulsion has been warmed up.

Experiments by Debot [7] not only add further support to the preceding explanation of the Herschel effect but also add some detail of mechanism. Debot showed that, if a photographic emulsion exposed to actinic light is treated with a bleaching bath which destroys the surface latent image, a subsequent exposure of this emulsion to red or infrared light can result in the formation of a new surface latent image. The exposure to the long wave length light has resulted in a transfer of latent image material from the interior of the grains to the surface.

In general, it appears from Debot's experiments that an exposure to long wave length light after pre-exposure to actinic light can produce four different results. Surface latent image silver can be transferred either to other surface specks or to specks in the interior of the grains; internal image silver can be transferred either to other internal specks or to the surface of the grains. All four processes may occur simultaneously during the secondary exposure of a normal emulsion, and the transferred latent image silver may attach itself to existing "sub-specks," thus building them up to the size necessary for development, or the silver may be deposited where it will not contribute to developability. In each process the mechanism of the transfer involves these steps: (1) ejection of an electron from a silver speck as a result of absorption of a red light quantum, (2) the trapping of the electron at some other point in the crystal, (3) "evaporation" of the excess silver ion from the initial speck, and (4) neutralization of that silver ion or some other interstitial silver ion by the electron at the new site.

An alternative explanation of the Herschel effect attributes it to an oxidation of the silver nuclei by some agent which is activated by the long wave exposure. This hypothesis is based principally upon the fact that certain dyes which desensitize an emulsion toward normal exposure actually promote the Herschel effect, or at least promote a reversal similar to it. However, the dyes in this case may act primarily as electron acceptors, preventing the return of electrons to the sensitivity specks. A strong Herschel effect can be obtained under conditions where there is no apparent oxidizing agent, and on the whole the evidence advanced in support of the oxidation hypothesis is inconclusive.

Extragranular Factors in Photographic Sensitivity

At least three factors external to the grain influence photographic sensitivity: (1) the pH of the gelatin, (2) the silver (or halide) ion concentration, and (3) the water content. As already mentioned (Chapter 2), the first two have irreversible effects upon the after-ripening which takes place during the manufacture of the emulsion. However, these factors also have reversible effects upon the sensitivity of the finished emulsion. The sensitivity decreases with increasing halide ion concentration (decreasing silver ion concentration), other things being equal. At constant halide ion concentration and water content, the sensitivity increases with increasing pH when the pH is adjusted and buffered before the final coating of the emulsion. Finally, when either the halide ion concentration or the pH is held constant and the water content is increased, the sensitivity at first increases; then it passes through a maximum (in the region of 12 to 16 per cent for the emulsion used by Sheppard and Graham [11]) and subsequently decreases.

The influence of all three factors may be accounted for qualitatively in terms of their influence on the reaction between halogen and gelatin. If the primary removal of halogen is effected through conversion to hypohalite (OBr^- or OCl^-), the influence of pH and halide ion concentration is exerted by way of an influence on the equilibrium

$$[OBr^-] = k \frac{[Br_2][H_2O]}{[H^+]^2[Br^-]}$$

according to the reaction scheme given in Chapter 3. The behavior of water is just what would be expected, since at first water is necessary for the hydrolysis of the halogen, but beyond a certain amount it acts simply to dilute the active hypohalite ion and thus to decrease the rate of reaction with the gelatin. It is doubtful, however, whether this explanation is complete for the action of halide ion on sensitivity.

Latent Image Production by X-rays

A latent image can be obtained by exposure of an ordinary photographic emulsion to x-rays. Certain differences are observed between light exposure and x-ray exposure phenomena, but these can be attributed to the much greater energy available in the x-ray quantum. Whereas a light quantum can produce only a single silver atom in the photolysis of silver halide, an x-ray quantum can produce hundreds to thousands of silver atoms. The latter photolysis is brought about by the action of secondary electrons liberated in the path of the initially liberated, highly energetic primary electron.

Despite the great number of silver atoms formed by the absorption of an x-ray quantum, considerably more would be produced if the energy were used to its greatest efficiency. The actual efficiency amounts to only 10 per cent or less. Günther and Tittel [12] found that this efficiency was nearly independent of the wave length of the x-radiation over the range 0.024 to 0.154 mμ, and that therefore the number of silver atoms formed was inversely proportional to the wave length. The actual number of atoms obtained per quantum absorbed varied from 930 to 148.

Except for very soft radiation, the absorption of one x-ray quantum is sufficient to make a grain developable, and there is evidence that, at least under some conditions, two or more adjacent grains can be made developable by the action of a single x-ray quantum. Since one quantum is sufficient to make a grain developable, there is no basis for a reciprocity law failure or an intermittency effect, and indeed none is observed in direct x-ray exposures. Solarization, however, can be obtained under proper conditions.

Only a very small fraction of the x-radiation falling upon a normal photographic emulsion is actually absorbed. Accordingly, intensifying screens often are used to increase the efficiency of the exposure. These screens contain a material, such as calcium tungstate, which emits fluorescent, photographically active light upon exposure to x-rays. The major portion of the latent image is then formed by action of the fluorescent light; therefore the photographic material becomes subject to the usual reciprocity law failure and intermittency effect.

REFERENCES

General

Mees, *The Theory of the Photographic Process*, Macmillan, New York, 1942, Chapters 6, 7.

Berg, "The Physical Chemistry of Latent Image Formation," in *Annual Reports on the Progress of Chemistry for 1942*, Chemical Society, London, 1943.

Webb, "Theory of the Photographic Latent Image Formation," *J. Applied Phys.* **11**, 18–34 (1940).

Specific

1. Berg, Marriage, and Stevens, *J. Optical Soc. Am.*, **31**, 385 (1941).
2. Kornfeld, *J. Optical Soc. Am.*, **31**, 598 (1941).
3. Webb and Evans, *J. Optical Soc. Am.*, **28**, 249 (1938); Berg and Mendelssohn, *Proc. Roy. Soc. London*, **A168**, 168 (1938).
4. Webb and Evans, *J. Optical Soc. Am.*, **28**, 431 (1938).
5. Cf. Burton and Berg, *Phot. J.*, **86B**, 2 (1946).
6. Webb, *J. Optical Soc. Am.*, **23**, 157 (1933).
7. Cf. Berg, *Phot. J.*, to be published.
8. Webb, *J. Optical Soc. Am.*, **30**, 445 (1940).
9. Bartelt and Klug, *Z. Physik*, **89**, 779 (1934).
10. Hilsch and Pohl, *Z. Physik*, **64**, 606 (1930).
11. Sheppard and Graham, *J. Franklin Inst.*, **230**, 619 (1940).
12. Günther and Tittel, *Z. Elektrochem.*, **39**, 646 (1933).

5.

The Mechanism of Development

Development of the photographic image, as carried out in normal practice, involves the reduction of the individual silver halide grains to particles of metallic silver. The process is generally termed chemical development, although direct development is a more distinctive term. *Each grain of the emulsion acts as a unit* in direct development in the sense that a grain either is developable as a whole or it is not developable.

There is a second type of development in which the silver is derived from a soluble silver salt contained in the developing solution itself. This type is termed (erroneously) physical development. It will be discussed later in the present chapter.

Development as an Oxidation-Reduction Reaction

The chemical reaction involved in either type of development is an oxidation-reduction reaction between silver ion and developer. The silver ion is reduced to silver, and the developer ion or molecule is oxidized in the process. To take a simple example, the development of silver bromide by hydroxylamine is accompanied by the oxidation of the hydroxylamine to nitrogen and water. The reaction can be written:

$$Ag^+Br^- + NH_2O^- \rightarrow Ag + \tfrac{1}{2}N_2 + H_2O + Br^- \quad (5 \cdot 1)$$

or simply

$$Ag^+ + NH_2O^- \rightarrow Ag + \tfrac{1}{2}N_2 + H_2O \quad (5 \cdot 2)$$

The reaction of other developing agents, although often more complicated, is fundamentally the same. The basic reaction in development is the reduction of silver ions to silver.

Direct Development of the Silver Halide Grain

In direct development, the reduction of the exposed grain starts at one or more discrete points on the grain surface, corresponding to the latent image nuclei, and proceeds from these points until eventually the entire grain is reduced. In general, reduction will not spread from one developing grain to another grain which does not contain a development center, unless the latter grain is in direct physical contact with the former or unless such contact is established during development of the former. When reduction of adjacent grains is instigated by development of a single exposed grain, it results in the formation of a clump of silver particles. The extent of clump formation depends to some extent upon the composition of the developer. Instigation of the reduction of normally undevelopable grains situated at some distance from a developing grain also has been observed, but only for developing solutions of unusual composition. For example, "infectious" development of this type can be obtained with a highly alkaline hydroquinone solution containing hydrazine.[1]

The shape of the developed grain depends upon the composition of the developing solution and the nature of the original silver halide grain. For example, a pure bromide emulsion developed in a hydroquinone solution which contains $0.025\,M$ reducing agent, $0.5\,M$ sodium carbonate, $0.02\,M$ sodium sulfite, and $0.02\,M$ potassium bromide yields silver grains which, under the optical microscope, appear to have the same shape as the original silver bromide. If the sulfite is increased from $0.02\,M$ to $0.6\,M$, or if the emulsion contains a small amount of iodide, perceptible distortion of the grain shape occurs during development. Development in some very active solutions is accompanied by marked distortion, and the silver particles formed bear little resemblance in shape to the original silver halide grains.

More detailed information on the structure of the developed silver grain has been supplied by the electron microscope. Figure 5·1 shows an electron micrograph of a partially developed silver bromide grain. (The unreduced silver bromide was dissolved out before the micrograph was made.) Development evidently was

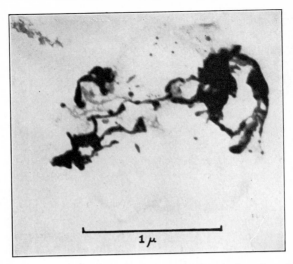

FIG. 5·1 Electron micrograph of partially developed silver bromide crystal, taken after the undeveloped portion had been dissolved out. (Hall and Schoen.)

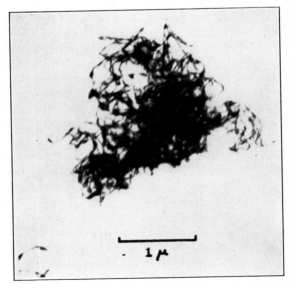

FIG. 5·2 Electron micrograph showing filamentary structure of completely developed grain. (Hall and Schoen.)

proceeding in an irregular fashion, and some of the silver is in the form of long, thin filaments. These filaments, however, are not simply the product of incomplete development. Figure 5·2 shows an electron micrograph of a completely developed grain. The silver occupies roughly the confines of the original grain, but evidence of filamentary structure remains. In some places, thin filaments project well beyond the probable boundaries of the original grain. Such filament formation is the normal occurrence in direct development. It will be considered in more detail subsequently.

Development as a Rate Process

The distinction which the developer makes between a sufficiently exposed grain (this term will be considered more explicitly later) and an unexposed or insufficiently exposed grain is primarily a matter of the time of reduction. Differences can appear in the physical character of the reduced silver according as it is obtained from exposed or unexposed grains, but the time factor is still the primary one. *The sufficiently exposed grain is reduced to metallic silver in a considerably shorter time.* This statement is subject to some qualification, since ordinary emulsions contain a small percentage of fog grains which will be rapidly reduced by the developer even without prior exposure. The statement is true for the great majority of grains, however. It is self-evident that the latent image material is in some way responsible for the distinction which the developer makes between exposed and unexposed grains. The primary task in formulating a theory of development is to discover why the latent image material accelerates the reduction process.

The classical Ostwald-Abegg hypothesis assumed that the latent image silver specks served merely as nuclei upon which silver formed in solution by the reduction of dissolved silver halide could condense. This hypothesis is not supported by the evidence and has been generally abandoned. It is highly probable that the *true action of the latent image silver is to accelerate or catalyze the actual reduction of silver ions.*

The following description of the development of an individual grain is in good accord with experimental evidence. The latent image silver nucleus or nuclei are in intimate contact with the silver halide which, it will be remembered, is an ionic crystal composed of silver ions and halide ions. The latent image silver acts as the initial accelerator or catalyst for the reaction between the developing agent and silver ions from the silver halide. The reduction of silver ions is accompanied by the formation of new silver around the latent image centers, and this silver in turn accelerates the reduction of more silver ions. Thus, the process of reduction of the individual grain continues as an auto-accelerated reaction.

Evidence from several sources indicates that the actual reduction occurs at or very near the interface between the silver and the silver halide. It may even be unnecessary for the silver ions to leave the solid state. Normal development can take place in the absence of any silver halide solvent other than water. If solution occurs at all in such a process, it probably is in the sense of a mobilization of silver ions in the water-adsorbed bromide ion sheath surrounding the grain. The silver ions move through this layer to some point on the silver nuclei where they are reduced.

The preceding considerations leave unanswered the question, how can silver accelerate the reduction of silver ions? The simplest approach to a solution of this problem is a consideration of the reaction between the developing agent and silver ions in solution —a reaction markedly catalyzed by colloidal silver. It can be considered as a simple prototype of the development reaction.

The Energy of Activation Necessary for Chemical Reaction

In the absence of the catalyst, direct collision of the reaction partners is a necessary condition for reaction, although not a sufficient one. Calculations show that most of the collisions between silver ions and the developing agent do not actually result in reactions in the system which we are considering; only a small fraction of them is fruitful. This situation is not unique for the reduction of silver ions by a developing agent; it is common to all except extremely fast chemical reactions. Evidently some special situation must exist for those collisions which do result in reaction.

Arrhenius explained this situation in terms of a critical energy requirement. He had observed that the rate of simple reactions could be represented by an equation of the type

$$\text{Rate} = AZe^{-E/RT} \tag{5·3}$$

where E is an energy term, R is the gas constant, T is the absolute temperature, A is a constant, and Z, the collision frequency, varies as $\sqrt{T}$. It is significant that the fraction $e^{-E/RT}$ is proportional to the number of molecules possessing energy at least E in excess of the average energy of all the molecules. The Arrhenius equation, therefore, implies that the number of molecules reacting in a unit time is proportional to the number which possess a suitable energy excess, or are in a suitably activated condition. Accordingly, E is termed the activation energy of the reaction. The activation energy should not be confused with the heat of reaction or with the free energy of the reaction. These are quite different concepts and usually have quite different numerical values.

At constant temperature the rate of a reaction can be changed by a change in either the factor Z or the activation energy E. Since the latter appears in the exponential part of equation 5·3, the reaction rate is very sensitive to the value of E. Any device that will bring about a decrease in E without causing a compensating decrease in Z will accelerate the reaction. One way in which a catalyst can accelerate a reaction is to bring about such a decrease in E.

The Mechanism of the Silver-Catalyzed Reduction of Silver Ions in Solution

Two basic mechanisms have been suggested to explain how silver nuclei can accelerate the reduction of silver ions by a developing agent. In the first it is assumed that the developing agent simply donates electrons to the silver nuclei. The nuclei then act essentially as tiny electrodes at which the silver ions become reduced. The reduction thus includes two essential steps: first, the transfer of electrons to the silver; second, the neutralization of the silver ions by the electrons. The steps can be symbolized by

$$R \rightarrow \epsilon + \text{oxidized } R \text{ (at the ``electrode'')} \qquad (5\cdot4)$$

and

$$Ag^+ + \epsilon \rightarrow Ag$$

where R is the developing agent. The activation energy of these two processes may be considerably smaller than that of the single direct transfer of an electron to a silver ion, such as would be necessary for reaction in the absence of the catalyst. Moreover, the transfer of an electron to the silver could occur at any point on the silver surface, and the reduction of the silver ion could occur at that or any other point on the surface. Thus, the catalyst might increase the rate of reaction by decreasing the activation energy, by eliminating the necessity of direct collision between silver ion and developing agent, or by performing both operations simultaneously.

Following this scheme, Bagdasar'yan [2] has calculated the kinetics of the reduction of silver ions in solution on the assumption that the transfer of electrons from developing agent to silver (equation 5·4) is the rate-controlling step. According to this calculation, the reaction rate should vary as some fractional power of the silver ion concentration and as the first power of the developing agent concentration. Experimental results [3] on the reduction of silver ions by hydroquinone agree completely with these requirements. The reaction of silver ions with hydroxylamine likewise shows a fractional power dependence upon the silver ion concentration. On the other hand, this dependence is not observed in the p-phenylenediamine reaction, where the rate varies with a fractional power of the reducing agent concentration instead. A similar dependence of rate upon a fractional power of the developing agent concentration is obtained in the hydroxylamine reaction. However, these discrepancies might result from oversimplification in the formulation of the electrode reaction rather than from a fundamental error in the basic concepts.

The second mechanism which has been proposed is based on the assumption that silver ions or developing agent or both are adsorbed by the silver nuclei, and that this adsorption results in a decrease in the activation energy necessary for the reduction of the silver ions. The silver catalyst, by adsorbing and deforming one or both reactants, causes the reaction to proceed over a path where less activation energy is required than if the two reactants simply collided in solution.

The observed dependence of the reaction rate upon a fractional power of the silver ion concentration is accounted for in the following way. If reaction does not occur until after the silver ions are adsorbed, the reaction rate is determined by the concentration in the adsorbed state, not by the concentration in solution. Over a limited but sometimes rather wide range, the concentration of a substance in the adsorbed state (C_a) can often be related to the concentration in solution (C_s) by means of the empirical equation

$$C_a = k'C_s{}^n \qquad (5 \cdot 5)$$

where n is a fraction. This equation is known as the Freundlich isotherm. If it is applied to the data on the reaction between silver ions and hydroquinone in a slightly alkaline solution, the dependence of the rate upon the silver ion concentration can be expressed as

$$\text{Rate} = k \cdot C_a = k'' \cdot C_s{}^n \qquad (5 \cdot 6)$$

The assumption that silver ions are adsorbed by silver is supported by direct measurements. These show that adsorption of silver ions by oxide-free silver surfaces starts when the silver ion concentration in solution is about 10^{-13}, which is lower than the silver ion concentration in all experiments in which silver catalysis of the reduction of silver ions has been detected.

The developing agent itself may or may not be adsorbed by the silver. For example, the kinetic evidence indicates adsorption of hydroxylamine and of p-phenylenediamine but not of hydroquinone. It seems probable that adsorption of silver ions is of much greater fundamental importance to development by most agents than adsorption of the developing agent itself. p-Phenylenediamine appears, however, to be an exception.

Mechanism of Development of the Exposed Silver Halide Grains

In the direct development of the solid silver halide, the fundamental mechanism of the catalysis is probably much the same as that in the reduction of silver ions from solution, just discussed. Several suggested mechanisms, which correspond to the first mechanism of the preceding section, are based on the assumption that the silver nuclei act essentially as tiny electrodes. The mechanism proposed by Gurney and Mott is an extension of their mechanism of latent image formation. According to this scheme, the silver nuclei acquire electrons from the developing agent, and interstitial silver ions are thereby attracted to the specks, where they are reduced to silver atoms. New interstitial silver ions are formed as the original ones are used up, and the process continues until the grains are completely reduced. It seems, however, that the new interstitial silver ions must be formed at or very near the surface of the grain; otherwise, an excess of bromide ions which are relatively immobile would quickly accumulate in the interior of the grain, and a prohibitive space charge would result. If the interstitial ions are formed at the grain surface, the excess bromide ions could escape into the solution, and no difficulty would arise on their account.

Other electrode mechanisms have been suggested,[4] but none (including the Gurney-Mott) is sufficiently supported by experimental evidence to warrant general acceptance. All the electrode mechanisms have in common the assumption that the silver nucleus can acquire electrons anywhere on its surface, but the reduction of silver ions is confined largely to the region of the silver-silver halide interface. The fundamental condition for direct development in all is that a transfer of electrons from developing agent to silver must take place much more easily than a direct transfer of electrons from developing agent to the silver halide crystal.

Direct development can be considered from the alternative point of view, which corresponds to the second mechanism discussed in the preceding section. In this treatment, the interface where the silver meets the silver halide is considered to be a region where the silver ions are already subjected to adsorption forces and are probably displaced somewhat from their normal positions. Less activation energy is required for reaction at this interface than at any other point on the crystal. Accordingly, the developer can reduce silver ions at the interface much more readily than at any other point on the silver halide surface.*

One distinct difference stands out between the two alternative points of view. According to the first, there is no need for direct contact between silver ion and developing agent, whereas according to the second there is. As yet there is no clear-cut evidence which allows a choice to be made between the two alternatives, but the available evidence does favor the latter. The clearest indication is given by the results of some kinetic studies[5] of development by hydroquinone and catechol in simple solution in the pH region of 8 to 9. There the development rate varies ap-

---

* For a more detailed discussion of the suggested mechanism of the catalysis, see the article by James, *J. Chem. Education*, **23**, 595 (1946).

proximately as the square root of the concentration of the active developing agent. This fact indicates adsorption of the ion prior to reaction (cf. equation 5·6). There is no reliable direct evidence for the adsorption of hydroquinone to silver itself, and the kinetic evidence shows that no significant adsorption occurs in the silver-catalyzed reduction of silver ions *from solution*. Accordingly, it is reasonable to assume that adsorption of the hydroquinonate ion by the silver bromide or the silver-silver bromide interface precedes the actual reduction of silver ions in the development of the silver bromide emulsion. This assumption agrees with Sheppard's suggestion that the developing agent is first adsorbed by the silver halide to form a complex with the silver ions.

The reactivity of the silver ions at the interface depends somewhat upon factors other than the silver-silver ion couple. For example, certain dyes which are strongly adsorbed to the silver halide through the medium of the silver ions can compete with the developer for possession of those ions. Such dyes markedly decrease the rate of reaction at the interface. Gelatin exerts a similar, but considerably smaller, retarding action. Adsorbed bromide ions can also retard the reaction in this way.

The Mechanism of Filament Formation

An explanation of filament formation has been attempted on the basis of a particular form of the electrode mechanism of development. This form is modeled after the Gurney-Mott latent image mechanism and is based on the assumption that interstitial silver ions from within the crystal are the ions actually reduced by the electrons obtained from the developer. The interstitial ions are reduced at the inside surface of the latent image speck, and the resulting accumulation of silver within a restricted space pushes out the silver above it, thus forming protrusions of silver. However, the filaments formed in development are markedly different in appearance from the knob-like protrusions of silver formed by excessive exposure of the silver bromide grains to light or to an electron beam where, according to the indications, the Gurney-Mott mechanism is operative.

A possible clue to the mechanism of filament formation is found in the evidence that the filaments formed in development do not have parallel edges [6] throughout their lengths, but show frequent angular enlargements in the plane of the ribbon. These enlargements often take the form of flat, triangular crystals (cf. Figs. 5·1 and 5·3), indicating that the sides of the filaments correspond to the octahedral (111) faces of silver crystals, so that the filaments may be considered as silver crystals which have grown chiefly in one dimension. Silver crystals of this type are not uncommon; macroscopic needle crystals have been grown by crystallization of silver vapor upon suitable nuclei, and fibrous silver crystals are formed both in the electrolysis of silver nitrate solutions under certain conditions and in the reduction of molten silver chloride by hydrogen. The mechanism of filament formation in these processes is primarily the mechanism of crystallization of the silver. The growth of such crystals very probably is associated with the mobility of newly formed or newly condensed silver atoms along the solid surface. This association suggests a corresponding explanation for the formation of filaments in development, when the newly formed silver atoms may, for a short time, possess considerable mobility.[7]

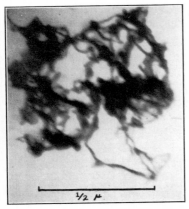

FIG. 5·3   Electron micrograph of partially developed grain, showing triangular enlargements of some filaments.

Numerous experiments have shown that migration of metal atoms along a solid surface is a rather common phenomenon, even at temperatures which are many hundreds of degrees below the melting point of the metal. This migration often requires very little energy. Now if, in development, the initial conditions are proper for the start of growth of a silver crystal in one dimension, the filament formation could continue readily by migration of the silver atoms to the points where they best fit into the growing crystal. Thus the orientation of the latent image nucleus may be of major importance in the determination of the nature of the crystal growth. Adsorption of gelatin or even of developing agent to certain crystal faces likewise may play a part in determining the ultimate size and shape of the individual crystals.

The Charge Barrier in Development

Although the catalytic action of the silver nuclei remains the fundamental basis for development, the surface condition of the silver halide grain can markedly affect the development process. It has already been mentioned that certain adsorbed substances can compete with the developer for possession of silver ions and hence retard the development process. A surface action of an entirely different nature is also present in many cases. This is the charge barrier effect, which is of considerable importance in determining the course of development by ionized developing agents.

If the development reaction is to take place at the interface, the reducing agent must penetrate to the surface of the silver halide grain at or very near the latent image centers before normal development can begin. If the active developer is a negatively charged ion, as many are, this penetration is opposed by an electrostatic effect. In the normal photographic emulsion, which contains an excess of halide ions, some of these excess ions are adsorbed by the surface of the grain. They induce the formation of an electric double layer that acts as a virtual barrier against the approach of negatively charged developing agents to the halide surface.

The fine details of the structure of the electric double layer surrounding a photographic grain are not known, but the simpler situation of a colloidal silver bromide particle in the absence of gelatin can be illustrated by Fig. 5·4. The bromide ions, being held rather rigidly to the surface, give the particle a net negative charge. This charge attracts ions of the opposite sign from the surrounding solution and tends to repel ions of the same sign. The result is an ionic atmosphere in which positive ions predominate. As the distance from the surface of the silver bromide increases, however, the predominance of positive ions decreases, until at a sufficiently large distance the negative charge of the surface no longer influences the distribution. The electrostatic charge at the particle surface sets up a potential gradient through the double-layer region. The curve in Fig. 5·4 illustrates, for the gelatin-free silver bromide, the drop in potential with distance from the surface.

The presence of gelatin undoubtedly causes some modification in the structure of the ionic double layer. Gelatin molecules are adsorbed to the bromide surface, and the silver halide particles are embedded in a gelatin gel. The gelatin itself becomes negatively charged when the surrounding medium is alkaline (Chap-

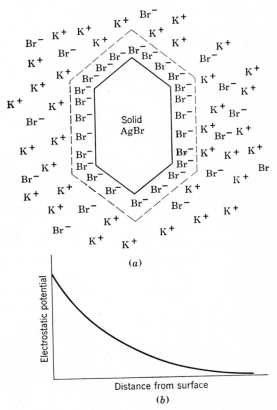

(a)

(b)

Fig. 5·4 Schematic illustration of electric double layer surrounding a silver bromide crystal. The curve illustrates the potential drop as a function of distance from the solid surface.

ter 2). Inasmuch as most practical developing solutions are alkaline, the charge of the gelatin probably enhances the total negative charge at the grain surface. Indeed, at least one kinetic effect in development has been definitely associated with the component of charge contributed by the gelatin. This and certain other kinetic effects will be considered in Chapter 7. For the present, discussion will be confined to the contribution of the charge effect to the fundamental basis for development.

Halide ions are not adsorbed so readily by silver as by silver halide, and hence the surface electric charge might be expected to be weaker locally wherever a silver nucleus was located on the surface of the grain. This factor alone, under proper circumstances, might conceivably lead to development. Many of the developing agents are active only in the form of negatively charged ions. If the electric charge barrier of an unexposed grain is large enough to prevent completely such a developer from reaching the surface of an unexposed grain, no reaction at all will occur. If the exposed grain, on the other hand, has a very low charge in the vicinity of the latent image centers, the kinetic energy of the ions of the developing agent will be sufficient to overcome the electrostatic repulsion at these centers so that the ions can reach the surface.

It is very doubtful that such an extreme case as the one just postulated ever occurs in practice. There is evidence, however, that in many instances the formation of large latent image centers results in a decrease in the charge barrier. As a consequence, the developer ions penetrate more readily to the larger latent image centers than to the smaller ones or to the surface of the unexposed grain. The change in the charge barrier then contributes to the discrimination between exposed and unexposed grains, because the kinetic energies of the ions in solution are distributed according to the Boltzmann principle. Consequently the fractional number of ions which can penetrate a given barrier will depend upon the magnitude of the latter. The smaller the barrier, the greater will be the percentage of ions which can reach the surface, and hence the greater will be the concentration of ions at the surface. Accordingly, the decrease which exposure produces in the magnitude of the barrier brings about an increase in the rate of reaction with the developer ions.

On the other hand, development often occurs under conditions such that the barrier effect makes no contribution whatsoever. The charge at the surface, in itself, can be of no significance when the developing agent is uncharged, and many agents of this kind are known to develop in much the same manner as the charged ones. Moreover, it is possible under some circumstances to develop *positively* charged silver bromide grains with negatively charged developer ions. The charge effect, in general, is less important as a fundamental *cause* of development than as a factor influencing the general kinetics of development.

Physical Development

A second type of photographic development is the so-called physical development. In its purest form, physical development *follows* the fixation process. The silver halide is first dissolved out in alkaline sodium thiosulfate or some other solvent which will not seriously attack the latent image. The image is then developed in a solution consisting of a reducing agent, a soluble silver salt, and certain substances which act to maintain the proper silver ion and hydrogen ion concentrations. The silver in this type of physical development thus comes from the soluble salt in the developing solution, not from the silver halide of the original grains.

The mechanism of physical development appears to be primarily that of a catalyzed reduction of silver ions. Silver ions from the solution are reduced at the surface of the silver (latent image) nuclei. The probable mechanism has been discussed previously (pages 73 to 75). Within certain limits, the mass of the developed silver is proportional to the number of suitable *latent image centers* rather than to the number of original silver halide grains which contained the latent image centers.

In a modified form, referred to as prefixation physical development, the silver halide is not dissolved out first. However, since the developer solution contains a strong silver halide solvent which dissolves the halide as development proceeds, both the silver halide and the soluble silver salt originally present in the developer contribute to the final silver image. Some direct development probably is involved, but the major action proceeds by way of solution.

Mixed Development

Physical development often encroaches to some extent upon direct development under practical working conditions, and under some conditions physical development may play a fairly important rôle. All the commercial developing solutions which employ organic reducing agents contain sodium sulfite or its equivalent. This substance forms with silver ions a soluble complex $Ag(SO_3)_2^{\equiv}$ and thus increases the solubility of silver bromide and silver chloride. The solvent does not increase the actual *equilibrium* silver ion concentration, but it does increase the rate at which silver ions pass into solution. (The silver ions in solution are formed by the equilibrium dissociation of the complex $Ag(SO_3)_2^{\equiv} \rightleftharpoons Ag^+ + 2SO_3^{=}$.) A high sulfite concentration and a low overall rate of development generally favor, relatively, the physical type of development. Some practical developing solutions, particularly the fine-grain variety, contain solvents even more drastic than sulfite. They promote physical development to an even greater extent.

Effective Size of the Latent Image Specks

Various attempts have been made to determine the number of silver atoms necessary to create a development center and the number of quanta necessary to make a grain developable. The two quantities are not necessarily identical. The number of light quanta absorbed in making a grain developable imposes an upper limit on the number of silver atoms that are necessary to form a development center. The actual atoms formed by the quanta, however, may be distributed among several centers.

It is known that some of the most sensitive grains are made developable by a very few quanta. Probably one is sufficient for some grains. In such a grain, one silver atom is sufficient to produce developability. But this, again, tells us nothing about the actual size of the development center, since the pre-existing nucleus contains silver sulfide and perhaps even metallic silver, both of which contribute to the developability.

There is no reason to assume that a fixed size threshold exists at which all nuclei acquire the power of initiating development. Orientation and position in the silver halide crystal may be of greater importance than mere size. Difficulty is even encountered in trying to establish a threshold of developability. Reduction of a grain must progress to the point where a measurable or microscopically visible amount of silver is formed before development of that grain can be detected. The time elapsing between the start of development and the point at which development can be detected is not the same for all grains, and it may vary over a wide range under some conditions. Hence, a grain which does not appear to be developable within a certain time of development may develop if given a longer time; the experimental time of development thus enters into the specification of a developable grain and a development center. If a well-defined border existed between development and the reduction of unexposed grains (fog formation), the problem could be met simply by specifying the grains which are reduced within the maximum development time. But the border is poorly defined, and development gradually merges into fog formation over a considerable range.

From the available evidence, it can be stated that the addition to some sensitivity specks of one silver atom (or its photolytic equivalent) each will considerably shorten the time required for the developer to reduce the grain involved. Conversely, the removal of one silver atom (or its equivalent) from certain development centers will considerably lengthen the time required for reduction. In this sense, a fairly critical threshold exists. Regarding the number of silver atoms which, if properly grouped together in the form of a nucleus, would make a grain containing no sensitivity centers unmistakably developable, only "informed guesses" can be made, other than that the nucleus definitely is of sub-microscopic size. Probably not more than a few hundred atoms are required, and possibly fewer than ten. The very existence of a fairly critical threshold, in the sense just considered, suggests that the total number is small.

Mechanism of Fog Formation

All the reduced silver which cannot be ascribed to development of a latent image is lumped together under the label of fog. Several causes of fog can operate simultaneously, and it is often very difficult to distinguish them experimentally. The cause of fog can lie either in the emulsion or in the developer or in both. Some emulsions show much greater fog than others, and some developers produce much greater fog (relative to image formation) than others.

Emulsion fog arises primarily from the catalytic action of nuclei of silver sulfide (with or without metallic silver) which have been formed during the manufacture of the emulsion. These nuclei have grown beyond the stage of mere sensitivity centers and act in much the same manner as the latent image in promoting the reduction of the silver halide grain. It may be expected that any emulsion of high sensitivity will contain some grains which are thus spontaneously developable.

A direct attack by the developing agent upon silver ions in solution, or upon unnucleated silver halide surface, also can give rise to fog. This reaction in itself should produce little silver during the course of normal development, but it can form nuclei of high activity under proper conditions. Subsequent catalytic reduction of the grains nucleated in this way, or of silver ions in the solution, can result in the formation of a significant amount of fog silver.

Several secondary causes of fog may be met in practice. The presence of certain impurities in an improperly prepared developing solution can lead to fog formation. Sulf*ide* ion is particularly troublesome in this respect. It forms silver sulfide nuclei which serve as catalytic centers for the reduction of the grains. Oxidation by air of some developing agents in the presence of the developing film gives rise to aerial fog. This type probably is caused by the action of a peroxide radical which is formed during the oxidation. The peroxide radical forms silver nuclei by reaction with the silver bromide, and these nuclei induce development of the grains containing them. Traces of copper salts in the developer will markedly promote this kind of fog.

REFERENCES

General

Mees, *The Theory of the Photographic Process*, Macmillan, New York, 1942, Chapter 8.

James and Kornfeld, "Reduction of Silver Halides and the Mechanism of Photographic Development," *Chem. Revs.*, **30**, 1–32 (1942).

Rabinovich, "Adsorption Theory of Photographic Development," *Trans. Faraday Soc.*, **34**, 920–926 (1938).

Sheppard, "Colloid Chemical Aspects of Photographic Development," article in *Colloid Chemistry*, Reinhold, New York, 1944. Vol. V, edited by J. Alexander.

James, "Recent Hypotheses Concerning the Mechanism of Photographic Development," *J. Chem. Education*, **23**, 595–601 (1946).

Glasstone, Laidler, and Eyring, *Theory of Rate Processes*, McGraw-Hill, New York, 1941.

Schwab, Taylor, and Spence, *Catalysis*, Van Nostrand, New York, 1937.

Specific

1. Stauffer, Smith, and Trivelli, *J. Franklin Inst.*, **238**, 291 (1944).
2. Bagdasar'yan, *Acta Physicochim. U.R.S.S.*, **19**, 421 (1944).
3. James, *J. Am. Chem. Soc.*, **61**, 648, 2379 (1939); *J. Phys. Chem.*, **45**, 223 (1941).
4. Cf. James, "Recent Hypotheses Concerning the Mechanism of Photographic Development," *J. Chem. Education*, **23**, 595 (1946).
5. James, *J. Chem. Phys.*, **14**, 536 (1946).
6. Jelley, *J. Phot. Soc. Am.*, **8**, 283 (1942).
7. James, *J. Chem. Phys.*, **11**, 338 (1943).

6.

Composition and Reactions
of the Developer

As already indicated, a developing agent must possess the property of being able to reduce sufficiently exposed grains at a substantially greater rate than unexposed or insufficiently exposed grains. Certain reducing agents, however, can be eliminated as possible candidates simply because they cannot reduce silver halide at all or can reduce only a small fraction of it. A simple ferrous salt, such as the sulfate, will serve as an example.

The Oxidation-Reduction Potential

When a solution of the ferrous salt is added to silver bromide, a certain amount of reaction occurs, producing silver and ferric ion. But the ferric ion can oxidize metallic silver. The net reaction is given by the equilibrium equation

$$Fe^{++} + AgBr \rightleftharpoons Fe^{+++} + Ag + Br^{-} \qquad (6 \cdot 1)$$

and the point of equilibrium lies far to the left. Only a very small amount of silver bromide is reduced. The equilibrium point of the reaction can be predicted quantitatively from a knowledge of the oxidation-reduction or "redox" potentials involved.

The concept of the redox potential has been used rather widely (and often erroneously) in connection with the theory of development. It will be useful to consider the concept in more detail in connection with the ferrous ion-silver bromide system, just to illustrate what can and what cannot be predicted from it.

If an inert electrode, such as platinum, is placed in a solution containing a mixture of ferrous and ferric ions, no chemical reaction with the electrode takes place, but an electric potential is set up between the electrode and the solution. The magnitude of this potential (the redox potential of the ferrous-ferric ion system) is determined by the ratio of the concentrations of the two ions according to the equation

$$E_{Fe} = E_0 + \frac{RT}{f} \log \frac{[Fe^{+++}]}{[Fe^{++}]} \tag{6.2}$$

where f is the value of the faraday, E_0 is a constant, and the brackets as usual indicate concentrations. Similarly, a silver electrode in a solution containing silver ions can set up a potential which follows the equation

$$E_{Ag} = E_0' + \frac{RT}{f} \log \frac{[Ag^+]}{[Ag]} \tag{6.3}$$

where, for most purposes, $[Ag]$ is constant. The equation for a silver-silver bromide electrode in the presence of bromide ions will be the same as 6.3, or, since the bromide ion concentration determines the silver ion concentration, it can be written:

$$E_{Ag} = E_0'' - \frac{RT}{f} \log [Br^-] \tag{6.4}$$

If, now, the silver-silver bromide electrode and the excess bromide ions are transferred to the ferrous-ferric ion solution containing the platinum electrode, an electric current will flow when an external electrical connection is made between the two electrodes *provided* the quantity $\Delta E = (E_{Ag} - E_{Fe})$ is not zero. If it is negative, ferric ions will oxidize silver. If it is positive, ferrous ions will reduce silver bromide. In either event, reaction will proceed until ΔE becomes zero. The direction of the reaction is determined by the fundamental thermodynamic principle that such a reaction can proceed only in the direction which leads to a decrease in free energy. The change in free energy to be expected is given by the equation

$$-\Delta F = \Delta Enf \tag{6.5}$$

where F is the free energy and n is the number of electrons involved in the reaction (one for the reduction of silver ions by ferrous ions).

The thermodynamic considerations show that ferrous sulfate cannot be an effective reducing agent for silver bromide because the ferric ions formed soon bring the net reaction to a halt. An examination of equation 6·2 shows, however, that anything which decreases the ratio $[Fe^{+++}]/[Fe^{++}]$ will decrease the value of E_{Fe} and hence will favor the reduction of the silver bromide. The decrease can be accomplished by adding oxalate, for example, to the solution. The oxalate forms a complex with both ferrous and ferric ions, but the ferric ions are held much more tightly than the ferrous; that is, the dissociation constant of the ferric complex is much smaller than that of the ferrous. The result is a large decrease in the ratio $[Fe^{+++}]/[Fe^{++}]$. For this reason, the solution containing the oxalate is much more effective in reducing silver bromide than a solution containing only a simple ferrous salt.

It should be noted, however, that the thermodynamic considerations do not determine whether a ferro-oxalate solution will be a developer. They show that it can reduce the silver bromide, and they show to what extent the reaction can proceed toward completion. They say nothing about the time which will be required, or whether exposure of the silver bromide to light will hasten the reaction. For example, sodium stannite fulfills the thermodynamic requirements for reaction, but it is not a developer. Apparently little or no activation energy is required for the reaction; in other words no catalyst is required, and reduction occurs without reference to light exposure. In general, no successful correlation has yet been made between developer activity and the redox potentials of the developers. Indeed, it is often impossible to determine, unambiguously, the redox potential of a developer under practical working conditions.

Classification of Developing Agents According to Structure

Several empirical correlations between developer ability and chemical structure have been suggested, but none includes all known developing agents. A correlation suggested by Kendall [1] has the widest applicability. It has a somewhat larger scope than the earlier correlations of Andresen and Lumiere. Kendall associates developer activity with the structural group a—$(C=C)_n$—b, where C≡C represents two carbon atoms joined by a double bond, n is zero or an integer, and a and b may be either hydroxyl (—OH) groups, amino (—NH$_2$) groups, or substituted amino groups. (In the substituted amino groups, one or both hydrogens are replaced by certain organic groups such as —CH$_3$, —C$_2$H$_5$, or —CH$_2$COOH.) The symbols a and b may represent either the same or different groups.

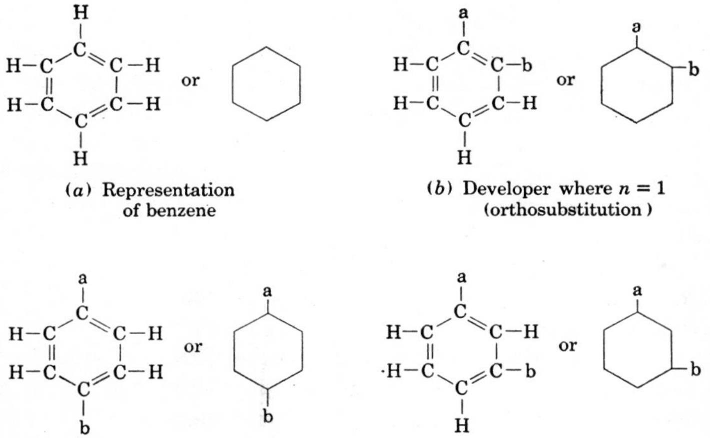

(*a*) Representation of benzene

(*b*) Developer where $n = 1$ (orthosubstitution)

(*c*) Developer where $n = 2$ (parasubstitution)

(*d*) Not a developer (metasubstitution)

FIG. 6·1   Substitutions in the benzene ring which will or will not convey developer properties.   The symbols a and b represent —OH, —NH$_2$, or substituted —NH$_2$ groups.

The simplest examples of developers falling under the Kendall classification are those for which n is zero.   Hydroxylamine, NH$_2$OH, is a good developer under proper conditions.   Two other representatives, hydrogen peroxide (HOOH) and hydrazine (NH$_2$NH$_2$), show developing properties under more restricted conditions.

The great majority of the developing agents which are included in the Kendall correlation, and indeed the great majority of all known developing agents, are aromatic compounds, principally simple benzene derivatives.   Benzene has the structure (in classical representation) shown in Fig. 6·1 (*a*).   The entire structure is usually represented by a simple hexagon, and the nucleus of six carbon atoms is referred to as the benzene ring. If two adjacent hydrogen atoms are replaced by the groups a and b, the resulting compound falls under the Kendall classification for n equals one Fig. 6·1 (*b*). If hydrogens at the opposite ends of the hexagon are replaced by a and b, n equals two, Fig. 6·1 (*c*). The adjacent positions shown in Fig. 6·1 (*b*) represent substitutions in the ortho or *o*-position; those at the opposite ends of the hexagon, Fig. 6·1 (*c*), substitutions in the para or *p*-position. Figure 6·1 (*d*) represents substitution in the meta or *m*-position, and the resulting compound either *is not* a developer or is a very weak one (with two exceptions, to be noted later in this section).

Because one or more of the hydrogen atoms of the benzene ring can be replaced by certain other atoms or groups without destroying the developer activity, the number of developers belonging to the benzene group is greatly increased. Thus, one or more hydrogens can be replaced by further hydroxyl or amino groups, or by alkyl groups or halogen atoms, and the compound still will act as a developer. Its developing properties are usually modified, however.

The Kendall classification easily can be extended to the derivatives of naphthalene and the polynuclear aromatic compounds. It also covers certain non-aromatic developers such as ascorbic acid (vitamin C). It fails to include one important group of developers however. This group contains compounds characterized by a valence change of a metal during the development process. Various ferro- and molybdo-complex ions, such as the oxalates and malonates, are represented in this group, which includes the historically important ferro-oxalate ion $Fe(C_2O_4)_2^=$. These complexes are oxidized to the corresponding ferri- and molybdi-complexes in the act of reducing silver ions. Certain other developing agents not covered by the Kendall classification include the inorganic substance, sodium hydrosulfite, and two aromatic meta derivatives, trioxymesitylene and oxyaminomesitylene.

Figure 6·2 gives the formulas of some developing agents of outstanding importance, either from a practical or a theoretical viewpoint. The amino compounds are shown as the free bases, although they are usually purchased in the form of salts, which are generally more stable and are generally more soluble in water. They are formed by direct addition of acid molecules to the free base, much as acids add to ammonia to form the ammonium salts.

The salts often are sold under trade names. Thus, methyl-*p*-aminophenol sulfate is known by several names, principally Elon

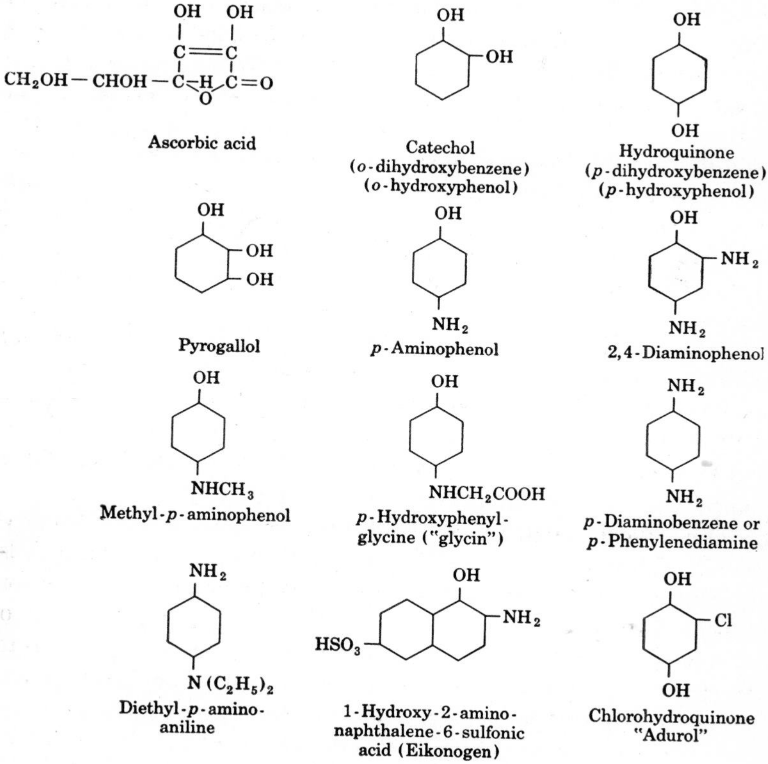

CH$_2$OH — CHOH — C$\cdots$H $\overset{\displaystyle \text{OH} \quad \text{OH}}{\underset{\displaystyle \text{O}}{\text{C}=\text{C}}}$ C=O

Ascorbic acid

OH

OH

Catechol
(*o*-dihydroxybenzene)
(*o*-hydroxyphenol)

OH

OH

Hydroquinone
(*p*-dihydroxybenzene)
(*p*-hydroxyphenol)

OH

OH
OH

Pyrogallol

OH

NH$_2$

p-Aminophenol

OH

NH$_2$

NH$_2$

2,4-Diaminophenol

OH

NHCH$_3$
Methyl-*p*-aminophenol

OH

NHCH$_2$COOH
p-Hydroxyphenyl-glycine ("glycin")

NH$_2$

NH$_2$
p-Diaminobenzene or p-Phenylenediamine

NH$_2$

N(C$_2$H$_5$)$_2$
Diethyl-*p*-amino-aniline

OH

NH$_2$

HSO$_3$

1-Hydroxy-2-amino-naphthalene-6-sulfonic acid (Eikonogen)

OH

Cl

OH

Chlorohydroquinone "Adurol"

FIG. 6·2   Structures of various developing agents.

and metol. Kodelon is a salt (usually the oxalate) of *p*-amino-phenol, and amidol is the dihydrochloride of 2,4-diaminophenol.

Dissociation and Ionization of Developing Agents

Although the amino compounds are generally dissolved in the form of salts in preparing developer solutions, the salts become completely dissociated when the solution is made sufficiently alkaline. Only the free bases exist in the practical developing solutions.

Developing agents containing one or more hydroxyl groups ionize in solution. The extent of the ionization depends upon the hydrogen ion concentration of the solution. The smaller the hydrogen ion concentration (that is to say, the more alkaline the solution), the greater will be the extent of the ionic dissociation. For example, methyl-p-aminophenol ionizes according to the equilibrium equation

$$CH_3NHC_6H_4OH \rightleftharpoons CH_3NHC_6H_4O^- + H^+ \qquad (6\cdot6)$$

The dependence of the ionization upon the hydrogen ion concentration is given by the expression

$$\frac{[CH_3NHC_6H_4O^-][H^+]}{[CH_3NHC_6H_4OH]} = K$$

or

$$[CH_3NHC_6H_4O^-] = \frac{K}{[H^+]}[CH_3NHC_6H_4OH] \qquad (6\cdot7)$$

where K is a constant for any given temperature. Its value is 4×10^{-11} at 20° C.

From equation 6·7, it follows that the concentration of the ionized methyl-p-aminophenol will equal that of the un-ionized species when the value of the hydrogen ion concentration is equal to K. When the hydrogen ion concentration equals $100\,K$, the concentration of ionized methyl-p-aminophenol will be only one one-hundredth that of the un-ionized form, and so on. Control of the concentration of the ionized form is quite important in development, since the ion is the actual developing agent. Consequently, control of the hydrogen ion concentration becomes of major importance to the control of development.

When the developing agent contains a second hydroxyl group this also may ionize, and such ionization may have an important bearing on the activity of the developing agent. For example, the divalent ion of hydroquinone is the real developing agent; consequently the ionization of the second hydroxyl group of hydroquinone is of major importance.

The ionization of hydroquinone takes place step-wise, and the concentrations of the two ionized forms are related to the hydrogen ion concentrations by the equations

$$\frac{[HOC_6H_4O^-][H^+]}{[HOC_6H_4OH]} = K_1; \quad K_1 = 1.46 \times 10^{-10} \text{ at } 20° \text{ C}$$

$$(6\cdot8)$$

and

$$\frac{[^{-}OC_6H_4O^-][H^+]}{[HOC_6H_4O^-]} = K_2; \quad K_2 \text{ is approx. } 4 \times 10^{-12} \text{ at } 20° \text{ C}$$

$$(6 \cdot 9)$$

The concentration of the doubly ionized form can be related to the concentration of the un-ionized form by combining equations $6 \cdot 8$ and $6 \cdot 9$ to give

$$[C_6H_4O_2^=] = \frac{K_1 K_2 [C_6H_4(OH)_2]}{[H^+]^2} \qquad (6 \cdot 10)$$

For many purposes, it is useful to classify developing agents according to the charge on the active form. Thus, the monovalent ion with a single negative charge is the active agent in a methyl-*p*-aminophenol (metol) developer, and the divalent ion with a

TABLE 6·1

CLASSIFICATION OF DEVELOPING AGENTS ACCORDING TO CHARGE

Charge	Agent
0	Sym-dimethyl-*p*-phenylenediamine, *p*-aminodimethylaniline, diaminodurene, and most of the other derivatives of *p*-phenylenediamine
−1	Metol, *p*-aminophenol, hydroxylamine, *p*-aminophenylglycine
−2	Hydroquinone, chlorohydroquinone, *p*-hydroxyphenylglycine, metol monosulfonic acid, ferro-oxalate ion, ascorbic acid
−3	Sodium hydroquinone monosulfonate
−4	Potassium hydroquinone disulfonate

double charge is the active agent in the hydroquinone developer. Table 6·1 lists a number of developing agents according to the charge of the active form.[2] The theoretical basis for the classification already has been given in Chapter 5; applications of it will be made in the next chapter.

Reaction of the Developing Agents with Silver Salts

When a developing agent reduces silver ions to silver, the agent itself is oxidized. The reaction involved in the development of silver halide by hydroquinone in the absence of sulfite can be represented by

$$C_6H_4(OH)_2 \rightleftharpoons 2H^+ + C_6H_4O_2^= \qquad (6\cdot11)$$

and

$$C_6H_4O_2^= + 2Ag^+ \rightleftharpoons C_6H_4O_2 + 2Ag \qquad (6\cdot12)$$

When the developing solution contains sulfite, quinone $(C_6H_4O_2)$ thus far has not been identified as a reaction product, but there is no reason to believe that it is not formed as an intermediate product. The products actually isolated from a used developer containing sulfite are hydroquinone monosulfonate and disulfonate,[3] but it is well established that quinone and sulfite in alkaline solution react rapidly to form hydroquinone monosulfonate, and this substance, upon oxidation in the presence of sulfite, goes over into the disulfonate.

It is believed that the oxidation of an organic compound such as hydroquinone takes place in steps, each involving the transfer of only one electron. On this basis, equation $6\cdot12$ should be broken up into two stages. The first involves the formation of semiquinone—a resonance-stabilized radical:

$$(6\cdot13)$$

The second is simply the reaction between the semiquinone thus produced and another silver ion to give quinone and a second atom of silver.

The organic developing agents which do not contain hydroxyl groups probably react in the un-ionized state. Ionization of the amino group according to the scheme $-NH_2 \rightleftharpoons -NH^- + H^+$, so far as the available evidence allows one to judge, is too small to be of significance. Thus, the reaction of *p*-aminodimethylaniline with silver ion can be represented by the overall equation

$$H_2N-\!\!\!\!\bigcirc\!\!\!\!-N(CH_3)_2 + 2Ag^+ \rightleftharpoons$$

$$HN=\!\!\!\!\bigcirc\!\!\!\!=N^+(CH_3)_2 + 2Ag + H^+ \quad (6 \cdot 14)$$

The reaction probably takes place in two steps, the first being

$$:N(CH_3)_2 \qquad \qquad \cdot N^+(CH_3)_2$$

$$\bigcirc \quad + Ag^+ \rightleftharpoons \quad \bigcirc \quad + Ag \qquad (6 \cdot 15)$$

$$:NH_2 \qquad \qquad :NH_2$$

Other developing agents of the benzene group react in a similar fashion. *p*-Aminophenol, for example, should yield the quinone-imide

$$O=\!\!\!\!\bigcirc\!\!\!\!=NH$$

but direct identification is difficult because of the great instability of this compound.

The oxidation products of the developing agents vary widely in stability and general reactivity. In the presence of sulfite, however, most of them react rapidly to form sulfonates, and only the sulfonates can be isolated from the conventional sulfite-containing developing solutions.

The Developing Solution

In addition to the developing agent or agents practical developing solutions usually contain (1) an alkali, added to adjust the hydrogen ion concentration (*p*H) to the most advantageous value for the particular purpose, (2) a preservative, usually sodium sulfite, and (3) potassium bromide. Other additions may be made for specific purposes.

The Alkali

The chief function of the alkali in development is to adjust the hydrogen ion concentration which, in turn, controls the concentration of the ionized form of the hydroxy developers, and hence the concentration of the actual developing agent. This is the principal reason for the practical emphasis on pH whenever the developing agent contains the OH group.

The development characteristics of the organic agents which do not contain hydroxyl groups also vary to some extent with the pH. The reason for this is not clear. A possible explanation involves the change in stability of the oxidation product of the developing agent. The reaction represented by equation 6·14 illustrates this idea. Experiment has shown that the addition of various agents which react readily with the quinone-imide oxidation product markedly increase the rate at which development proceeds. It appears, therefore, that the oxidation product is in some way interfering with the development process. The stability of this oxidation product in solution depends markedly upon the hydrogen ion concentration. Increase in pH decreases the stability, and hence increases the rate of removal of the oxidation product by way of decomposition. This, in turn, decreases the extent to which the oxidation product can interfere with the development process. Accordingly, the measured effect of an increase in pH is an increase in the rate of development.

A secondary but very important function of the alkali in practice is to maintain the hydrogen ion concentration at as nearly constant a value as possible. The development reaction is accompanied by the liberation of hydrogen ions. If not controlled, this can produce a large increase in the hydrogen ion concentration (decrease in pH) and, as a consequence, a serious decrease in the rate of development. Accordingly, it is desirable to use an alkali which has a high *buffer capacity*. Even such a buffer cannot completely prevent the change of hydrogen ion concentration during development, but it can greatly decrease that change.

Buffer capacity depends upon the presence in the solution of two components, one which can combine with hydrogen ions and one which can dissociate to give up hydrogen ions. As an example, a mixture of a very weak acid HA and an excess of its ion A^- (added in the form of the sodium or other completely dissociated salt) can act as a buffer. The acid HA can ionize to yield hydrogen ions, and the ion A^- can combine with hydrogen ions to form undissociated acid. The net hydrogen ion concentration of the solution is determined by the usual relation

$$\frac{[H^+][A^-]}{[HA]} = K \tag{6·16}$$

If, now, a small amount of strong acid (hydrogen ion) is added to the solution, the major portion of it will combine with some of the excess A^- to form HA, since K is a constant. Conversely, if a small amount of a strong base, such as sodium hydroxide, is added, the initial removal of hydrogen ion by reaction with the hydroxyl ion of the base is largely compensated by a dissociation of HA. In either event, some change in pH occurs, but it is small in comparison with the change produced in the absence of the buffer.

Several alkalies are available for practical use. Those most commonly employed are sodium hydroxide, sodium carbonate, and members of the borate group. The latter are usually the sodium metaborate (Kodalk) and the sodium tetraborate (borax). The entire pH range from about 8 to 13 can be covered by the proper use of these agents, although the buffering capacity is weak at some points. Excellent buffering can be obtained over the range 8.0 to 10.0 with the metaborate-tetraborate-boric acid system. This system cannot be used, however, for organic developers which have their active groups in the ortho position, because borate forms relatively inactive complexes with such developing agents.

Sulfite

The oxidation products of the developing agents usually have an undesirable influence on the course of development. The retarding action of the oxidation product of p-aminodiethylaniline has been mentioned already. Similar but less marked effects are produced by the oxidation products of the p-aminophenols. On the other hand, development by hydroquinone actually is accelerated by quinone or its decomposition product. The latter effect also is undesirable for most purposes, as it is uneven and difficult to control.

In addition to the kinetic effects, the oxidation products of most of the organic developing agents decompose in alkaline solution, and the products are usually colored materials which stain the emulsion. It is common practice, therefore, to add a substance which removes the oxidation products rapidly and harmlessly. Sodium sulfite is by far the most satisfactory agent for this purpose.

In alkaline solution, sulfite reacts with quinone to form hydroquinone monosulfonate ion:

$$+ SO_3^= + H_2O \rightarrow \quad\quad + OH^- \quad\quad (6\cdot17)$$

The quinone formed during development is removed almost quantitatively by this reaction. The monosulfonate is a colorless, soluble substance which probably plays no rôle of significance in the development process. It is a weak developing agent, but its rate of reaction is too small to enable it to compete with hydroquinone under most practical conditions.

The oxidation product of methyl-*p*-aminophenol (metol) reacts with sulfite in a similar manner. Metol monosulfonic acid, again a soluble, colorless product, is formed.[4] In this case, the monosulfonic acid is a fairly strong developing agent. Although its rate of reaction is less than that of the parent substance, it probably takes some part in subsequent development.

The reactions of the oxidation products of hydroquinone and metol are typical of those of most of the aromatic developers. Apart from the few developing agents where reaction between the oxidation product and the sulfite is not possible, reaction usually occurs with the formation of the monosulfonate. When the monosulfonate is oxidized, a quinone-like product is formed which usually can react with a second molecule of sulfite to form a disulfonate.

The stain-preventing action of the sulfite does not carry over to the removal of stain once formed. The stain is not produced by the quinone itself but by an oxidation and polymerization product (or products) of the quinone. Sulfite will not convert this material into a colorless product.

Sulfite plays another part in the chemistry of the developer solution, this time as a preservative. The organic developing agents in alkaline solution react rather readily with oxygen from the air. Hydroquinone, for example, reacts according to the equation

$$\bar{O}\text{—}[\text{ring}]\text{—}\bar{O} + O_2 + 2H^+ \rightarrow O\text{=}[\text{ring}]\text{=}O + H_2O_2 \qquad (6 \cdot 18)$$

Sulfite removes the quinone in the same way as before. It also removes the peroxide, since the latter readily oxidizes sulfite to sulfate. At the same time, the sulfite markedly decreases the rate of oxidation of the hydroquinone.

The preservative action of the sulfite is not simply a matter of preferential reaction between sulfite and oxygen. The rate of uptake of oxygen by a solution containing both sulfite and hydroquinone is many times smaller than the rate of uptake by the hydroquinone alone, other factors remaining constant. The effect is a genuine retardation of the oxidation of the hydroquinone.

Sulfite is a preservative for all hydroquinone derivatives where rapid reaction with the quinone is possible. On the other hand, sulfite has no effect on the rate of oxidation of tetramethylhydroquinone (durohydroquinone), where no reaction between the sulfite and the quinone takes place. Moreover, several substances besides sulfite are known to decrease the rate of oxidation of hydroquinone, and each of these reacts rapidly with the quinone. These facts suggest that small amounts of quinone, formed by an initial oxidation of some of the hydroquinone, strongly catalyze the subsequent oxidation of the remainder. Sulfite suppresses this catalysis by removing the catalyst and in this way decreases the measured rate of oxidation.

A quinone catalysis of the oxidation of durohydroquinone and trimethylhydroquinone actually has been demonstrated by direct experiment. The data on the oxidation of the durohydroquinone can be explained by a simple mechanism.[5] In the absence of a catalyst the oxidation takes place in two steps, a slow one forming the semiquinone, and a rapid one forming the quinone.

$$\text{durohydroquinone dianion} + O_2 \xrightarrow{\text{slow}} \text{semiquinone radical} + O_2^- \qquad (6\cdot19)$$

$$\text{semiquinone radical} + O_2 \xrightarrow{\text{rapid}} \text{duroquinone} + O_2^- \qquad (6\cdot20)$$

The catalysis results from the rapid reaction between the duroquinone thus produced and the original durohydroquinone to give more semiquinone:

$$\text{duroquinone} + \text{durohydroquinone dianion} \rightleftharpoons 2\ \text{semiquinone radical} \qquad (6\cdot21)$$

This reaction effectively short-circuits the first or slow step in the oxidation.

The rate of the catalyzed oxidation of durohydroquinone, as expected from this mechanism, is directly proportional to the concentration of the quinone. The same is true of the oxidation of trimethylhydroquinone *for sufficiently small concentrations of quinone*. At higher concentrations, however, the rate approaches a maximum, and further increase in trimethylquinone concentration produces only a very slight increase in reaction rate. In the oxidation of hydroquinone itself the maximum rate probably is reached at such a small concentration of quinone that the catalysis escapes direct measurement.

Sulfite retards the oxidation of many of the other developing agents, again probably by removing the catalyzing quinone. No genuine retardation has been observed where no reaction takes place between the sulfite and the oxidation product.

It will be noted from equations 6·11 and 6·18 that the oxygen oxidation of hydroquinone does not change the net hydrogen ion concentration of the solution (two hydrogen ions are "liberated" in forming the divalent ion according to equation 6·11, and two are used up in forming hydrogen peroxide according to equation 6·18), whereas the reaction between the sulfite and quinone yields hydroxyl ions (equation 6·17). Thus, oxygen oxidation of a hydroquinone-sulfite solution leads to a *decrease* in hydrogen ion concentration (increase in pH). This supplies one more reason for the use of a good buffer in the developer solution.

In addition to the functions just considered, sulfite exerts a solvent action on silver chloride and silver bromide. The sulfite ion forms a soluble complex $Ag(SO_3)_2^{\equiv}$ with silver ion. Some development effects resulting from the increase which large concentrations of sulfite produce in the solubility and rate of solution of the silver salts will be considered in the next chapter.

Bromide

Potassium bromide often is added to the developing solution as a fog restrainer and as an aid to the obtaining of more uniform development. The solubility of silver bromide in water or aqueous solution changes with the concentration of excess bromide ion in a rather complicated fashion, as already mentioned in Chapter 2. Excess bromide ion also is adsorbed by the silver bromide surface. Both factors operate to change the rates of development and fog formation, both relative and absolute. The small amounts of bromide usually added to the developing solution (0.05 M or less) generally depress the rate of fog formation to a greater degree than the rate of development; therefore more efficient development is obtained. High concentrations of bromide, under some circumstances, promote fog because of the solvent action upon the silver bromide.

Bromide can exert an effect upon the development characteristics quite apart from its action on fog, as by changing the relative rates of development at the different exposure levels. The action here is complex, but the most important factor appears to involve the charge barrier effect. This subject will be discussed in more detail in the next chapter.

Color Development

In color development of the coupler type, the oxidation product of the developing agent becomes of major importance, and removal of the oxidation product by sulfite is not desired. The primary development process is still the reduction of exposed silver halide grains to metallic silver. The developer or the emulsion layer, however, contains a compound (a coupler) which reacts with the oxidation product of the developing agent to form a dye. The emulsion is coated in several layers, each sensitive to a particular region of the spectrum. By suitable control of the development and by use of several couplers, it is possible to form the proper dye in each layer to give an adequate color representation of the light image producing the original exposure. In the final stages of processing, the silver is removed, and only the dyes remain to form the color image.

The developing agents used for this type of color development are generally members of the p-phenylenediamine group. The parent substance is not a good developer for this purpose, but replacement by alkyl groups of the two hydrogens of one amino group leads to the formation of good color developers. It is possible with a single developing agent to obtain all three basic dyes for three-color photography. Thus, with p-aminodiethylaniline as the developing agent, a yellow dye of formula I is obtained when the coupler is acetoacetic ester; a cyan (blue-green) dye of formula II is obtained with 1-naphthol as coupler; and a magenta dye of formula III is obtained with *p*-nitrobenzyl cyanide as coupler.

$$(CH_3)_2N \underset{}{\longleftrightarrow} N = COOCH_3$$
$$\underset{CO_2C_2H_5}{|}$$ I

$$(CH_3)_2N \underset{}{\longleftrightarrow} N = \underset{}{\longleftrightarrow} = O$$ II

$$(CH_3)_2N \underset{}{\longleftrightarrow} N = C \underset{}{\longleftrightarrow} NO_2$$
$$\underset{CN}{|}$$ III

The mechanism of the reaction by which the dyes are formed has not been completely worked out.

REFERENCES

General

Mees, *The Theory of the Photographic Process*, Macmillan, New York, 1942, Chapters 9, 10, 12.
Clerc, *La technique photographique*, Paul Montel, Paris, 3rd ed., 1942, Vol. 1, Chapter 28.
Kolthoff and Laitinen, *pH and Electro Titrations*, Wiley, New York, 1941.

Specific

1. Kendall, *Proc. IX Intern. Congr. Phot.*, *Paris*, **227** (1935).
2. James, *J. Phys. Chem.*, **43**, 701 (1939).
3. Kauffmann, *Ber.*, **40**, 4550 (1907); Pinnow, *Z. wiss. Phot.*, **13**, 41 (1914).
4. Lehmann and Tausch, *Phot. Korr.*, **71**, 17, 135 (1935).
5. James and Weissberger, *J. Am. Chem. Soc.*, **60**, 98, 2084 (1938).

7.

General Kinetics of Development

The simplest study of the kinetics of development, from the theoretical point of view, would be that of the development of a single, typical silver bromide grain by a developing agent in a simple solution. This study has not been carried out. Some experiments by Meidinger and by Rabinovich approach these conditions, however.

Kinetics of Development of Large, Single Grains

Meidinger [1] investigated the kinetics of development of large individual silver bromide grains in a metol-hydroquinone solution. From microscopic observations he determined the rate of initiation of development R_i and the rate of continuation of development throughout the grain R_c. The initiation rate R_i was determined from the time which elapsed between the penetration of the developer to the grain and the appearance of the first traces of reduction visible under the microscope. This rate increased with increasing light exposure until a maximum was reached. In the region of solarization, the rate decreased. The continuation rate R_c, on the other hand, was independent of the exposure. Both R_i and R_c decreased with increasing bromide concentration in the developer, but the decrease in R_i was relatively much greater at low bromide concentrations. Both rates increased when the pH of the developer was increased, and both rates decreased when the developer was diluted with water. Rabinovich and coworkers, using a hydroquinone developer, observed that the rate of increase of the visible silver-silver bromide interface in the early stages of development of some large, thin grains varied roughly in direct proportion to the extent of the interface.[2]

The preceding results are in adequate agreement with the mechanism of development already given. An increase in the extent of the silver-silver bromide interface increases the amount of silver bromide in contact with the catalyst at any time and hence should increase the rate of reaction. An increase in the amount of exposure increases the amount of catalyst and, presumably, the amount of interface, provided no solarization occurs. Solarization, on the basis of the rehalogenation hypothesis, decreases the amount of interface which the developer can reach. The relative effect of bromide upon R_i can be explained on the basis of the electric barrier effect as described subsequently in connection with the induction period, although it is possible that some other factor also may be involved. The experimental procedure followed by Meidinger and Rabinovich is not free from objections, however, since they used grains which were considerably larger than those commonly found in photographic emulsions, and the gelatin which they used had been desensitized by treatment with iodine.

Relation between Density and the Size and Number of Developed Grains

The development of a normal photographic emulsion presents a more complex situation. Development rates are usually determined from measurements of changes in optical density. As development proceeds, however, density may increase in either or both of two essentially distinct ways: (1) by increase in the average size of the developed silver particles, that is, by increase in the degree of completion of development of those grains which are developing; and (2) by increase in the *number* of developing or developed grains.

Two extreme cases may be imagined. In the first, all the grains start to develop at the same time; that is, the period of initiation of development is the same for all, and development of any one grain parallels that of any other grain. Increase in density then is caused solely by increase in the size of the silver particles. In the second case, the initiation periods vary in magnitude, and the duration of the initiation period for any given grain is much greater than the duration of reaction beyond the initiation period. At any intermediate stage of the gross development of the emulsion, the image is made up essentially of completely or almost completely developed grains. Density then is determined by the number of developed grains. Between these two extremes, the entire range of combinations of the two is possible.

The suggestion has been made on theoretical grounds that the density should increase in direct proportion to the increase in the total projection area of all the developing silver particles; that is, the relation $D = kn\bar{a}$, where n is the number of silver particles per unit area and $\bar{a}$ is the average projection area per particle, should hold. Experimentally, it has been shown that the density increases proportionately with the number n when the average size of the particles remains constant. There is doubt, however, about the general validity of the assumed proportionality between D and $\bar{a}$. If the number of particles is held constant, the following relation often holds to a reasonably good approximation:

$$\frac{M}{D} = Bd + C \qquad (7\cdot1)$$

where M is the mass of silver per unit area of emulsion, d is the diameter of the average projection area of the silver particle (considered as a circle), and B and C are constants. The validity of this equation has not been established over a wide range of particle shapes, however, and it is possible that B and C do not remain constant over such a range.

The quantity M/D in equation $7\cdot1$ is termed the photometric equivalent, but it is far from being a universal constant. It can vary many times over from emulsion to emulsion, and even for a single emulsion it can vary with the conditions of development and with the exposure. When an emulsion having a rather wide distribution of grain sizes is given full development in a conventional developer, the photometric equivalent decreases with increasing exposure over a considerable range. The reason for this behavior is that the large grains are statistically more sensitive than the small ones, and thus the developable grains that predominate at the low exposures are the large ones. As exposure increases, the *average* size of the developed grains decreases. Emulsions which have a narrow range of grain sizes show little variation of photometric equivalent with exposure.

The behavior of the photometric equivalent during the course of development often indicates why the density is changing,[3] especially if the emulsion has a narrow range of grain sizes. If, with such an emulsion, the photometric equivalent remains essentially constant with increasing density, the increase in density is brought about primarily by an increase in the number of developed grains, and the average size of the silver grains remains essentially constant. If, on the other hand, the photometric equivalent increases as development proceeds, the average silver particle size is increasing according to equation 7·1.

Kinetics of Development under Simplified Conditions

In studying the kinetics of development of a simple emulsion, it is often possible to adjust conditions so that the majority of the grains develop as an ensemble in which the course of development in each grain substantially parallels that of development in any other grain. Development of motion-picture positive film exposed to give ultimate densities which lie well in the shoulder region of the characteristic curve follows this course in some simple developing solutions. This is true of development by sulfite-free hydroquinone solutions [4] of pH 8 to 9, used in the absence of oxygen. Under these conditions, the rate of development by hydroquinone varies approximately as the square root of the concentration of the divalent ion $C_6H_4O_2^=$. This variation holds whether the change in concentration is caused by a change in total hydroquinone content of the solution, or simply by a change in pH.

The rate of development by hydroquinone cannot be described uniquely in terms of the concentration of either the un-ionized hydroquinone or its monovalent ion. It can be described only in terms of the concentration of the divalent hydroquinonate ion. This fact shows that the divalent ion is the active developing agent. The dependence of rate upon the square root of the concentration implies that the ion reacts in the adsorbed state (cf. equations 5·5 and 5·6). Since there is no substantial evidence of adsorption of hydroquinone to silver nuclei, it may be assumed that the adsorption involves the silver bromide or the silver-silver bromide interface. There is independent evidence to support this assumption.

The addition of bromide to the hydroquinone solution decreases the rate of development, and the decrease is much more marked

at the start of the reaction than in the later stages. This result is
in complete agreement with Meidinger's observations of the effect
of bromide on the rate of development of individual silver bromide
grains (page 104). Quantitatively, the effect of bromide on the
rate at which development starts in the hydroquinone solution is
accurately described by the equation

$$\log t = \alpha \log [Br^-] + \text{constant} \qquad (7 \cdot 2)$$

where t is the time of appearance of the image, and α is a fraction.

Quinone, one of the reaction products, accelerates development.
Small amounts of sulfite decrease the measured rate because the
sulfite removes the quinone formed in the reaction, but such small
amounts do not alter the kinetics of development in any other
significant way. Large amounts of sulfite, however, introduce
complications which will be treated subsequently.

The Induction Period

A definite induction period exists for development by some
agents under proper conditions.[5] In the induction period region,
the rate of formation of density increases with the time of develop-

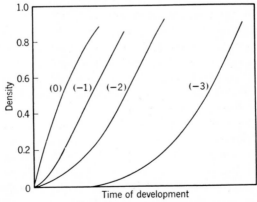

FIG. 7·1 Effect of the charge of the developing agent upon the shape of the
initial portion of the density-time of development curve.

ment; as a result the initial part of the density-time of development curve is concave in shape, as shown by curves (-1), (-2)
and (-3) of Fig. 7·1. A marked induction period is obtained
with the simple, sulfite-free hydroquinone developer used under

the conditions described in the preceding section. In this case, a part of the acceleration of development can be attributed to the action of the quinone which is accumulating in the solution, but a marked acceleration persists even when sulfite is added to prevent the accumulation of quinone. Moreover, the acceleration indicated by the density change is *in addition to* the acceleration caused by the increase in the extent of the silver-silver bromide interface. It is probable that, because of the nature of the relation between density and the mass of silver (equation 7·1), the acceleration resulting from the increase in interface will not show up in the density plot. This idea is supported strongly by the fact that, when certain other developing agents (for example, diaminodurene) are used under the same conditions, the density plots do not show induction periods (curve 0, Fig. 7·1) even though the density bears the same relation as before to the mass of silver. A curve with a concave region at the foot is obtained for such a developer only when the mass of silver (instead of density) is plotted against the time of development. Thus, the expected increase in rate with increase in interface is revealed only by the silver plot, not by the density plot.

An induction period is obtained only when the developing agent acts in the form of a negatively charged ion,[5] and its magnitude depends primarily upon the amount of charge on the ion, not on its chemical nature. Figure 7·1 shows typical curves produced by developing agents of charge 0, −1, −2, and −3.

The induction period can be explained in terms of a change in the magnitude of the charge barrier protecting the individual silver halide grains. In the early stages of development, an increase in the size of the silver speck is accompanied by a decrease in the magnitude of the barrier (see Chapter 5). The local decrease in the barrier permits a larger percentage of the developer ions to reach the solid surface, and the rate of the reaction is increased. The relative effect is greater, the greater the charge of the developing ion and the greater the magnitude of the original barrier. Increase in the halide ion concentration of the developing solution produces an increase in the magnitude of the barrier and hence a corresponding increase in the relative extent of the induction period for the charged developers. Meidinger's observation that the rate of initiation of development is more sensitive to bromide ion concentration than is the rate of continuation of development finds an explanation in this effect of bromide ion on the charge barrier. Uncharged developing agents, on the other hand, are not impeded by the barrier, and hence development by them does not show an induction period.

As already mentioned, sulfite in small amounts decreases the measured rate of development by hydroquinone because it removes quinone which otherwise would accelerate the reaction. Sulfite produces a similar decrease in the initial rates of development by all the *doubly charged* developing ions tested, *except* where the sulfite does not react with the oxidation product. This fact strongly suggests that the accelerating action of the oxidation product is tied up with a decrease in the barrier charge. Such a decrease probably results from adsorption of the oxidation product, or a decomposition product thereof, by the silver halide. When the developing agent is *uncharged*, the oxidation products do not increase but often *decrease* the rate of development: small amounts of sulfite and other substances which remove these products increase the rate of development. The singly charged ions show intermediate results when reaction between sulfite and the oxidation product occurs readily.

The barrier effects discussed thus far originate solely or primarily in the electrostatic action of the adsorbed halide layer. The electric charge of the gelatin also affects the rate of development by negative ions in alkaline solution. When the developer is used in a solution containing a very low total salt concentration, the retarding action of the gelatin charge can be quite significant. This charge is diminished and the rate of development is increased by the addition of neutral salt. Thus, the rate of development of motion-picture positive film by ascorbic acid is increased about sixfold when the potassium ion concentration is increased from $0.05 \, M$ to $1.0 \, M$ by the addition of potassium nitrate. The effect of salt is considerably greater when the developing agent is doubly charged than when it is singly charged, and potassium salts produce greater acceleration than the corresponding sodium salts.

The Kinetics of Practical Development

The rate of development, as measured under the conditions usually employed in practice, is often a complex quantity. Usually, it is not possible to determine from the available data whether the change in density is primarily a matter of change in the size or in the number of silver particles or whether it is because of both. Changes in development conditions may alter the relative importance of size and number without the alteration becoming evident from the simple kinetic data.

Development under the usual practical conditions generally is complicated in other ways. The measured rate often depends upon the interaction and combination of the rates of a number of separate stages, such as rates of diffusion of the developer through the gelatin layer, of penetration of the double-layer barrier, of adsorption of the developing agent, of reduction of silver ions to silver, of solution of the silver halide, and of accumulation or elimination of the reaction products. It is not surprising, therefore, that theoretical interpretations of data obtained under these circumstances are often somewhat ambiguous.

The methods of expressing the rate of development generally fall into three groups. These depend upon (1) the time of appearance of the image, (2) the rate of increase of density for a fixed exposure, and (3) the rate of increase of gamma.

The Watkins formula is sometimes taken as a practical basis for the first method. This formula states that

$$t_D = W \cdot t_a \qquad (7 \cdot 3)$$

where t_D is the time required to obtain the density D, t_a is the time of appearance of the image, and W is the *Watkins factor*. Within limits, W is approximately constant for changes in concentration, temperature, and pH. It varies to some extent with the nature of the emulsion and the amount of exposure, and it varies markedly with the nature of the developing agent. The time of appearance of the image, however, is generally of less practical importance than the rate of increase of density or gamma.

Rate measurements based upon the change of gamma, in turn, are generally of greater practical usefulness than those based upon the change of density. Neither method gives a complete representation of the rate of change of the photographic characteristics, however, since the toe and shoulder regions of the characteristic curve do not always show precisely the same rate of change as the straight portion. The rates of change of density and of gamma sometimes are determined with the aid of approximation equations such as those given in the following section. Useful rates can be obtained, however, simply by measuring the slope of the density- or gamma-time of development curves at some specified value of density or gamma.

The Progress of Development under Constant Conditions

Various formulas have been suggested to represent the progress of development when the developer composition is held constant. The simplest of these is

$$\frac{dD}{dt} = k(D_\infty - D) \tag{7·4}$$

where D_∞ represents the density for complete development. It is doubtful whether this formula has any theoretical significance as applied to development. At present, it is best considered as an empirical equation which fits the data over a limited range. Wide departures from it often are observed, and it is not surprising in view of the complex nature of development. Nor is it surprising that none of the various elaborations which have been suggested has led to an expression of general validity. One equation of this kind,[6] in its integrated form, is the following:

$$D = (A \log t + B) \log E + C \log t + G$$
$$= \gamma \log E + C \log t + G \tag{7·5}$$

where A, B, C, and G are constants which depend upon concentration, pH, and temperature (and probably the nature of the emulsion as well). The equation holds over a wide range of concentrations of developing agents and of pH for metol-hydroquinone solutions, but only when applied to the straight portion of the characteristic curve and to intermediate stages of development. It fails at very low gamma and at gamma values approaching the maximum.

A simple equation of the same form as 7·4, but expressing the rate of change of gamma instead of density, is of some importance. In its integrated form, the equation is

$$\gamma = \gamma_\infty(1 - e^{-kt}) \tag{7·6}$$

where γ_∞ is the limiting value of γ for the emulsion involved. This equation gives a more accurate representation of the progress of development in most cases than equation 7·4, but it still is not rigorous. The equation is used primarily to determine γ_∞, the ultimate contrast of the photographic material. The value of k in the equation depends markedly upon the nature of the developer, its temperature, and to some extent upon the nature of the emulsion. It also tends to decrease for some time as the emulsion is kept, whereas γ_∞ is practically independent of the age of the emulsion during its useful life.

Diffusion Effects in Practical Development

Sheppard and Mees showed that the absolute time required for the developer to penetrate the thickness of the emulsion is small, amounting in general to only a few seconds. The composition of the developer in the immediate vicinity of the developing grain, however, may differ considerably from the original composition of the solution when development is rapid. The developing agent is being used up, reaction products are forming, and diffusion is not sufficiently rapid to restore the original developer composition. The latter is shown by the fact that agitation of the developer has an important effect on the rate of rapid development.

If no agitation whatever is used, development by a normally rapid-acting solution becomes noticeably retarded and often uneven in character. Increase in the rate of agitation produces an increase in the rate of development, the latter rate eventually approaching a maximum. Figure 7·2 illustrates the effect. The experiments [7] were carried out with motion-picture positive film and a normal metol-hydroquinone developer (Kodak D-16). Agitation was obtained by the "brush" method, in which a soft, camel's-hair brush is drawn back and forth over the surface of the film.

The absolute rate of diffusion of an individual molecule in the gelatin probably is not affected by such agitation, but the net rate of diffusion is. The net rate of diffusion between the surface of the emulsion and the points where the actual development is occurring (the grains within the emulsion) is determined by the concentration gradient. The rate of diffusion of a particular molecular species is given by the equation

$$\frac{dM}{dt} = A \cdot P \frac{dc}{dx} \tag{7·7}$$

where dM is the amount which diffuses in time dt, A is the area of the film, P is the diffusion coefficient, and dc/dx is the concentration gradient.

In the absence of agitation, a quiescent layer of solution forms along the emulsion surface. Selective diffusion of the developing agent, alkali, and the like into the gelatin tends to change the concentration in this layer of developer. New developer can be supplied only by diffusion from the bulk of the solution. On the

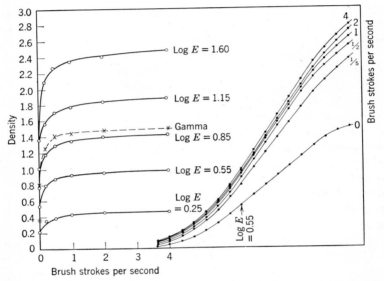

Fig. 7·2 Effect of agitation upon the rate of development by a rapidly acting developer. The characteristic curves obtained for various rates of brushing are plotted on the right-hand side of the figure; gamma and densities for various exposures are plotted, as functions of the rate of brushing, on the left-hand side. (Ives and Jensen.)

other hand, bromide ion being liberated in the development reaction diffuses out toward the quiescent layer, which thus becomes richer in bromide ion than is the bulk solution. Both effects decrease the concentration gradient between the surface of the emulsion and the reaction sites. Agitation disrupts the quiescent layer and keeps the surface of the emulsion in direct contact with developer of the same composition as the bulk of the solution. This, in turn, increases the concentration gradient between the surface and the points where the reaction is taking place within the emulsion, and thus increases the rate of rapid development.

It will be noted that the effect of agitation is of little significance when the rate of development is very small. When the specific rate of the chemical reaction is very much smaller than the rate of diffusion, the former controls the measured rate and the latter is of no importance. On the other hand, if the specific rate of the chemical reaction is very much greater than the rate of diffusion, the molecules of the developer react practically as soon as they reach the reaction sites, and thus diffusion controls the overall, or measured, rate of the development process.

Bromide in Practical Development

Soluble bromides usually retard the rate of fog formation to a greater extent than they retard the rate of development of the latent image, provided the bromide ion concentration does not exceed a few grams per liter. Likewise, bromide ion generally decreases the rate of growth of density in the lower exposure regions to a relatively greater extent than in the higher exposure regions. If development is carried to equal gamma values in a series of solutions varying only in bromide content, the entire characteristic curve is usually displaced with increasing bromide ion concentration toward larger exposure values.

In a series of characteristic curves representing simply a change in development time, it is often found that all the straight line extensions (Fig. 1·3) pass through a common point when they are extrapolated toward the log E axis. When the developer contains little or no bromide, this confluence point generally lies on or very near the log E axis. The exact position and even the existence of the point depends upon both the developer and the emulsion. (Some emulsions fail to give a confluence point with any developer, and a few developing solutions fail to give a confluence point with any emulsion.) Addition of bromide in sufficient quantity shifts the confluence point downward below the axis (Fig. 7·3). The extent of the shift has often been used to express the sensitivity of the developing agent to bromide, and this sensitivity in turn has been used as a basis for classifying developing agents. The most extensive work of this sort was carried out by Nietz,[8] and his relative values, sometimes erroneously referred to as reduction potentials, have been widely quoted. These relative values, however, are not constant, as they depend upon the conditions under which they are determined. The bromide effect on development by a single agent can change markedly with a large change in pH or in concentration of the developing agent.

The electric charge effect appears to be one important factor which influences the depression of the confluence point. The available data show a considerably larger depression for the doubly charged agents than for chemically similar singly charged or un-

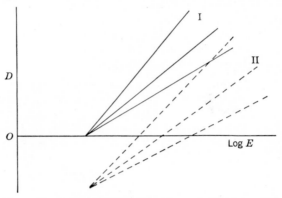

FIG. 7·3 Generalized straight line extensions of the characteristic curves, showing depression of the confluence point due to bromide. I, no bromide; II, added bromide.

charged agents. It is unlikely, however, that the charge effect is entirely responsible for the differences in bromide depressions between the various developing agents. For example, bromide also may influence the development rate by affecting the adsorption of developing agents to silver bromide or by altering the concentration of the activated complex formed between the developing agent and the silver ion. The search for a complete explanation of the bromide depression is hampered because many of the data in the literature are not comparable and because sometimes important variations in the conditions within a single set of tests have been disregarded.

Effect of Change in Total Concentration of Developing Solution

Simple dilution of a ferro-oxalate developer containing no bromide produces a relatively simple change in development conditions. Primarily, the change is in the concentration of the de-

veloping agent, since no sulfite is present and the rate of development is almost independent of pH. Sheppard and Mees found
that the rate of development in a ferro-oxalate solution containing
little or no bromide varied almost directly with the total concentration. A nearly constant degree of development was obtained
when the product of time and concentration was constant regardless of the specific value of either.

Dilution of most of the commonly employed developers produces a more complicated change. Not only is the concentration
of the developing agent decreased, but the sulfite concentration,
bromide concentration, and total salt concentration are decreased
as well. Moreover, the pH is often changed. The complicated
change in development rate which can result is well illustrated by
Chibisoff's data.

The initial composition of the developing solution was as
follows:

Developing agent	0.05 M
Sodium sulfite crystals	100 grams
Sodium carbonate crystals	54 grams
Potassium bromide	1 gram
Water to make	1000 ml

Development was carried out at 15° C. Table 7·1 gives the
gamma values obtained when the product of concentration and
time of development is constant. Data of this type can be used to
determine empirically the dilution required to yield a specified
gamma for a given time of development, or conversely the time
required for a given concentration. It should not be assumed,
however, that a developer formula of substantially different
composition from that just given will yield results which are
strictly parallel to those shown in Table 7·1.

TABLE 7·1

VALUES OF GAMMA FOR VARIOUS DEVELOPING AGENTS WHEN
CONCENTRATION × TIME IS HELD CONSTANT

Concentration	1	0.5	0.25	1	0.5	0.25	1	0.5	0.25
Time	1	2	4	2	4	8	4	8	16
Catechol							0.35	0.60	0.70
Pyrogallol				0.42	0.48	0.52	0.75	0.95	0.81
p-Aminophenol				0.32	0.49	0.63	0.59	0.88	0.94
Metol		0.37	0.56	0.67	0.81	0.98	1.20		
Amidol		0.39	0.60	0.43	0.76	1.12	1.04		

Concentration of the Developing Agent

Data showing the effect of change in concentration of the developing agent alone are scarce. Many of the older data cannot be used, since pH control was neglected. Several anomalous results reported in the literature can be explained adequately on the basis of a change in pH. An example is found in the reported optimum concentrations of amidol and metol, beyond which an

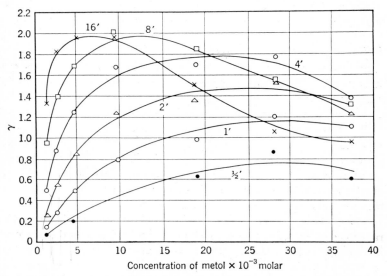

FIG. 7·4 Dependence of development rate upon metol concentration. Gamma is plotted against metol concentration for several times of development. (Kan-Kagan.)

increase in concentration produced a decrease in rate of density formation. The increase in concentration simply produced a drop in pH which was accompanied by an actual *decrease* in the concentration of the active developing agent (the ion).

It is to be expected that an increase in the concentration of the active developing agent will result in an increase in development rate. Such is actually the situation in general, but the quantitative form of the increase often is not simple. Results obtained by Kan-Kagan illustrate the point. A metol developer containing 0.127 N sulfite was used. The pH was adjusted to 10.6. Changes in the concentration of metol produced considerable variations in the shape of the characteristic curves, corresponding to changes in the relative rates of development of the various exposure steps. The rate of growth of density increased with increasing metol concentration. The gamma values corresponding to the longer times of development, however, passed through a maximum (Fig. 7·4). The drop in gamma at the longer development times probably was caused by the increase in general fog, which was considerable. It should be noted in considering results of this type that data obtained with a single emulsion are not necessarily typical and that conclusions based on such data cannot safely be generalized.

Effect of the Alkali

Specification of the pH of a developing solution is of primary importance. Fortunately, pH values can be determined with ease and considerable accuracy now that glass electrode pH meters are available as routine laboratory instruments.

The suitable pH range for practical development varies widely with the nature of the developing agent. Most of the organic agents, especially those containing active hydroxyl groups, do not develop at a useful rate unless the solution is alkaline. The rate of development increases with the alkalinity, for reasons given in the previous chapter, eventually approaching a maximum.

A few organic agents, such as amidol, will develop at a useful rate even in a slightly acid solution. Ferro-oxalate is most useful in acid solution; it shows little dependence on pH over the range of 4 to 7. It cannot be employed at pH values much above 7 unless oxygen is strictly excluded from the system. Dissociation of a hydrogen ion is not involved in the determination of the reaction rate in this case. Increases in alkalinity can influence the development rate of ferro-oxalate only by increasing the gelatin charge barrier effect (an effect which is scarcely noticeable when the total salt concentration is high) and by promoting the formation of ferrous and ferric hydroxides or intermediate hydrolysis products of ferrous and ferric ions.

Figure 7·5 shows [9] the dependence of density upon pH for a fixed exposure and time of development; each curve represents a different developing agent used in a conventional solution containing sulfite. The pH dependence of the agents varies considerably. For example, the change in rate of development by p-aminophenol (curve IV) produced by a given change in pH is less than one fourth of that of hydroquinone (curve II). It is to be expected, of course, that the rate of development by singly ionized agents should show less dependence upon pH than that by doubly ionized agents. Once again, however, the presence of several complicating factors has thus far prevented a general quantitative formulation of the pH effect in the conventional developing solutions.

Data on the effect of various buffers show that the specific nature of the buffer has only a slight effect on the rate of develop-

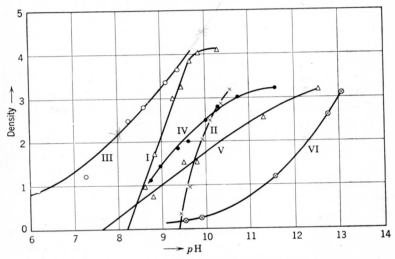

Fig. 7·5 Dependence upon pH of density obtained for a fixed exposure and time of development. I, pyrogallol; II, hydroquinone; III, metol; IV, p-aminophenol; V, p-hydroxyphenylglycine; VI, p-phenylenediamine. (Reinders and Beukers.)

ment. Even the slight variation noted may be caused simply by a variation in total salt concentration. One important exception, however, is noted in the use of borate buffers with orthohydroxy developers because a complex is formed between the borate and the —C(OH)=C(OH)— grouping, and the developer activity is markedly reduced as a result. Borate buffers, accordingly, should not be used with pyrogallol, catechol, or other developing agents having two active hydroxy groups in ortho positions.

In practice, several factors enter into the choice of a buffer for a particular developer. Buffer capacity in the desired pH region, solubility of the buffer salts, and cost of the buffer salts are all of importance. Some buffers adversely affect the properties of the fixing bath. Trisodium phosphate, for example, should not be used when a potassium alum fixing bath is employed.

Salt Effects

The rate of development by the charged agents depends upon the total salt concentration and upon the specific nature of the ions formed by dissociation of the salt. Usually this effect is unimportant in practice, since most developing solutions normally contain a rather high salt concentration, and moderate variations have little influence on the development rate. For this reason, the very existence of a salt effect is often overlooked.

The concentration of positive ions (principally sodium) is already $1 N$ or greater in the developing solutions commonly employed in practice. An increase in the rate of development by hydroquinone can be achieved in such a solution by the addition of a large amount of potassium nitrate, but considerable variations in sodium ion concentration will produce no detectable change. The salt effect is even smaller in developers containing metol or other singly charged agents. Relatively large variations in salt concentration are of little or no practical significance in such developing solutions, except where large additions of salt produce a marked decrease in the swelling of the gelatin. Sodium sulfate, for example, is often added to the solution to control the swelling of the gelatin when development must be carried out at tropical temperatures. Such additions of sodium sulfate decrease the rate of development under proper conditions, presumably by retarding diffusion of the developer into the emulsion.

Sulfite

The development rates of most of the agents used commercially would be altered if the oxidation products of the agents were allowed to accumulate. Thus, the oxidation products of hydroquinone, pyrogallol, and p-hydroxyphenylglycine accelerate development, while the oxidation products of metol, p-aminophenol, and p-aminodiethylaniline retard development over most or all of its course. Sulfite changes the development rates of solutions of these and many other agents simply by combining with the oxidation products to form sulfonates.

Since the amount of sulfite required to remove effectively the oxidation product is usually rather small, the quantities of sulfite normally employed in development are more than adequate. Fairly large changes in sulfite concentration can then be made without changing the rate of development in this way. Some of the substituted *p*-phenylenediamines are exceptional in this respect, however, and even such agents as hydroquinone and *p*-hydroxyphenylglycine may show some effects of oxidation products when the overall rate of development is large, even though the sulfite concentration is also large.

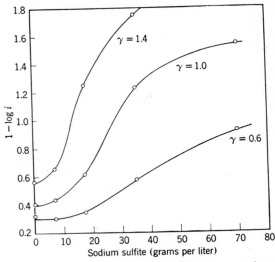

Fig. 7·6 Variation of emulsion speed with sulfite content of an iso-ascorbic acid developer.

With some developing agents, changes in the sulfite concentration can produce a measurable change in development rate as a result of the general salt effect. Sulfite contributes 50 per cent or more of the total salt concentration in most practical developers.

The solvent action of sulfite on silver chloride and bromide undoubtedly has some effect on development rates, but data are not available on this point for developers of the conventional composition. A more important practical aspect of this solvent action is the tendency of high-sulfite developers to give less graininess, other things being equal, as discussed in the last section of this chapter.

Large concentrations of sulfite can change the relative rates of development for different exposures, and in this way change the measured emulsion speed for incomplete development. The effect is illustrated in Fig. 7·6 by some data obtained with ascorbic acid as developing agent. The measured speed (expressed as $1-\log i$) is plotted against sulfite concentration for development carried to a constant gamma. Sulfite produced a marked increase in the measured speed for each of the three gamma values represented. An increase of this type, however, has been obtained only when the active developing agent was a negative ion. It is probable that the charge barrier effect once more is involved. The solvent action of the sulfite may disrupt the adsorbed bromide ion layer and in this way make the latent image centers formed by the smaller exposures more accessible to the developer ions than they were originally.

The Temperature Coefficient

The rate of most chemical reactions increases with increase in temperature, and development is no exception. Because the

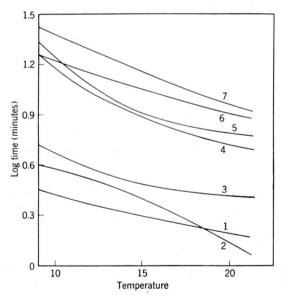

FIG. 7·7 Dependence of time of development required to obtain a fixed gamma upon temperature of the developing solution. 1, amidol; 2, metol; 3, pyrogallol; 4, *p*-aminophenol; 5, catechol; 6, hydroquinone; 7, *p*-hydroxy-phenylglycine. (Chibisoff.)

variation of rate with temperature is often large, adequate temperature control is of considerable practical importance.

Once more, the rate variation is not simple. Reaction rates, diffusion rates, and degrees of ionization all are influenced by temperature. Each component plays a part in determining the ultimate temperature dependence of development under most practical conditions. Figure 7·7 illustrates the variation of rate for several developing agents. Here the logarithm of the time required to obtain a fixed gamma is plotted against the temperature in degrees centigrade. The plot is almost linear for some developing agents; for others the variation from linearity is considerable.

The temperature dependence is increased by the addition of bromide to the developer, and it is generally decreased by an increase in pH. The dependence also often varies with the nature of the photographic emulsion, but some data suggest that it becomes independent of the nature of the emulsion when sufficient bromide is added to the developer. For example, Ferguson found that a pyrogallol developer containing 10 grams of potassium bromide per liter gave practically the same temperature dependence for all emulsions tested. The rate of development in these tests doubled for each 10° C increase in temperature.

The Metol-Hydroquinone Combination

Metol and hydroquinone are often employed in the same developing solution because the combination not only has desirable features of the components but has further practical advantages which the components individually do not possess. The rate of development is generally greater than would be predicted by a simple addition of the individual rates. The development characteristics often combine desirable features of each individual agent. The flexibility of the combination is so great that metol-hydroquinone developers can be used for practically any development requirements within the scope of black-and-white photography.

It has been suggested that a complex between the individual developing agents is formed in a metol-hydroquinone solution, and that this complex constitutes a substantially new developing agent of superior properties. There is no evidence, however, that such a complex can exist in alkaline solution. An explanation based on the charge effect [10] seems preferable, although even this explanation may not be wholly adequate. According to it, metol, by virtue of its smaller charge, starts development of the individual grains. The number of grains which have started to develop at any given stage of the process, therefore, depends upon this component of the developer. Once reduction has progressed beyond the induction period stage, the hydroquinone takes a much greater part in the development, and the overall character of development then shifts toward that of the hydroquinone type. The extent of the ultimate shift will depend upon the relative concentration of hydroquinone and the pH of the solution. In general, the greater the concentration of hydroquinone or the greater the pH, the more closely the development characteristics will approach those of hydroquinone.

Fog

It is desirable to regard fog as characteristically different from the density produced by image development. In the presence of a developed image, however, it is usually impossible to separate quantitatively the densities arising from the two sources. The amount of fog in a given area must decrease with increasing image density, because some of the grains which might have been reduced as fog have developed as image. To add to the difficulty of separation, the optical density of fog usually does not bear exactly the same relation to the mass of silver as the image density does. Under some conditions, the difference may be negligible; under others, it may be considerable. There is no assurance that the photometric equivalent (M/D) of the fog, determined in the absence of the image, is the same as that of fog formed in the presence of the image. It is quite likely that the presence of the developing image changes to some extent the form, distribution, or amount of fog silver, particularly when a considerable amount of silver halide solvent action is occurring. For example, silver ions in solution which, in the absence of an image, would produce fog nuclei by reduction may, in the presence of an image, simply develop out upon the image centers.

For practical purposes, the significant factor in specifying fog is the ratio of the rate of fog formation to that of image development. Shiberstoff has determined the variation of this ratio with the developing agent and the temperature, using the developer formula given on page 117. He expressed the rate of image formation in terms of the reciprocal of the time required to obtain a

density of 1.5 for a specified exposure, and the rate of fog formation in terms of the reciprocal of the time required to obtain a
density of 0.3 for the unexposed material. He then determined
the value of the ratio

$$U = \frac{\text{image rate}}{\text{fog rate}} = 100\,\frac{t(\text{fog})}{t(\text{image})}$$

The results are given in Table 7·2. It is seen that the selectivity
varies considerably with the developing agent. It also decreases
with an increase of temperature, showing that the rate of growth
of fog increases more rapidly than that of the image (cf. Chapter 5).

The value of U, as determined above, will depend upon the
nature of the emulsion and upon the formula in which the developing agent is tested. Even the order in which certain of the developing agents fall can be changed by suitable variation of these factors.

TABLE 7·2

THE SELECTIVITY OF ACTION OF VARIOUS DEVELOPING AGENTS

Developing Agent	U at 15° C	U at 20° C	U at 25° C
p-Aminophenol	500	500	250
Catechol	267	227	191
p-Hydroxyphenylglycine	259	210	150
Metol	240	180	200
Pyrogallol	200	136	100
Bromohydroquinone	159	131	95
Chlorohydroquinone	196	123	106
Hydroquinone	93	75	50

Fog generally has a complex origin. Emulsion fog and developer
fog often are produced simultaneously, and other types may be
superimposed upon them under certain conditions. Experimentally, a partial separation between emulsion fog and development
fog can be made by use of emulsions specially prepared for the
purpose; limited kinetic studies have been made in this way.
These have indicated a marked difference in the effect of sulfite on
the two types of fog produced when hydroquinone is used as
developing agent. A small amount of sulfite decreases the rate
of emulsion fog formation, just as it decreases the rate of development. On the other hand, the sulfite *increases* the rate of developer
fog formation. The quinone formed in the initial stages of the

fogging reaction evidently interferes with the further formation of developer fog, probably by destroying incipient catalytic centers. Substances other than sulfite which remove quinone produce a similar increase in this type of fog.

With most developers, both types of fog formation are more sensitive than image development to changes in the bromide content of the solution. Accordingly, bromide is often used as an *anti-foggant* in development. Certain other substances, such as 6-nitrobenzimidazole, have a similar action, either separately or in combination with bromide.

In most cases of practical development, high concentrations of sulfite tend to promote fog formation, particularly when the rate of development is low. This effect probably is associated with the solvent action of the sulfite, because other silver halide solvents, such as ammonia, thiosulfate ion, and thiocyanate ion exert a similar action. A small amount of sodium thiosulfate, accidentally transferred to the developer from the fixing bath, can result in a considerable increase in fog under proper conditions.

The physical character of the fog can be changed by the solvent action. This change may be accompanied by a change in appearance and in the photometric equivalent. In extreme cases, the color of the fog is yellow or even grayish white in reflected light, and reddish in transmitted light. The photometric equivalent is considerably larger than that of image silver, and it may even amount to several times the latter.

The origin of other types of fog, such as aerial fog and sulfide fog, has been discussed already. These types appear largely as a result of accidental circumstances in practical development, and a discussion of the kinetics of formation would involve an expenditure of space quite out of proportion to their practical or theoretical importance.

Practical Usefulness of Various Developing Agents

The question of the practical usefulness of any developing agent involves both the purpose for which it is to be used and the general composition of the solution in which it is to be used. A complete coverage of even the most important aspects of the question would involve an enormous amount of work. At present, conclusions drawn from the available data are valuable for certain purposes but are subject to definite limitations.

The development of image relative to fog formation has been discussed already. The selectivity factor U is a valuable criterion of usefulness for many purposes. On the other hand, high emulsion speed is frequently the factor that determines the selection of a developer.

Various measurements have been made of the relative emulsion speed obtained with different developing agents. There is a marked lack of agreement in the results of various investigators, emphasizing the dependence of relative measurements of this sort upon the development conditions and the nature of the photographic material used. Table 7·3 gives some data obtained under different conditions by three investigators.

TABLE 7·3

Effect of the Developing Agent on Sensitivity (Emulsion Speed)

	Data by		
Agent	Neitz	Shiberstoff and Bukin	James (for sulfite-free solutions)
Methyl p-amino-o-cresol	100	....	100
Pyrogallol	76	30.1	...
Hydroquinone	46	25.1	100
Metol	10	22.7	100
Chlorohydroquinone	6.3	29.7	...
p-Aminophenol	7.6	17.6	95.5
Catechol	5.5	26.8	97.8
p-Hydroxyphenylglycine	...	25.1	69.3

Shiberstoff has introduced a factor which he calls the degree of perfection of the developing agent. This factor Z is proportional to the product of the maximum emulsion speed and the maximum gamma obtained:

$$Z = K \cdot S_m \gamma_m$$

Under the conditions he used, p-aminophenol, p-hydroxyphenyl glycine, and catechol are the most perfect agents, whereas hydroquinone is the least perfect of those tested. Shiberstoff points out, however, that the rate of development is of considerable importance in determining the practical usefulness of a developing agent. Accordingly, he introduced a new concept, the degree of practicability, defined by the relation

$$P = \frac{Z}{t'}$$

where t' is the time required to obtain γ_m. On this basis, the agents tested fall in the following order of decreasing practicability: metol-hydroquinone combination, metol, pyrogallol, p-aminophenol, bromohydroquinone, catechol, eikonogen, chlorohydroquinone, p-hydroxyphenylglycine, and hydroquinone. Once again, however the relative values should depend upon the development conditions and upon the nature of the emulsion; generalizations having a wide range of validity cannot be drawn from the available data.

The graininess of the developed image supplies another basis for practical comparison. In a later chapter, the subject of graininess will be dealt with in detail. For the present purposes, graininess may be defined simply as the inhomogeneity of the image as seen by the observer. It becomes particularly evident in large-scale enlargements and in motion-picture projections viewed close to the screen.

The outstanding developing agent which, by itself, gives low graininess (fine-grain development) is p-phenylenediamine. The exact reason for this is unknown. p-Phenylenediamine has a strong solvent action for silver halide, however, which favors the physical type of development. Moreover, the addition of its isomer, m-phenylenediamine (not a developer) to low-activity solutions of certain developing agents reduces the graininess of the developed silver image, probably because of the solvent action of the diamine.

Apart from p-phenylenediamine and possibly o-aminophenol, the developing agents themselves show little difference in the graininess of the images they develop. Fine-grain development is largely a matter of the composition of the developing solution. Relative rates of direct development, solution of the silver halide, and physical development bear an important relation to the graininess produced. Solutions of low or moderate rates of development give reduced graininess when certain silver halide solvents are present. Typical solvents include sodium sulfite (in large amounts), ammonium chloride, certain organic amines, and potassium or ammonium thiocyanate. Kodak D-76 and D-23 are representative of the developers which depend solely upon sodium sulfite; DK-20 represents a group containing thiocyanate.   Once again, the decrease in graininess apparently is connected with a tendency to shift toward physical development.   It should be noted that all developers which give low graininess do so only at a sacrifice in effective emulsion speed.   Negatives to be developed in *p*-phenylenediamine, for example, require at least three times the normal exposure.

The use of a solvent can be overdone.   Thus, the strong solvent thiosulfate generally produces an increase in graininess.   The change in graininess produced by a given solvent also depends upon the emulsion in question.   It is quite possible to obtain an increase in graininess with one emulsion and a decrease with another, the same addition of solvent to the developing solution being used.

REFERENCES

General

Mees, *The Theory of the Photographic Process*, Macmillan, New York, 1942, Chapter 11.
Chibisoff, "Theory of the Photographic Process," *Kinophotoizdat*, Moscow, 1935 (in Russian).

Specific

1. Meidinger, *Physik. Z.*, **36**, 312 (1935).
2. Rabinovich, Bogoyavlenski, and Zuev, *Acta Physicochim. U.R.S.S.*, **16**, 307 (1942).
3. Sheppard and Ballard, *J. Franklin Inst.*, **206**, 659 (1928); James, *ibid.*, **240**, 83, 229 (1945).
4. James, *J. Phys. Chem.*, **44**, 42 (1940).
5. James, *J. Franklin Inst.*, **240**, 15 (1945).
6. Elvegard, *Z. wiss. Phot.*, **41**, 81 (1943); 42, 65 (1944).
7. Ives and Jensen, *J. Soc. Motion Picture Engrs.*, **40**, 107 (1943).
8. Nietz, "The Theory of Development," Monograph 2 on *Theory of Photography*, Eastman Kodak Co., Rochester, N. Y. (1922).
9. Reinders and Beukers, *Ber. VIII intern. Kongr. Phot., Dresden*, 171, (1931).
10. Reinders and Beukers, *Phot. J.*, **74**, 78 (1934); James, *J. Franklin Inst.*, **240**, 327 (1945).

8.

Fixing and Washing

Only a portion of the total silver halide of the original emulsion is reduced to silver during the development of a normal photograph. The remaining silver halide impairs both the immediate usefulness of the photograph and its permanence, and hence should be removed. In the fixing process, the residual silver halide is dissolved out of the film without damaging the metallic silver of the image.

Some Factors Affecting the Solubility of Silver Halides

The solubility of silver halide in the fixing solution can be treated simply as an equilibrium problem, without reference to the mechanism of solution. Let us consider first the solubility of silver halide in pure water. The amount that dissolves is controlled by the product of the concentrations of silver and halide ions, that is, by the solubility product. This is a constant for any given temperature:

$$[Ag^+][X^-] = K \text{ at constant temperature} \qquad (8 \cdot 1)$$

The values of K for silver bromide and silver chloride are of the orders of 10^{-13} and 10^{-10}, respectively, in the region of normal processing temperatures ($18°$ to $24°$ C). If neither silver nor halide ion is in excess, the solubility in terms of moles per liter is given by the square root of K. If a slight excess of halide ion is present (not enough to form complex ions to any significant extent) the solubility will be even less. In either event, the solubility is so small that washing the silver halide out of the emulsion with pure water is not in the least feasible.

According to equation 8·1, the solubility of silver halide in water can be increased by any device that will reduce the concentration of either silver ion or halide ion. If the concentration of silver ion, for example, is decreased by the addition of some agent that will form a complex with it, the halide ion concentration must increase in order that K of equation 8·1 remain constant. This increase in halide ion concentration is brought about by the solution of more silver halide. Hence, the solubility of the silver halide is increased by the addition of the complex-forming agent. The function of the fixing agents is to form complexes in which the silver ions are tightly bound. Examples of such complex-forming substances have been encountered already in preceding chapters. Thus, sulfite forms the soluble complex $Ag(SO_3)_2^{\equiv}$, ammonia forms the complex $Ag(NH_3)_2^{+}$, and halide ions in considerable excess form soluble complexes of uncertain composition. A number of other substances are known which form complexes of the general formula $AgA_2^{(2n-1)-}$, although this is not the only form which silver complexes can take. The complex is dissociated slightly into silver ions and A molecules or ions according to the relation

$$\frac{[Ag^+][A^{n-}]}{[AgA_2^{(2n-1)-}]} = K' \qquad (8\cdot2)$$

This equation determines the permissible silver ion concentration in the solution, provided the substance A does not form other complexes with silver ions and thus introduce further complications in the quantitative formulation. In general, the smaller the silver ion concentration, as given by equation 8·2, the greater will be the solubility of silver halide in a solution of A.

Sulfite and ammonia are not strong solvents for silver bromide, since K' is too large in each of them. It is of the order of 10^{-8} for ammonia and 10^{-9} for sulfite in the temperature range of 18° to 24° C. Certain other substances form complexes which have much smaller dissociation constants and hence are much stronger solvents for silver bromide. Thus, thiosulfate ion forms a complex having a dissociation constant of the order of 10^{-14}, and cyanide ion forms a complex having a constant of about 10^{-19}. Solutions of either substance in sufficient concentration act as strong solvents for silver bromide. It is evident that the bromide is more soluble in a cyanide solution than in a thiosulfate solution of equal concentration, but the cyanide is objectionable for photographic use because of its poisonous nature. The thiosulfates, particularly in the form of the sodium salt (hypo), are used almost exclusively as fixing agents in practice.

Although the existence of a silver thiosulfate ion complex of the formula $Ag(S_2O_3)_2^{\equiv}$ seems well established,[1] it probably is not justifiable to treat the solution of silver bromide in thiosulfate quantitatively in terms of the formation of this complex alone. Some evidence [2] points to the existence of at least one additional complex ion, probably $Ag(S_2O_3)_2^{\overline{\equiv}}$. The various complex salts which have been isolated in solid form, however, need not be considered. At least four of these salts have a stable existence at room temperature, but they dissociate into ions in solution, and it is possible to formulate all four as composed simply of Na^+, Ag^+, and $Ag(S_2O_3)_2^{\equiv}$.

Since silver iodide has a solubility product of only 10^{-16} at $20°$ C, iodide ions greatly depress the solubility of silver bromide in thiosulfate solution. Even the small percentages of silver iodide present in most negative materials have a marked effect upon the total solubility of silver salt in the fixing bath.

Ideally, a fixing agent should dissolve the silver halide without attacking the silver of the image. Sodium thiosulfate does not completely fulfill this requirement, inasmuch as it does attack the silver to some extent, the rate of solution being greatest when the silver is in the finest state of division. The rate is materially increased by the presence of oxygen, which may play an essential part by oxidizing the silver. In appreciably acid solutions which also contain bisulfite, sulfur dioxide apparently plays the part of an oxidizing agent in increasing the rate of solution of the silver, and the action becomes very marked in strongly acid solutions. Ammonium thiosulfate solutions appear to attack the silver image more readily than sodium thiosulfate solutions. In practice, however, the amount of silver dissolved by the conventional fixing bath is usually of little importance unless fixation is prolonged considerably beyond the time normally required for removal of the silver halide. A notable exception is post-fixation physical development, where the solvent action can destroy much of the latent image.

Rate of Fixation

The total solubility of silver halide in a thiosulfate solution determines the maximum capacity of that solution to dissolve the silver halide. However, the practical usefulness of the solution as a fixing bath is determined primarily by other considerations. One of these is the rate of fixation, or the total time required to fix a given type of emulsion in the bath in question.

Sheppard and Mees [3] investigated the kinetics of fixation of a silver bromide emulsion in dilute solutions of sodium thiosulfate. They found that the rate was not altered by the addition of 0.1 M potassium bromide to the solution but was substantially increased by agitation. These findings suggested that the rate is controlled by a diffusion process. The rate of diffusion dM/dt of thiosulfate to a surface of area A at a distance d within the emulsion is given by the regular diffusion formula

$$\frac{dM}{dt} = A \cdot P \frac{dc}{dx} \qquad (8 \cdot 3)$$

where dc/dx is the concentration gradient and P is the diffusion coefficient.

If the rate of formation of the silver thiosulfate complex ion is large in comparison with the rate of diffusion, the thiosulfate is used up practically as soon as it reaches the surface of the grain, and the concentration at this point is maintained at substantially zero. During the early stages of fixing, therefore, when the concentration of thiosulfate in the bulk solution and at the emulsion surface is substantially constant, the concentration gradient will be constant, being proportional to the inverse of the distance d below the emulsion surface and proportional to the bulk concentration M. The rate of fixation will equal the rate of diffusion; it can be written:

$$\frac{dM}{dt} = \frac{kMAP}{d} \qquad (8 \cdot 4)$$

which is the Nernst equation for the rate of a diffusion-controlled reaction. The data of Sheppard and Mees are in agreement with this expression, although they do not constitute a completely adequate test of it.

Most of the experimental work which has been done on the kinetics of fixation is based upon determinations of the clearing time, that is, the time required for the disappearance of the last visible trace of silver halide. Measurement of the clearing time involves the determination of the point at which the fixing rate becomes negligible so far as the eye can judge. It is not entirely satisfactory as a quantitative measure of the fixing rate. Results

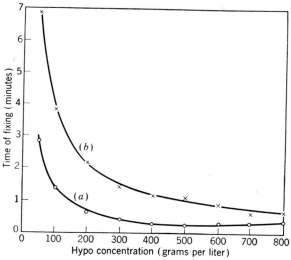

FIG. 8·1 Dependence of time of fixing upon hypo concentration. (*a*) Fine-grain emulsion. (*b*) Coarse-grain emulsion. (Russell.)

based on this method usually have at least semi-quantitative value, however, and the clearing time is obviously of direct practical interest. It has been found to vary with (1) the nature of the emulsion, (2) the thiosulfate concentration, (3) the nature of the cation, (4) temperature, (5) agitation, (6) the degree of exhaustion of the fixing bath, and (7) the presence of other salts.

The clearing time varies considerably with the size of the silver halide grains, being shorter for fine-grain emulsions than for coarse-grain ones, other things being equal. This is shown by Fig. 8·1, where curve (*a*) represents data for a fine-grain emulsion, curve (*b*) a coarse-grain emulsion. The result is to be expected on the basis of equation 8·4, since the fine-grain emulsions present a greater total area per unit weight of silver halide. Likewise, the clearing time varies with the mean diffusion path in the emulsion, and so it is larger for thick emulsions than for thin ones. The hardness of the gelatin has very little effect, if any.

The variation of clearing time with concentration of thiosulfate is also illustrated in Fig. 8·1. The time decreases rapidly with increasing concentration at first, but subsequently it levels off and shows little change beyond 300 to 400 grams per liter. The shape of the curve at the higher thiosulfate concentrations, however, sometimes departs markedly from that shown in Fig. 8·1. Many of the older data in the literature show a region of optimum concentration where the measured clearing time was a minimum. This optimum region usually occurred at about 300 to 400 grams per liter, and at higher concentrations the clearing time increased markedly. At least some of these data, however, apply to the time required to clear film which had been introduced directly into the thiosulfate solution without prior development. Conditions are not specified for the remaining data of this kind.

Alnutt [4] observed that, under otherwise identical conditions, curves showing optimum concentrations were readily obtained when dry film was introduced into the fixing solution, and curves showing no optimum were obtained when the film was first soaked in developer or in plain water. (The soaked film, of course, corresponds more closely than the dry to practical fixing conditions.) However, Alnutt found that the temperature of the fixing bath influences the shape of the concentration curve. His data for prewetted film show evidence of an optimum concentration when the temperature of a sodium thiosulfate solution was at 15° C but no evidence of an optimum at higher temperatures. His data for ammonium thiosulfate solutions show a definite optimum at 15° but none at 25°. It is possible that the shape of the concentration curve may vary also with the nature of the photographic emulsion and the pH of the solution, but these factors have not been investigated adequately.

The cause or causes of the optimum have not been established with certainty. Sheppard has suggested that a balance between the effects of two opposing influences is involved. The first is the normal mass action effect of increasing concentration. This is predominant at the lower concentrations, where increase in thiosulfate concentration produces a corresponding increase in the fixing rate. The second is the effect of salt in depressing the swelling of the gelatin. When the decrease in swelling counter-balances the mass action effect, the rate of fixing reaches its maximum value. If this explanation is correct, the shape of the concentration curve should be influenced by pH changes and by the addition of a neutral salt such as sodium sulfate.

The rate of fixing, particularly of emulsions containing iodide, is dependent upon the nature of the cation. As indicated by the

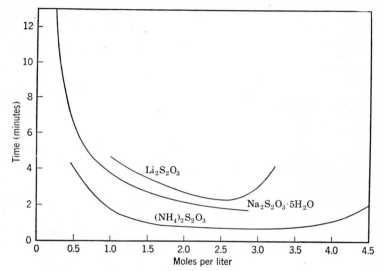

Fig. 8·2 Dependence of clearing time upon the concentration of various thiosulfates at 20° C. (Curves based upon data by Alnutt.)

data in Fig. 8·2, the clearing time of a typical negative emulsion in ammonium thiosulfate solution is quite substantially shorter than that in sodium thiosulfate solution of equal concentration. Lithium thiosulfate, on the other hand, is somewhat slower in its action than sodium thiosulfate. The fixing rates of potassium and calcium thiosulfates, as indicated by other data, are considerably slower than that of the sodium salt.

Because of its faster action on emulsions containing iodide, ammonium thiosulfate is used commercially in the formulation of rapid-fixing solutions. Baths which are satisfactory in general properties can be prepared with ammonium in place of sodium thiosulfate, and the substantially shorter fixing times required by such solutions offer a distinct advantage wherever it is important to fix the emulsion in the shortest possible time. However, ammonium thiosulfate offers no practical advantage over the sodium salt in the fixing of the usual paper emulsions (chloride, chlorobromide, or pure bromide).

Ammonium thiosulfate suffers the disadvantage that it is less stable in the solid form than the sodium salt. Moreover, the solid residue obtained by evaporation of partially exhausted fixing baths containing ammonium thiosulfate is less stable in the presence of light than that obtained from the corresponding sodium thiosulfate baths. However, a photographic image fixed by ammonium thiosulfate does not lose stability on this account, provided the emulsion is given a normally thorough washing.

The clearing time decreases with increasing temperature. Apparently, the action is twofold. Both the swelling of the gelatin and the normal rate of diffusion in solution increase with increasing temperature. The net effect on the rate of fixation varies with the experimental conditions and with the concentration of the thiosulfate. The increased swelling of the gelatin, however, may seriously threaten the mechanical stability of the film if the temperature becomes too high, and the best working temperature for most purposes lies in the range of $16°$ to $24°$ C.

The clearing time is decreased by agitation, the reason being similar to that already given for rapid development. Agitation increases the rate of supply of fresh solution to the surface, and thus it increases the thiosulfate concentration gradient between the surface of the gelatin and the silver halide grains within.

The clearing time can be changed by the addition of salts other than the thiosulfate. For example, the addition of ammonium chloride to sodium thiosulfate solution under proper conditions decreases the clearing time of emulsions that contain iodide. The effect depends upon both the concentration of thiosulfate and the concentration of ammonium chloride. It is most marked at low thiosulfate concentrations, and an optimum ammonium chloride concentration is observed for any particular thiosulfate concentration.

Strauss found that sodium chloride accelerated fixing to some extent but that sodium bromide retarded it. The effect of bromide was not marked, however, and Sheppard and Mees had found that $0.1 \ M$ bromide was without measurable effect at low thiosulfate concentrations. Sodium iodide has a powerful retarding effect upon the fixing process. Since most commercial silver bromide emulsions, particularly the negative materials, contain silver iodide, the accumulation of iodide in the bath during repeated use can become an important factor in determining the useful life of the bath under practical working conditions.

The clearing time changes with the degree of exhaustion of the fixing bath. The change in time is in the direction to be expected from a knowledge of the change in composition of the solution. These changes, and the accompanying alterations in the properties of the fixing bath, will be considered subsequently.

The clearing time does not in general represent the time when all the silver halide has been converted into silver thiosulfate complex. Small residues of silver halide still remain. It is desirable to extend the fixing time well beyond the clearing time for two reasons, firstly to allow conversion of the invisible silver halide residue into thiosulfate complex, and secondly to decrease the concentration of the complex and of halide ion in the gelatin layer. The evidence in general indicates that the fixing may be regarded as complete for practical purposes if the time is extended to about twice that required for clearing. This criterion, however, is a practical one rather than a universally applicable principle.

The Acid Fixing Bath [5]

The fixing agent in straight black-and-white photography is commonly employed in an acid solution. (This is not true for color photography because acid may adversely affect the dyes formed in coupler development.) The acid serves a dual purpose. (1) It permits the direct use of potassium alum (potassium aluminum sulfate) or chrome alum (potassium chromium sulfate) as hardeners in the fixing bath. These materials are not effective as hardeners in neutral or alkaline solution. (2) It neutralizes any alkaline developer which may be carried over, thus quickly stopping development and preventing the formation of stain. If the developed film were transferred directly to an *alkaline* thiosulfate solution, the reducing action of the developer in combination with the solvent action of the thiosulfate might lead to the formation of dichroic fog. Furthermore, stain might be formed by oxidation products of the developing agent which are not adequately removed by the now diluted sodium sulfite.

The use of acid, however, entails certain complications. Thiosulfate ion is unstable in acid solution, decomposing primarily according to the equation

$$S_2O_3^= + H^+ \rightleftharpoons HSO_3^- + S \qquad (8 \cdot 5)$$

The reaction passes through a definite induction period before the formation of sulfur is apparent. Kinetic evidence indicates that the reaction is autocatalytic, sulfur in the form of colloidal particles acting as the catalyst. This means that the solution deteriorates rapidly after sulfur appears in it. Fortunately, however, the decomposition of the acid thiosulfate solution can be greatly retarded by the use of a preservative, provided the pH of the solution is not too low. Bisulfite (often added as sulfite, but existing largely as bisulfite in the acid solution) acts as an effective preservative. The basis for the preservative action is implied in equation 8·5. The addition of bisulfite ion shifts the equilibrium toward the left, in accordance with the principle of mass action. This shift decreases the concentration of sulfur in solution and retards the formation of the colloidal catalyst.

A secondary path of decomposition, unaffected by the presence of bisulfite, may also act to retard the total rate of decomposition. Small quantities of polythionates are formed, by either decomposition or oxidation of the thiosulfate, and these react with sulfur to form higher polythionates.

Even in the presence of sulfite, sulfurization will occur eventually. The sulfurization life of the bath, that is, the time that can elapse before sulfur begins to precipitate, depends markedly upon the hydrogen ion concentration. The accelerating effect of hydrogen ions on the decomposition is indicated by equation 8·5. In practice, the thiosulfate bath is generally used above a pH of 4.0, except when chrome alum is added as hardener. The chrome alum fixing baths are generally somewhat more acid, but the use of a lower pH is at the expense of a loss in stability.

The hardener is used in the fixing bath to decrease the hazard of mechanical injury to the gelatin layer. The latter, in a swollen condition, is easily scratched, torn, or distorted by mechanical action. Unhardened gelatin is most susceptible to such action during the washing process and during transfer from the washer to the drying apparatus. During fixation the swelling will be repressed to a considerable extent either by the salt present or by virtue of a pH lying in the region of the isoelectric point. During washing, however, the salt is removed, and the pH generally rises progressively to a value well above the isoelectric point. The gelatin thus will swell to the maximum for that pH and temperature. The use of a hardener in the fixing bath restrains the swelling and thus reduces the danger of mechanical injury. Hardening becomes more important the higher the processing temperature, as the swelling increases rapidly with temperature.

The decrease in swelling of the gelatin layer can be used as a practical measure of hardening. The swelling can be measured either by the change of weight of the gelatin layer or by the change in thickness (volume). A more convenient but somewhat more arbitrary method involves the change in melting temperature of the gelatin. The simplest measurements of melting temperature are made by placing strips of film in a water bath, raising the temperature of the bath at a definite rate, and noting the temperature at which the gelatin layer melts or shreds off the film support. The measured temperature depends somewhat upon both the rate of heating and the extent of agitation.

The hardening agent generally used in the fixing bath is potassium alum, $KAl(SO_4)_2 \cdot 12H_2O$. The extent of the hardening produced varies with both concentration and pH. This is illustrated by the schematic curve in Fig. 8·3, which shows that the hardness increases with pH until a maximum is reached beyond which it decreases. Little or no hardening action is obtained in alkaline solution.

The mechanism of hardening is not completely understood. It is probable that some type of aluminum-gelatin complex formation occurs in which the aluminum ion (or possibly an intermediate hydrolysis product) reacts with the $-COO^-$ groups of the gelatin chains to form cross-linkages between the polypeptide chains (see Chapter 2). This reaction increases the forces holding the chains together in the three-dimensional network of the rigid jelly. According to this view, three factors operate to produce a maximum in the hardening curves: (1) the free $-COOH$ groups of the gelatin end and side chains become increasingly ionized to $-COO^-$ with increasing pH; (2) the concentration of aluminum ions decreases with increasing pH because of the formation of the insoluble hydrous alumina, $Al_2O_3 \cdot x(H_2O)$, and related basic aluminum sulfites and sulfates; (3) the formation of colloidal alumina particles at the surface of the gelatin inhibits the penetration of aluminum ions into the gelatin because the colloid adsorbs the ions. The last two effects diminish the rate of hardening and, as they increase in magnitude, they eventually outweigh the first effect, and thereby account for the existence of the maximum in the hardening curve.

Any other factor which restrains penetration or reduces the concentration of aluminum ions should also decrease hardening.

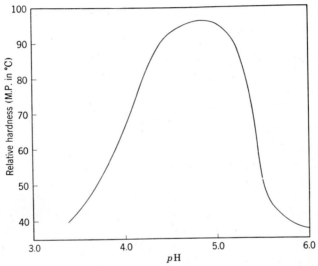

FIG. 8·3 Variation of hardening with the pH of a potassium alum fixing bath.

Thus, polycarboxylic acids (such as citric) and hydroxycarboxylic acids (such as lactic) inhibit hardening by binding the aluminum ions into complexes.

Besides aluminum, only chromium is of much practical importance as a hardener for the photographic emulsion during processing. The chromium is generally used in the form of chrome alum, $KCr(SO_4)_2 \cdot 12H_2O$. The mechanism of chromium hardening is still a subject of controversy. An optimum pH which is lower than that for aluminum is observed in chromium hardening, and it corresponds approximately to the point at which chromic oxide and the basic chromic sulfate start to form. Probably the chromic ion is the chief hardening agent, and apparently it can form cross-linkages between the polypeptide chains by reacting with either the —COO⁻ group or the NH_2 group.

It has been noted already that the stability of thiosulfate in solution is an important consideration in the determination of a lower practical limit to the pH of the fixing solution. There are other limiting factors to consider, however. Decrease in pH beyond the optimum for hardening is accompanied by a decrease in hardening, and too low a pH is a disadvantage to the subsequent washing process. On the other hand, several factors enter to set a rough upper limit to the permissible pH of the practical solution. If the pH is too high, the bath is no longer effective in preventing stain. Increase in pH beyond the optimum is likewise accompanied by a loss in hardening power. Finally, if the pH becomes too high, the hardening agent tends to sludge out in the form of the hydrous oxide and related basic salts. The useful range of pH for the potassium alum fixing bath generally lies in the region of 4 to 6. The chrome alum baths are generally used in the region of 3 to 4 to obtain optimum hardening and low sludging tendency.

Since contamination from the developer tends to increase the alkalinity during use, the solution should be well buffered against an increase in pH. This is accomplished by use of mild acids, such as acetic, or acid salts, such as sodium bisulfite, to adjust the pH to the desired value. Boric acid, used in aluminum-containing fixing baths in the presence of acetic, propionic, or butyric acid, contributes specific properties by extending the useful hardening life and decreasing the sludging tendency as the pH of the bath increases by contamination with the developer. An acid that forms a relatively undissociated complex with the hardening agent should not be used, since such an acid will adversely affect the hardening properties of the solution.

Washing

The fixed photographic material contains considerable amounts of thiosulfate. Removal of this ion will result in a marked improvement in the stability of the silver image. The principal purpose of washing is to remove the thiosulfate, together with the usually small but not negligible amount of soluble silver thiosulfate complexes which remain in the film. When film or plate materials on stable supports are adequately fixed and washed, their silver images are permanent for practical purposes. If, however, the washing has been insufficient, the color (tone) of the silver image may change upon being kept at high humidity, and particularly at both high humidity and high temperature. This color change is known as fading. It is a result of a reaction between the thiosulfate and the finely divided silver, leading to the formation of yellowish or brown silver sulfide. An overall yellowish stain, particularly noticeable in the clear portions, can result from decomposition of the silver thiosulfate complex to form silver sulfide.

The washing of photographic materials coated on water-impervious supports, such as glass or cellulose nitrate or acetate film, is a straightforward process, and the thiosulfate can be adequately eliminated by a practical washing procedure. In the following discussion, the use of films or plates is implied unless otherwise stated. Washing of materials coated on fibrous supports, such as paper, represents a special case where complete removal of the thiosulfate is not possible by the ordinary washing process. The treatment of such materials will be considered separately.

At the outset, it will be useful to distinguish two extreme types of washing. In the first type, the film (or plate) is placed in a vessel of water and allowed to stand, either with or without stirring, until equilibrium is attained. At the equilibrium point, the rate of passage of thiosulfate from the film to the water equals the rate of passage from the water to the film. The amount of thiosulfate originally present in the film will be reduced to a definite fraction of the original amount, the magnitude of the fraction depending upon the volume of the water in the vessel. The vessel is now completely emptied and filled again with water. When equilibrium is again attained, the amount of thiosulfate in the film has again been decreased, and by the same fractional amount as in the first washing. If the process is continued, the amount of thiosulfate in the film decreases exponentially with the *number of changes* of water.

In the second type, a continuous supply of fresh water is maintained at the film surface as, for example, by directing a rapidly flowing stream of fresh water against the surface. The rate of washing then is a continuous function, and is determined by the rate of diffusion of the thiosulfate from the gelatin layer. The rate of diffusion can be expressed simply by the equation

$$\frac{dM}{dt} = A \cdot P \frac{dc}{dx} \tag{8·6}$$

where dM is the amount of thiosulfate which diffuses in time dt, A is the area of the film, P is the diffusion coefficient, and dc/dx is the concentration gradient in the gelatin layer. When a particular film is processed in a specified manner and washed under conditions of constant temperature and pH, the diffusion coefficient is substantially constant and the rate of washing (removal of thiosulfate) is determined by the concentration gradient. If a continuous supply of fresh water is actually maintained at the gelatin surface, the concentration of thiosulfate in this water layer is zero, and the effective gradient has its maximum value for whatever concentration of thiosulfate may be in the gelatin layer. If the water layer at the surface contains thiosulfate, the concentration gradient will be smaller, and the rate of washing will be smaller.

Virtually all practical washing practices involve compromises between the two types just described. The water may be changed at regular intervals, but without allowing time for equilibrium. Then, both the frequency with which the water is changed and the rate of diffusion will affect the time required for washing. Other washing devices maintain essentially a continuous flow. It is possible to approach quite closely conditions where the concentration gradient is proportional to the amount M of thiosulfate remaining in the film. Integration of equation 8·6 shows that, under such conditions, the concentration of thiosulfate in the film drops exponentially with the washing time.

Factors Affecting the Diffusion-Controlled Rate of Washing

The rate of washing increases with the temperature of the wash water. However, high temperatures produce excessive swelling of the gelatin and thus increase the danger of mechanical damage to the emulsion. A wrinkling or reticulation of the gelatin often is obtained when the temperature of the water is too high, and this reticulation does not disappear when the film is dried. For most practical purposes, temperatures in the range of 18° to 24° C are generally recommended, and the temperature chosen should be approximately that of the fixing bath.

The rate of washing depends upon the pH of the water and upon the composition of the fixing bath. Treatment of partially washed materials with dilute alkaline solution (preferably 0.03 to 0.3 per cent ammonia) for a few minutes appreciably increases the rate of subsequent washing. A controlled addition of ammonia to the wash water sometimes is used to effect the same result. Alkaline treatments have the disadvantage, however, that they often remove or decrease hardening and thus promote softening and excessive swelling of the gelatin.

The change in the rate of washing with pH probably is associated with the change in the electrical state of the gelatin. At pH values below the isoelectric point, the positive charge of the gelatin tends to retain a negative ionic atmosphere within the layer. In alkaline solution, where the gelatin is itself negative, the opposite is true.

The rate of washing of film fixed in an alum fixing bath often is lower than that of film fixed in a non-hardening bath.[6] The effect of alum on washing depends upon the pH of the fixing bath and the kind of alum present. With potassium (aluminum) alum, the retarding effect is strong at pH 4.1 and decreases with increasing pH until a value between 4.7 and 5 is reached. At higher pH, the rate of washing shows little or no dependence upon the presence or absence of alum. The reason for the effect of alum on washing is not clear. The retarding action does not parallel the increase in hardening of the gelatin. Indeed, the latter often is at a maximum at a pH of around 5, whereas the effect of the alum upon washing is insignificant at that pH. Moreover, chrome alum does not exert nearly so great a retarding action as the corresponding aluminum compound. Adsorption of the thiosulfate to alumina or to the hardening complex has been suggested, but adequate proof of adsorption has not been obtained. Another possible factor is that of the influence of alum on the pH of the gelatin layer. Alum acts as a buffer in the pH range where the retarding effect is pronounced, and thus it may retard washing by retarding the adjustment of the gelatin pH to that of the wash water.

The rate of washing in certain salt solutions, such as sodium sulfate solution or sea water, is greater than that in plain water.

However, the salt from sea water must itself be removed to a large extent by subsequent washing in plain water, since small quantities of thiosulfate are especially destructive in the presence of chloride ion. Even including the time required to remove the sea salt, the total washing time is shorter than that required by fresh water alone.

Washing involves not only removal of thiosulfate ion but removal of residual silver salts as well. However, the quantity of the residual silver salts already should have been lowered to a practical minimum by adequate fixation, as described on page 139. It is good practice in washing studies to compare results obtained with two widely different fixing times to insure that the washing rate is independent of the fixing time.

Removal of the silver thiosulfate complex by washing usually follows rather closely the removal of thiosulfate ion. Factors that produce a change in the rate of elimination of one produce a similar change in the rate of elimination of the other. An exception to this general statement appears in some experiments by Crabtree, Eaton, and Muehler [6] on washing film which had been fixed in a partially exhausted bath of pH 4.1. The bath contained potassium (aluminum) alum as hardener. The data show that small quantities of silver salt were retained by the film even after prolonged washing and that the amount of silver salt retained depended upon the amount of film which previously had been fixed in the bath. If the pH of the fixing bath was raised above 5, however, the silver salt was completely eliminated by washing. No retention of silver was observed at any pH or following any degree of exhaustion when the fixing bath contained no hardener.

Washing of Papers

The washing of paper prints is more complicated from the theoretical viewpoint than the washing of film or plates. The initial rapid diffusion, which follows equation 8·6 rather closely, eventually degenerates into a very sluggish process. Although the main bulk of the thiosulfate can be removed within the first two or three minutes of washing, a harmful residue remains behind which will not be reduced to a tolerable amount in less than 30 to 60 minutes, depending upon the thickness of the paper support. Residues of the order of 64 milligrams of $Na_2S_2O_3 \cdot 5H_2O$ per square meter (0.04 mg per sq in.) may remain in single weight prints after 6 hours of washing; this quantity is not significantly lowered by prolonging the washing up to 20 hours.

The washing of the usual photographic paper represents a compromise between the washing of at least two different parts: the gelatin layer and the paper base. The washing of the gelatin layer follows the same pattern as that of film or plates, as discussed previously. The washing of the paper base, particularly in

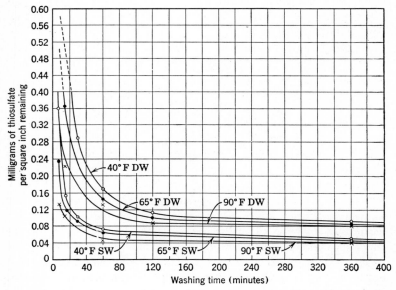

Fig. 8·4 Washing curves for typical single-weight (SW) and double-weight (DW) photographic papers. (Crabtree, Eaton, and Muehler.)

its later stages, is the sluggish process. For this reason, factors that affect the washing of the gelatin only do not affect the washing of paper prints except during the earliest part of the process.

Figure 8·4 shows the general form of the washing curve in the later stages, where the washing of the paper predominates. The rate of elimination of thiosulfate approaches zero while appreciable amounts of thiosulfate still remain in the paper. Double-weight paper (DW) retains approximately double the amount retained by single-weight paper.

The thiosulfate retained by the paper after prolonged washing appears to be adsorbed. Adsorption is strongly suggested by some experiments of Crabtree, Eaton, and Muehler, in which the thiosulfate content of paper which had been soaked for varying times in a dilute thiosulfate solution was determined. The paper was prepared in the same way as normal photographic paper, except that the silver halide was omitted. Table 8·1, in which the thiosulfate concentrations have been calculated from their published data, gives some typical results. The solution used contained 0.0004 grams sodium thiosulfate pentahydrate per liter.

TABLE 8·1

UPTAKE OF THIOSULFATE BY PHOTOGRAPHIC PAPER BASE

Time of Treatment, Minutes	Weight of Absorbed Solution, Milligrams per Square Decimeter	$Na_2S_2O_3 \cdot 5H_2O$ in Milligrams per Square Decimeter
5	700	0.31
15	770	0.34
30	830	0.74
60	770	0.99
120	830	1.53
330	830	2.15

The data in Table 8·1 show that the amount of thiosulfate taken up by the paper increases steadily with increasing time, whereas the total amount of solution in the paper becomes essentially constant within a few minutes. The data do not indicate whether the adsorption is by the paper fibers or by the sizing.

The extent to which washing should be carried to assure permanence of the image depends upon the degree of permanence desired. Film and prints destined for archival use require the maximum degree of permanence obtainable and, on the basis of results from accelerated fading tests, this means practically complete elimination of thiosulfate and silver complexes. Film and prints for ordinary commercial and amateur use do not require such stringent elimination. Crabtree, Eaton, and Muehler [6] have suggested the following values as the "maximum permissible concentration of thiosulfate" (as $Na_2S_2O_3 \cdot 5H_2O$) for commercial and archival use:

Material	Commercial Use Mg per sq in.	Commercial Use Mg per sq dcm	Archival Use Mg per sq dcm
Motion-picture film			
Fine-grain duplicating positive	0.02	0.30	0.08
Normal fine-grain release positive	0.05	0.80	0.15
High-speed negative	0.20	3.0	0.80
Film used by photofinishers and amateurs	0.15–0.25 [1]	2.3–3.9 [1]	0.80 [1]
Industrial type A x-ray film	0.15–0.25 [1]	2.3–3.9 [1]	0.80 [1]
Paper			
Double-weight	0.20–0.25	3.0–3.9	Nil
Single-weight	0.10–0.15	1.5–2.0	Nil

[1] Data apply to coatings on one side of the film.

When it is necessary to reduce the thiosulfate content of paper beyond that which can be attained by normal washing, as when storage conditions are adverse or when the material is destined for archival use, recourse must be had to the use of chemical agents. Alkaline baths are sometimes used as "assists" to promote the leeching out and subsequent washing away of thiosulfate, but the complete removal of thiosulfate is not obtained in this way unless the alkaline baths are employed for excessive times. It is preferable to use *hypo-eliminators* which quantitatively oxidize the thiosulfate to the innocuous sulfate without attacking the silver image. Chemical agents that convert thiosulfate to tetrathionate are not satisfactory, since tetrathionate easily effects sulfiding of silver images.

Muehler's hydrogen peroxide-ammonia mixture is quite effective as a hypo-eliminator. In practice, the well-fixed prints, which have been washed in plain water for 15 to 30 minutes, are treated for 5 to 6 minutes in the eliminator solution and finally washed about 5 minutes. The solution, which has a pH value in the range 9.8 to 10.2, reacts quantitatively with the thiosulfate according to the equation

$$Na_2S_2O_3 + 4H_2O_2 + 2NH_4OH \rightarrow Na_2SO_4 + (NH_4)_2SO_4 + 5H_2O$$

Sodium chlorite in a suitably buffered, mild acid solution is another promising hypo-eliminator. Eliminators of this type are not required for the treatment of film and plate materials, however, and their use with such materials may even be disadvantageous because of their tendency to soften and blister the usual film or plate emulsion.

Complete removal of the silver thiosulfate complex has special importance for white papers, since small amounts can produce a noticeable stain upon decomposition. The practice of following the initial fixation by a treatment in a second bath of fresh fixing solution is useful in promoting complete removal of the silver salt.

REFERENCES

General

Mees, *The Theory of the Photographic Process*, Macmillan, New York, 1942, Chapter 13.

Clerc, *La technique photographique*, Paul Montel, Paris, 3rd ed., 1942, Vol. 1, Chapter 29.

Specific

1. Bassett and Lemon, *J. Chem. Soc.*, **1933**, 1423.
2. Ölander and Adelsohn, *Svensk Kemi Tid.*, **58,** 33 (1946).
3. Sheppard and Mees, *Investigations on the Theory of the Photographic Process*, Longmans, Green and Co., London, 1907.
4. Alnutt, *J. Soc. Motion Picture Engrs.*, **41,** 300 (1943).
5. Sheppard, Elliott, and Sweet, *J. Franklin Inst.*, **196,** 45 (1923).
6. Crabtree, Eaton, and Muehler, *J. Soc. Motion Picture Engrs.*, **42,** 9 (1943); *J. Franklin Inst.*, **235,** 351 (1943).

9.

Sensitometry I, Exposure and Development

Photographic *sensitometry* is the science of measuring the sensitivity of photographic materials. It consists of the quantitative measurement of the relation between the density of the photographic image and the treatment to which the material has been subjected. The methods of exact sensitometry have become important to the users as well as to the manufacturers of photographic materials.

The trend in modern sensitometry is to obtain data which can be interpreted in terms of practical results. All methods of measuring sensitivity require a standard light source, a method of giving a graduated set of known exposures, a method of development that will give reproducible results, and a method of interpreting the response of the material to the process of exposure and development. If the results are to have practical significance, the radiant energy of the light source, the time and intensity of the exposure, and the developer formula and development conditions must be in accordance with those used in practice. In addition, the response of the film must be interpreted in terms of that required from the material as it is commonly used. The above requirements will of course be different for different photographic materials, and will in fact depend upon the use for which they are intended.

Sensitometers

The instrument used to produce a precise set of graded exposures on a photographic material is called a *sensitometer*. The essential elements of a sensitometer are shown in Fig. 9·1. A light source of known luminous intensity which is emitting radiation of a

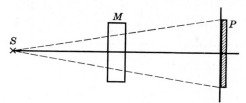

FIG. 9·1 Schematic diagram of the essential elements of a sensitometer.

known spectral composition is shown at *S*. The photographic material *P* is illuminated by the light source in such a manner that all points on the surface receive the same amount of radiant energy per unit time. The exposure-modulating device *M* is placed between the light source and the photographic material.

Light Sources

It is very important that the spectral composition of the light source used in a sensitometer be both *known* and *appropriate*. The spectral sensitivity curves for three typical photographic emulsions are shown in Fig. 9·2 together with the energy distribution for average noon sunlight and for light from a tungsten source. Curve *A* is for an ordinary blue-sensitive emulsion, *B* is for an orthochromatic blue-green-sensitive emulsion, *C* is for a panchromatic emulsion, *D* is the energy distribution for mean noon sunlight, and *E* is the energy distribution for a tungsten light source. If the ordinates of curves *A*, *B*, and *C*, respectively, are multiplied by the corresponding ordinates of curve *D*, the curves A_d, B_d, and C_d shown in Fig. 9·3 are obtained. The curves A_e, B_e, and C_e as shown in the same figure are obtained when the ordinates of curves *A*, *B*, and *C* are multiplied by the corresponding ordinates of curve *E*. A comparison of the areas under curves A_d and A_e in Fig. 9·3 gives the relative effectiveness of sunlight and tungsten light as a source for use with a blue-sensitive emulsion. In a similar manner, a comparison of the areas under the other two sets of curves in this figure gives the relative effectiveness of sunlight and tungsten light when used as a light source with an orthochromatic emulsion and a panchomatic emulsion, respectively. It is apparent from Fig. 9·3 that the energy distribution of the light source used for exposure is an important factor in sensitometry, since both the absolute and the relative response of photographic materials to exposure depend markedly on the energy distribution of the light source.

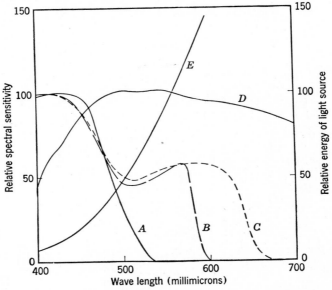

Fig. 9·2   Spectral sensitivity curves (*A*, *B*, *C*) for three typical photographic materials together with the energy distribution curves for mean noon sunlight (*D*) and a tungsten light source (*E*).

In practical sensitometry, the light source used to expose a given photographic material in the sensitometer must emit radiation which is *equivalent spectrally* to that used in practice to expose this same material.   The light sources used in early sensitometric investigations had been developed as standards of luminous intensity rather than to be a spectral match for the light sources used in taking pictures.   Among the sources which have been used are the standard candle, the Hefner lamp, the acetylene flame, and the standardized incandescent lamp.   Of these sources, the calibrated incandescent lamp offers many practical advantages.   However, the highest filament temperature of modern incandescent lamps is only about 3400° K, whereas the effective equivalent color temperature of the sun is approximately 5400° K. In order to obtain a spectral match between the radiation from an incandescent lamp and the several light sources used to make photographs, it is necessary to introduce a selectively absorbing filter between the light source and the exposure plane of the sensitometer.

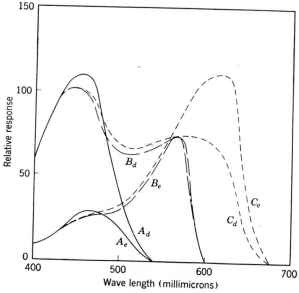

Fig. 9·3 The relative responses of photographic materials to mean noon sunlight and to a tungsten light source.

It is relatively easy to obtain a spectral match between the light source in the sensitometer and the artificial light sources used in practice; it is more difficult to obtain a spectral match between an artificial light source and sunlight. Dyed gelatin filters, such as the Wratten No. 79, give approximately the desired radiation when used in combination with the correct controlled source. These gelatin filters, although very stable, are not reproducible with sufficient precision to be useful in a primary standard. The International Congress of Photography in 1928 adopted a resolution defining the international unit of photographic intensity as one visual candlepower of radiation of the quality emitted by a

2360° K source screened with a Davis-Gibson liquid filter. The Davis-Gibson filter is very stable and precisely reproducible. The formula for the filter to be used with a 2360° K source is shown below.

Solution A

Copper sulfate, $CuSO_4 \cdot 5H_2O$	3.707 grams
Mannite, $C_6H_8(OH)_6$	3.707 grams
Pyridine, C_5H_5N	30.0 cc
Water (distilled) to make	1000.0 cc

Solution B

Cobalt ammonium sulfate, $CoSO_4 \cdot (NH_4)_2SO_4 \cdot 6H_2O$	26.827 grams
Copper sulfate	27.180 grams
Sulfuric acid (sp gr 1.835)	10.0 cc
Water (distilled) to make	1000.0 cc

Each solution is used in a cell 10 cm thick, the cells being in tandem.

Modulation of Exposure

Since exposure is the product of time and intensity, sensitometers may employ either a time-scale or an intensity-scale modulation system. Exposure is usually expressed in meter-candle-seconds and can be impressed either continuously or intermittently. Instruments for controlling exposure have been classified by L. A. Jones [1] into intensity-scale and time-scale sensitometers, subdivided as follows:

Type I.   Intensity-scale (sensitometers); I variable, t constant
      A. Exposure intermittent
          1. Wedged exposure
          2. Stepped exposure
      B. Exposure non-intermittent
          1. Wedged exposure
          2. Stepped exposure
Type II. Time-scale (sensitometers); I constant, t variable
      A. Exposure intermittent
          1. Wedged exposure
          2. Stepped exposure
      B. Exposure non-intermittent
          1. Wedged exposure
          2. Stepped exposure

Sensitometers using intermittent exposures were in general use until about 1920, but they have the very serious fault that a photographic material does not integrate intermittent exposures for anything less than a critical frequency. This is shown in Fig. 9·4, where the two sensitometric curves, A and B, represent data on the same material derived from intermittent and non-intermittent exposures of identical magnitude. In general, different values of gamma and inertia will be obtained from intermit-

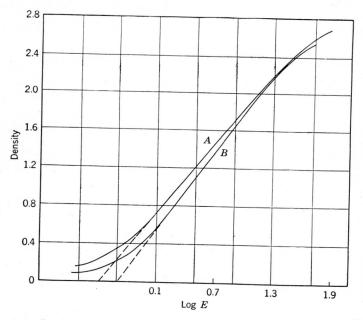

FIG. 9·4   Sensitometric curves from (A) non-intermittent and (B) intermittent exposures on a single material.

tent and non-intermittent exposures of the same material. Since the intermittency effect is associated with reciprocity failure (see Chapter 4), it is not the same for different materials, and the relative sensitometric values for different materials as obtained with intermittent exposures may not be the same as those obtained with non-intermittent exposures. To simulate the common practice in exposing photographic materials, the modulating device in the sensitometer must therefore be of the non-intermittent type. The exception would be an intermittent exposure device which impressed the exposures at a rate above the critical frequency.

In comparing time-scale and intensity-scale sensitometers it is again necessary to point out that, if the sensitometric data are to be applied to the practical use of photographic materials, the data must be obtained under conditions similar to those under which the material is to be used. For most negative materials,

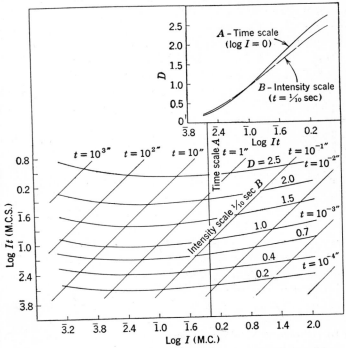

FIG. 9·5 Reciprocity failure curves for a panchromatic emulsion.

this means a short, continuous, intensity-scale exposure at a relatively high level of intensity. In astronomy, however, it means long exposure times at a very low level of intensity. Sound recording is an example of the opposite extreme where the exposure given the photographic material is of the order of 1/20,000 second at very high levels of intensity.

The importance of selecting the proper intensity level is demonstrated by Fig. 9·5, which illustrates again the reciprocity law failure discussed in Chapter 4. The curves in this figure show the values of log It required to produce densities of 0.2, 0.4, 0.7, 1.0,

1.5, 2.0, and 2.5, respectively, for various values of log I. If time-scale and intensity-scale sensitometers were to give the same sensitometric data these curves would have to be straight lines parallel to the log I axis. Any ordinate across the curves, such as A, represents the data obtained with a time-scale sensitometer. Likewise, any line drawn through the curves at an angle of 45° to the coordinates, such as B, represents the data obtained with an intensity-scale sensitometer If the density values are plotted against the exposure It for the set of intercepts produced by the lines A and B, respectively, the curves shown in the inset of Fig. 9·5 are obtained. These curves, which are the characteristic curves as obtained with time-scale and intensity-scale sensitometers, show the large differences that can occur between the two types of measurements. It should be noted that these two curves apply to only one level of intensity for the time-scale curve and to only one time for the intensity-scale curve. A complete set of curves could be drawn for both scales by employing the other lines parallel to A and B. It is clear that the curves within a given set can differ from each other appreciably.

Time-Scale Sensitometers (Type II)

Despite their many disadvantages, time-scale sensitometers were the earliest to be adopted in practice because of the difficulty of obtaining satisfactory instruments using an intensity scale. Until relatively recent years, it has been very difficult to obtain unvarying light sources and a strictly reproducible intensity modulator. These experimental difficulties led Hurter and Driffield to perform their classical work on sensitometry with a sensitometer employing a rotating sector disk giving intermittent exposures on a time-scale basis. Since the exposure is made by allowing the sector disk to make several revolutions, the long period variations in light intensity act upon the whole of the strip at the same time and do not affect the relative exposures given each strip. A typical sector disk is shown in Fig. 9·6. Since each successive aperture is one half as large as the preceding one, the innermost ring gives an exposure of half of the total time of operation; the next, one fourth; the next, one eighth; and so on, there being nine sectors in all in this particular disk.

As soon as it was possible to maintain the light source at a constant intensity for a period of time long enough to make an ex-

posure, the errors arising from the intermittency effect could be
eliminated by driving the disk at such a speed that it made the
exposure in a single revolu-
tion. Such a sensitometer
was designed by L. A. Jones [2]
particularly as a control instrument for use with motion-
picture film. A schematic
diagram of this instrument is
shown in Fig. 9·7. The lamp
house contains a carefully
standardized tungsten filament lamp of a precision
type. The light, after passing through a filter, is reflected by a mirror to the
exposure plane. The expo-

Fig. 9·6   Sector disk.

sure modulator is a cylindrical drum which makes one revolu-
tion for each exposure. The drum is driven by a synchronous

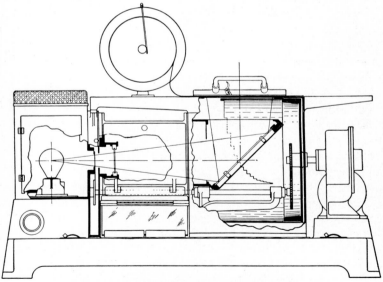

Fig. 9·7   Schematic diagram of type II-B sensitometer.

motor to assure accurate exposure times, and it has twenty-one
apertures increasing as powers of $\sqrt{2}$. For ordinary work, gelatin

filters are placed between the light source and the exposure plane to produce a source-filter combination giving radiation comparable with that used in practice for the particular material being exposed. When desired, however, a Davis-Gibson filter can be used in place of the gelatin filters. Other similar non-intermittent time-scale sensitometers have been described which give longer or shorter exposure times by employing different types of sector wheels.

Intensity-Scale Sensitometers (Type I)

With the advent of steady light sources and reproducible intensity modulators, intensity-scale sensitometers have largely replaced time-scale sensitometers. By employing an exposure time in agreement with that used in practice and varying the intensity sufficiently to obtain a range of densities, the sensitometric data derived are directly applicable to the photographic material under practical operating conditions. The time of exposure would, of course, be different for different materials, depending upon the purpose for which the material is commonly used. The exposure time is commonly controlled by single-aperture sector disks, rotating drums with a single opening, or, when longer exposures are required, electronic time-control switches.

The most common method of modulating the intensity of the light falling on the sample employs an accurate step tablet or optical wedge. The exposure is made with these variable-density step tablets or wedges in contact with the photographic material. These wedges and tablets can be made by properly casting gelatin containing dyes or colloidal carbon. In practice, it is very difficult to make wedges or tablets that do not modify the spectral composition of the light falling on the sample. Even if they absorb uniformly in the visible spectrum, they frequently absorb the ultraviolet and the infrared selectively. For much sensitometric work, it is possible to use wedges made by suitable exposure and development of a photographic material. If such wedges are developed in a metol-hydroquinone developer, they will be very nearly neutral throughout the visible spectrum and the near infrared and near ultraviolet. Intensity-scale sensitometers employing these various types of step tablets or wedges are in general use for obtaining sensitometric data and for controlling photographic operations. However, unless these tablets are essentially non-selectively absorbing and have been carefully calibrated, they are not suitable for primary standards in a sensitometric laboratory.

In addition to the modulation of intensity by optical wedges, several systems of intensity modulation have been introduced which are based upon the principle of a diaphragmed optical system. Although there are many special forms of this system for modulating the intensity of light in a sensitometer, they are all dependent upon the simple law of optics that for a lens of given focal length the illuminance of the image is a function of the effective diameter of the lens; that is, the light is modulated in much the same way as the effective exposure of the common camera is reduced by stopping down the lens. Although satisfactory diaphragmed optical-system type of intensity-scale sensitometers have been designed [3, 4] they have not been used extensively in practice because of their relative complexity as compared to instruments employing a wedge or step tablet to modulate the exposure. With a wedge in contact with the photographic material all the intensity-scale exposures are made simultaneously, whereas with the diaphragmed optical system the exposure at each intensity level must be made independently since the aperture must be changed to change the illuminance of the sample. On the other hand, modulating the exposure by a diaphragmed optical system does not affect the spectral composition of the radiant energy from the light source.

Development of the Sensitometric Samples

It is very difficult to develop photographic materials evenly and reproducibly because of the effect of development products on the rate of development (see Chapter 7). These products are formed most abundantly in the most exposed regions of the material, and if they are not removed by agitation or by a chemical reaction in the developer, they lead to uneven and non-reproducible results. As in all phases of sensitometry, the development must be carried out in such a manner that the results will be reproducible and will conform to those obtained in practice.

In most reactions between a photographic material and a developer, the change in specific gravity of the solution containing the reaction products is sufficient to set up convection currents. In vertical development without agitation, the reaction products, which usually have a higher specific gravity than the developing solution, drift to the bottom of the tank, and the rate of development accordingly varies from the upper part of the sample to the lower. These reaction products generally retard development, and the resulting difference in photographic density between the ends of a sample developed in a vertical tank without agitation can be as high as 10 per cent.

Many modifications of the vertical method of development have been proposed to eliminate the uneven development usually produced by this method. The object of all these modifications is to agitate the developing solution and the sample so as to remove constantly the development products from the region being developed. One of the earliest methods of insuring a flow of the developing solution over the sample during vertical development was to enclose the sample in a tube and to shake the tube by hand so that the sample moved from one end to the other. The flow of the developer over the sample was produced by the motion of the sample through the solution, and thus air could be excluded by filling the tube with the developing solution. It was found that the irregular motion produced when the tube was shaken by hand was more efficient in producing even and reproducible results than the regular motion produced when the tube was shaken by mechanical means. The British and American Standards Committees [5] adopted a similar system employing a vacuum bottle partly filled with the developer. The sample is fastened to a long narrow strip of glass or metal attached to the stopper. Because of the vacuum jacket surrounding the tube, handling produces only a negligible temperature rise.

Harrison and Dobson [6] secured an effective flow of the developer over the sample by employing a plunger which moved up and down near the face of the sample. Many modifications of this system have been used in developing machines.

In many sensitometric laboratories, such as those operated by the motion-picture industry and the manufacturers of photographic materials, special developing machines are employed which give a very uniform image and very reproducible results. A section of a developing machine for sensitometric strips is shown in Fig. 9·8. A relatively slow, uniform circulation of the developer in the vertical direction is produced by the propeller which forces the developer down into the well and up past the sensitometric strips as shown by the arrows. In addition to this general circulation of the developer, a much more vigorous agitation is produced by the vertical paddles which move back and forth close to the surface of the samples. The temperature of the developing solutions is maintained constant by the thermostatically controlled water jacket.

Although developing machines are employed extensively for quantity work, there are many instances where it is desirable or necessary to carry out development in a tray. To obtain even and reproducible results with tray development, a considerable amount

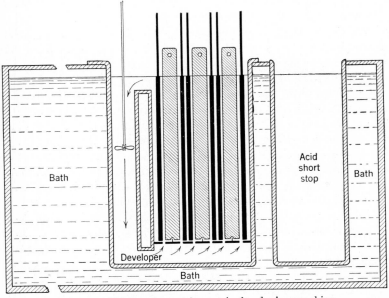

Fig. 9·8   Section of a sensitometric developing machine.

of developer must be used in order that the loss of the developing agent by oxidation will not be serious. During the process of development, local concentration of development products must be avoided by careful, irregular rocking of the tray. In general, uniform mechanical rocking of the tray should be avoided because it produces standing waves in the developer which result in uneven development. Although it is difficult to control the temperature of the solution during tray development, good results can be obtained by using special water-jacketed trays or by setting the tray containing the developer in a much larger tray containing water at the desired temperature.

Another method of obtaining even development is to brush the strips continuously during development with a soft, flat, long-haired brush. Clark [7] studied this method of development at length and found that brush development gives a very uniform image and that the right type of brush does not damage the emulsion. However, it is very difficult to obtain reproducible results with the brush development technique because the rate of development depends upon the rate at which the development products are removed by brushing.

Developers for Sensitometric Work

If the purpose of a sensitometric procedure is to determine the properties of the material used in practical photography, the developers and development conditions should conform as nearly as possible to those used in practice. On the other hand, developers used for scientific investigations of the principles of photography should be reproducible to specification and should be stable with respect to time and usage. Many of the developers used in practice in the past have not met these requirements, and a p-aminophenol developer recommended by Sheppard and Trivelli [8] was adopted at the Eighth International Congress of Photography as the standard for scientific sensitometric work. However, the present metol-hydroquinone (M.Q.) developers are reproducible to specification and are sufficiently stable with respect to time and usage for sensitometric work. These developers, which are also used extensively in practice, are now used almost exclusively in sensitometric laboratories since, as in all phases of sensitometry, it is desirable to conform as nearly as possible to the practical procedure.

REFERENCES
General

Mees, *The Theory of the Photographic Process*, Macmillan, New York, 1942, Chapter 16.

Jones, *Photographic Sensitometry*, Eastman Kodak Co., Rochester, New York, 1935.

Specific

1. Jones, *J. Franklin Inst.*, **189,** 303 (1920).
2. Jones, *J. Soc. Motion Picture Engrs.*, **17,** 536 (1931).
3. Jones and Morrison, *J. Franklin Inst.*, **228,** 445 (1939).
4. Bornemann and Tuttle, *J. Optical Soc. Am.*, **32,** 224 (1942).
5. *Phot. J.*, **80,** 341 (1940).
6. Harrison and Dobson, *Nature*, **114,** 752 (1924).
7. Clark, *Phot. J.*, **65,** 76 (1925).
8. Sheppard and Trivelli, *Proc. VII Intern. Cong. Phot.*, *London*, 174 (1928).

10.

Sensitometry II, Density and Its Measurement

The amount of photographic image produced by the exposure and development of a light-sensitive material can be measured either in terms of the mass of silver per unit of projection area in the photographic deposit or the amount of light stopped by the image. Hurter and Driffield[1] in their classical work on sensitometry reported that the optical density of a silver deposit in a photographic image was directly proportional to the mass of silver per unit of projection area. Although this conclusion was confirmed by some subsequent workers, later investigations have shown considerable departures from this linear relation. Since the purpose of the photographic image is to modulate the light passed through or reflected from the deposit, the most significant practical property of the image is its light-stopping power. Consequently, the concept of optical density as developed in the following sections will be based entirely upon the optical properties of the photographic image. The relation between the optical properties of the image and the mass of silver per unit of projection area has been discussed in Chapters 1 and 7.

Optical Density

When radiant energy falls on the photographic image, some is reflected backward, some is absorbed, some is scattered, and some is transmitted through undeviated, as illustrated in Fig. 10·1.

The flux of radiant energy $*P_o$ is incident on the deposit A, where some is reflected backward and some is passed through. The transmitted flux of radiant energy P_t has the distribution indicated by the envelope surrounding P_t. The exact spatial distribution of the transmitted light depends upon light-scattering properties of the individual deposit.

The light-stopping power of the deposit is measured in terms of its *optical density D*, which is defined by

$$D = \log_{10} \frac{P_o}{P_t} \quad (10 \cdot 1)$$

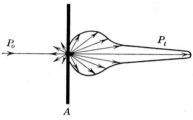

The ratio P_o/P_t is known as the *opacity O*, and the ratio P_t/P_o is known as the *transmittance T*. Equation $10 \cdot 1$ may now be rewritten:

Fig. 10·1 Distribution of light reflected and transmitted by a photographic image.

$$D = \log_{10} O = -\log_{10} T \quad (10 \cdot 2)$$

This concept of density is often applied not only to photographic deposits but also to other materials, such as light filters and colored glass.

Types of Density

A number of different numerical values of density can be obtained for the same deposit depending upon the geometry of the optics used to measure P_o and P_t. *Diffuse density* is given by equation $10 \cdot 1$ when the radiant flux is incident normally on the sample and all the transmitted flux is measured, or in accordance with the optical reversibility principle, when the incident radiant flux is perfectly diffuse and only the specularly transmitted component is measured. These two methods of measuring diffuse

* P_o is measured in power units such as ergs per second or watts. In deriving the general concept of density, this more precise physical quantity is employed in place of the usual quantity intensity which, in photographic literature, is used in a loose sense as being measured in either visual units such as meter-candles or physical units such as ergs per square centimeter per second.

density are illustrated in Figs. 10·2 (*a*) and 10·2 (*b*). *Specular density* is given when the radiant flux is incident normally on the sample and only the normal component of the transmitted flux is measured, as shown in Fig. 10·2 (*c*). *Doubly diffuse density* is given when the radiant flux incident on the sample is completely diffuse and all the transmitted flux is measured, as shown in Fig. 10·2 (*d*).

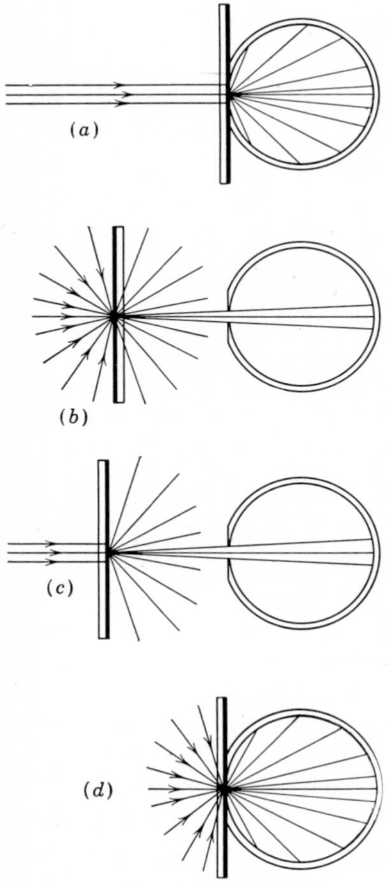

For a given sample, specular density is higher than doubly diffuse density, which in turn is higher than diffuse density.

It is very important to note that, although P_o is customarily defined as the flux of radiant energy incident on the sample and P_t as the flux of radiant energy transmitted by the sample, in practice *P_o is the flux of radiant energy measured by the photometer when the sample is not in place, and P_t is the flux of radiant energy measured by the same photometer when the sample is in place.* For example, when P_o is measured as shown in Fig. 10·2 (*b*), the flux measured is not the total flux from the diffuse radiant flux incident on the sample, but only that specular component of the diffuse flux which is measured by the

FIG. 10·2   Geometry of the optics used to measure different types of density.

photometer when no sample is in place.

The effect of scattered light upon the relative values of specular or diffuse density was a source of disagreement between Hurter and Driffield and their critics. Hurter and Driffield measured approximately specular densities and Abney measured approxi-

mately diffuse densities. Abney correctly ascribed the difference
between the values he obtained and those obtained by Hurter and
Driffield to the light-scattering property of the silver deposit,
but Hurter and Driffield thought that it was due to interreflections
between Abney's diffusing medium and the negative. In 1898
Chapman Jones confirmed Abney's idea that the loss of light by
scattering gave a higher value for specular density than that for
diffuse density.

In 1909 Callier made a large number of measurements to deter-
mine the relation between specular density $D\|$ and diffuse density
$D\hspace{-2pt}\parallel\hspace{-4pt}\parallel$. He designated the ratio of $D\|$ to $D\hspace{-2pt}\parallel\hspace{-4pt}\parallel$ as Q, and this ratio is
commonly referred to as the *Callier Q factor*. According to Cal-
lier's measurements Q is a constant at all values of density for a
given material. Bloch and Renwick [2] later showed that Q is not
constant for all values of density but can be expressed as a logarithmic function of density. They found that when the logarithm
of diffuse density is plotted against the logarithm of specular
density, straight lines are obtained. Tuttle [3] verified the findings
of Bloch and Renwick with experiments performed many years
later.

The value of Q varies not only with density but also with
gamma. In Fig. 10·3 the values of Q for the densities on five
sensitometric strips of motion-picture positive film which were
developed to different gammas are plotted against diffuse densities. It is evident that for a given density the value of Q depends
upon the gamma to which the strip was developed. In the same
strip, the value of Q increases rapidly with density up to densities
of about 0.3 and then decreases somewhat. The Q factors used in
this figure were calculated from densities of the silver plus base.
The Q factor for silver plus base is important in some operations,
such as sound recording, whereas the Q factor of the silver deposit
alone is important in other operations, such as granularity measurements. Usually the effect of the base may be neglected but, if
the film has a gray base, the values of the Q factor for the silver
deposit and the base together will be appreciably lower than
those for the silver deposit alone. For low densities, where the
density of the silver deposit is of the same order of magnitude as
the density of the base, measurements of the Q factor without
corrections for the density of the base will always lead to a value
which approaches unity.

The density of a photographic deposit which is spectrally selective in its absorption depends upon the spectral characteristics of the incident radiant energy and the spectral sensitivity of the device employed to measure the transmitted or reflected flux. The

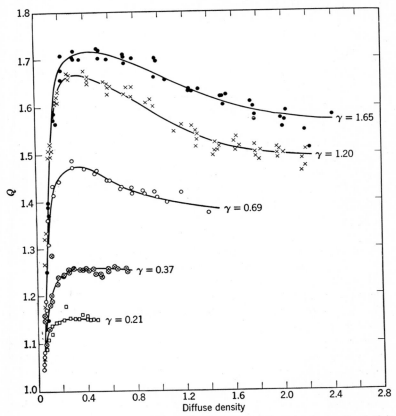

Fig. 10·3 The variation of Q with gamma and diffuse density. (Sandvik.)

density for any given wave length of radiant energy is of interest and can be measured. Spectrophotometer traces showing the densities of two different photographic deposits at different wave lengths are shown in Fig. 10·4. Curve A in this figure is representative of most photographic deposits since they are nearly non-selective in their absorption. However, some developers such as pyrogallol produce negatives having a yellowish color, and spectrophotometer traces for these materials are similar to curve *B* in Fig. 10·4. Very fine-grain materials also show selective absorption as a result of selective scattering of the light. A broad classification of density according to its spectral selectivity follows:

a.	At any wave length	*c.*	Printing
b.	Visual	*d.*	Photoelectric

This classification applies to all three main types of density: diffuse, specular, and doubly diffuse. The classification of each of

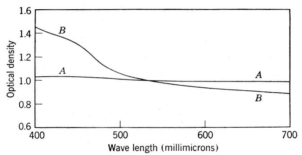

FIG. 10·4   Spectrophotometer traces for a photographic material developed in (*A*) a non-staining and (*B*) a staining developer.

these three types of density depends upon the spectral quality of the light source and the spectral response of the receiver employed to measure P_o and P_t.

Density at any wave length is usually measured by illuminating the sample with nearly monochromatic radiant energy and measuring the quantities P_o and P_t with any receiver which has sufficient sensitivity. The other classes of density are measured by illuminating the sample with a light source having the spectral quality of a tungsten radiator at 3000° K and measuring the quantities P_o and P_t with a receiver having the required spectral sensitivity. In the determination of visual density the spectral sensitivity of the element used to measure the light flux is that of the normal photopic eye, whereas for printing density it is the blue-green sensitivity of the common photographic papers. These required spectral sensitivities can be obtained by the proper combination of a photoelectric tube and filter. The spectral sensitivity of the receiver employed to measure photoelectric density is that of the surfaces used in commercial photoelectric tubes.

This broad classification of density on the basis of spectral selectivity can in turn be subdivided into several different types based upon other light sources and other light-measuring devices.

Two of the most important spectral types of density are visual and printing. With a deposit which is spectrally non-selective, these two types of density are of course identical. However, in

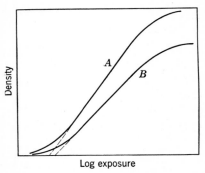

FIG. 10·5 Characteristic curves for a colored photographic image. Curve *A* is for printing density, and curve *B* is for visual density.

general, colored images give characteristic curves having different gammas according to whether visual or printing density is measured. Two such curves are shown in Fig. 10·5. These curves are representative of those most commonly obtained in practice in that they have nearly the same inertia point, with the result that there is nearly a constant ratio between the values of printing and visual density as measured on a single photographic deposit. Jones and Wilsey [4] examined the spectral selectivity of photographic images in detail. The *color coefficient* χ was defined by these men as the ratio between the printing gamma and the visual gamma ($\chi = \gamma$ printing/γ visual).

For negatives developed with non-staining developers, such as ferrous oxalate and hydroquinone, the value of χ is low, usually below 1.1. With developers containing pyrogallol and very little sulfite, the value of χ may be as high as 2.75 because of the high printing density of the yellow stain image produced under such conditions and the relatively low density of this image as measured visually. It has been shown that the yellow image produced by pyrogallol is a non-silver image consisting of yellow oxidation products. Frayne [5] has shown that the color of fine-grain images is a function of density. At least part of the color of these fine-grain images must therefore be attributed to the light scattered by the grains.

The density in a developed photographic image which is not the result of exposure to light is known as *fog*. A density as normally measured includes both that produced by fog and that produced by exposure to light. Although the printing characteristics of a negative are related to the total densities in the negative regardless of whether these densities are the result of fog or exposure to light, it is nevertheless sometimes desirable to be able to correct the density readings for fog. As a first approximation, it is satisfactory to subtract the fog density in the unexposed region from all densities. However, this correction is only a first approximation since the fog density is higher for the unexposed areas on the plate than it is for the areas that received relatively heavy exposures. The exact correction for the contribution of fog to a given density is assumed to be proportional to the number of silver halide grains *not* developed, since some of the grains which would produce fog in an unexposed region are exposed in the area producing the image density. Formulas to be used in making exact fog corrections have been suggested by Meidinger,[6] Wilsey,[7] and Nietz.[8]

Densitometers

The instruments used to measure photographic absorption are called *densitometers*. Although these instruments are essentially photometers, it is better to retain this term for an instrument that measures the intensity of light.

Many of the early densitometers were simply modified forms of a bench photometer. In such an instrument, two light sources are used and an intensity balance is made with the sources unscreened and with one source screened by the sample to be measured. The photometer head, in which the intensity balance is made, may be any one of the several used in photometric work, such as the Bunsen grease spot or the Lummer-Brodhun head. Although the density of the sample can be computed from the transmittance values thus obtained, such instruments are clumsy to use, and the light sources must be maintained constant. Densitometers of the bench type have been replaced very largely by instruments which compare two beams of light from a single source. The best known and the most widely used instrument for the matching of the two beams is the Martens photometer.

Many of the densitometers used in photographic work are merely instruments which are used to compare the density to be measured with the density of a calibrated wedge or series of wedges. These instruments have the advantage that they are relatively simple to make and easy to use. A simple form of the comparator which is widely used is that of Capstaff and Purdy; it is sketched in Fig. 10·6. Light from the source A passes through the circular photographic wedge W and onto the opal glass H. The sample is placed in contact with this opal glass, and the observer on looking through the eyepiece J sees a

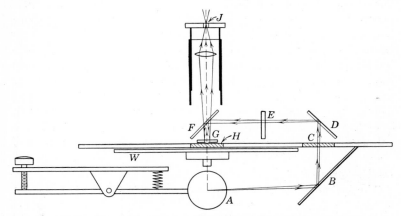

Fig. 10·6   Schematic diagram of the Capstaff-Purdy densitometer.

circular spot of light illuminated by the opal glass. The light passing through the sample is modulated by *both* the sample and the wedge. Light from the source A also enters the eyepiece J by the path B, C, D, E, F, and G. The opal glass C and the ground glass E are placed in the comparison beam as shown to insure that the illumination of this beam is uniform. The comparison beam is reflected by the semi-transparent mirror F onto mirror G, which has a small area in the middle from which the silver has been removed. On looking through the eyepiece, therefore, the observer sees a field illuminated by the comparison beam in the middle of which is a small spot illuminated by light that has passed through the sample and the wedge. The area illuminated by the comparison beam remains of a fixed brightness, and the density of the wedge in the beam passing through the sample is then adjusted until the small central spot disappears and the entire field appears uniform. Since this requires that the sum of the densities of the sample and the wedge should be constant, the density of the sample can be measured in terms of the density of the wedge. It should be noted that the accuracy of this instrument depends not only upon the ability of the operator to obtain a match, but also upon the accuracy of the calibration of the photographic wedge.

Many densitometers have been made in which radiation-sensitive electrical devices replace the human eye. These instruments have the advantage that they eliminate visual fatigue, frequently attain higher precision, and increase the reading speed. The accuracy of visual readings cannot exceed about 0.008 in density because of the inherent characteristics of the eye, and even experts can make only five or six readings a minute and then only for a limited period. Physical densitometers have been built which will read densities with an accuracy of 0.0004 and some will make as many as 50 readings a minute.

The earliest physical densitometers, which were designed by astronomers and spectroscopists, incorporated a thermopile and a galvanometer. Transmittance was computed from the galvanometer readings with and without the sample in place. Thermoelectric instruments have little advantage in speed over visual instruments. They are affected by temperature variations, are of low sensitivity, and most of their response is in the extremely long wave length region of the spectrum. These instruments are of little value in the measurement of materials which are spectrally selective.

Photoelectric tubes are free from many of the shortcomings of the thermal devices because they respond instantly and, with the proper tube filter combinations, their response can be made to match quite closely that of the human eye or the printing medium. However, the output of these tubes must be amplified, with the result that, in general, they are less stable than thermal devices. This instability has limited the use of photoelectric tubes in densitometers but, with the recent progress in electronics, satisfactory direct-reading instruments have now been constructed.

Photoresistive cells, of which the selenium type is best known, have been used for densitometers because of the greater current available as compared to the photoemissive cells. With these cells a much less sensitive indicating instrument can be employed. Unfortunately, they are inherently less stable and considerably slower to respond than the photoemissive types. No photoresistive cell instrument has been an unqualified success.

The barrier-layer, self-generating photoelectric cells have been used in many physical densitometers. They are stable and simple, they have a high current output, and the spectral response lies almost entirely in the visible spectrum. Several densitometers consisting of a light source, a barrier-layer cell, and a microammeter have been designed.

Since all the radiation-sensitive devices used in physical densitometers have a response which is approximately a linear function of the illuminance, the direct-reading instruments all have non-linear scales, and their accuracy decreases rapidly as density increases. Single-scale direct-reading instruments are not satisfactory for measurements of densities over 1.3. This defect has been partially overcome by the production of galvanometers which have an expanded scale at the low deflection end. Some of these expanded-scale instruments are calibrated to a density of 3.0 and can be read with considerable accuracy up to a density of 2.0. Densitometers which use a photoelectric tube and an amplifier with a logarithmic response have also been constructed. Although it may be that in the future satisfactory logarithmic amplifiers will be built, at present they are not an unqualified success because of their lack of stability and their failure to provide an exact logarithmic response.

The disadvantage of the non-linear density scale on physical densitometers has been overcome in many instruments by using the radiation-sensitive device, not to measure the light intensity, but to ascertain the equality of two light intensities. The tube is used to adjust the setting of a modulating device, such as an optical wedge or mechanical diaphragm, in such a manner that there is an intensity balance between the beam passing through the sample and the modulator and the comparison beam of fixed intensity. These instruments are fundamentally the same as the Capstaff-Purdy instrument described previously except that the light balance is obtained by means of a photoelectric tube and an associated electronic circuit for adjusting the modulator.

The Measurement of Density by Reflection

For many purposes, such as a print on paper, it is necessary to measure the optical properties of the image by reflected light. The relationship between the transmission of a photographic image and the light reflected from it when it is placed in contact with an opaque support has been the subject of many investigations. If R represents the ratio of the light reflected by the base to the light reflected by the image, the *reflection density* D_r is defined by the following formula:

$$D_r = \log \frac{1}{R} \tag{10·3}$$

This definition of reflection density is analogous to that for transmission density. According to Jones, Nutting, and Mees,[9] the relation between the transmittance of the sample and its reflection density is given by the equation

$$D_r = \log \frac{1}{(1 - C)T^2 + C} \tag{10·4}$$

C being a constant. It is clear that reflection density is not exactly equal to twice the transmission density. The exact relation between transmission and reflection density depends upon the diffusing properties of the photographic deposit and the base, and upon the nature of the illumination.

As with transmission density, the numerical value of reflection density depends upon the character of the optical system. The distribution of the reflected light is one of the most important optical factors that influence the measured value of reflection density.

The reflected light from a photographic print has both a specular and a diffuse component. The reflection density values obtained with a given densitometer depend upon the relative amounts of each of these two components accepted by the light-measuring element of the instrument. For viewing a photographic print, it is desirable to arrange the lighting and viewing conditions in such a manner that the amount of the specularly reflected light reaching the observer's eye is a minimum; if these viewing conditions are not fulfilled, the image of the light source as seen on the picture will produce an unpleasant glare. In photographic paper sensitometry, the illumination and the angle of acceptance of the measuring element of the densitometer are arranged to eliminate the principal specular component and to measure the diffusely reflected light. A satisfactory way to fulfill these conditions is to illuminate the sample with light that is incident on the paper at an angle of 45° and to measure the light that is reflected normally to the surface. The various forms of densitometers discussed previously can be adapted to read reflection density. However, when densitometers using polarized light are employed, precautions must be taken to insure that the measuring beam has not been polarized by reflection.

REFERENCES

General

Mees, *The Theory of the Photographic Process*, Macmillan, New York, 1942, Chapter 17.

Jones, *Photographic Sensitometry*, Eastman Kodak Co., 1935.

Specific

1. Hurter and Driffield, *J. Soc. Chem. Ind.*, **9,** 455 (1890).
2. Bloch and Renwick, *Phot. J.*, **56,** 49 (1916).
3. Tuttle, *J. Optical Soc. Am.*, **12,** 559 (1926).
4. Jones and Wilsey, *J. Franklin Inst.*, **185,** 231 (1918).
5. Frayne, *J. Soc. Motion Picture Engrs.*, **36,** 622 (1941).
6. Meidinger, *Z. physik. Chem.*, **114,** 89 (1924).
7. Wilsey, *Phot. J.*, **65,** 454 (1925).
8. Nietz, *Theory of Development*, Eastman Kodak Co., 1922.
9. Jones, Nutting, and Mees, *Phot. J.*, **38,** 342 (1914).

11.

Sensitometry III, Interpretation of Sensitometric Data

Sensitometric data are usually expressed in graphic form, and the numerical constants derived from the curves are used to express the characteristics of the photographic materials. One of the most useful curves is that obtained by plotting the optical densities of the deposits against the logarithms of the exposures as shown in Fig. 11·1 (also see Chapter 1). This curve, which is correctly called the *characteristic curve*, is popularly known as the H & D curve because it was first plotted by Hurter and Driffield in 1890. The characteristic curve is sometimes described as being S-shaped, but actually a considerable portion is usually a straight line within the limits of experimental error.

The Characteristic Curve

For a given density interval ΔD there is a corresponding $\log E$ interval, $\Delta \log E$; and the ratio $\Delta D / \Delta \log E$ of these intervals is known as the *gradient G*. Except for the straight portion of the curve, the gradient is not constant. For the straight portion the gradient is equal to the tangent of the angle α formed between the straight portion of the curve and the $\log E$ axis. This tangent is commonly called *gamma*. It should be noted that gamma gives information pertaining only to the slope of this straight portion of the curve and tells nothing about the other portions.

The projection of the straight portion of the characteristic curve on the $\log E$ axis (MN) determines the log exposure range over which direct proportionality exists between D and log E. This log E interval is called *exposure latitude* and is expressed in exposure units, either on a natural or a logarithmic scale. Although density is directly proportional to the logarithm of exposure only throughout the straight portion of this curve, nevertheless exposure differences in the range represented by the curved portions of the curve are reproduced as density differences. The portion C to A in which the gradient increases from zero to that repre-

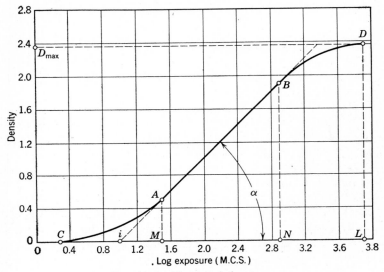

Fig. 11·1   Characteristic curve.

senting the straight portion is known as the *toe* of the curve. The portion B to D in which the gradient decreases to zero from that of the straight portion is known as the *shoulder* of the curve. The value of density corresponding to point D is D_{max}, the maximum density obtainable with this material under the conditions of exposure and development used to obtain these sensitometric data.

The term exposure latitude, as defined above, should not be confused with the *total scale* (CL, Fig. 11·1), which is the exposure range within which the material is capable of rendering differences in object luminance * by density differences. The total scale of

* See Table II in the Appendix.

most negative materials is considerably larger than the luminance range in the majority of scenes. The total scale of a given material is not a constant because its value depends upon the extent to which development is carried (γ) and, to a lesser extent, upon the processing factors and exposure conditions.

When the straight portion of the characteristic curve is extended to cut the log E axis, the value of log E at the point of intersection is called *inertia i* (*i*, Fig. 11·1). The equation of this straight portion is

$$D = \gamma(\log E - \log i) \qquad (11·1)$$

The Determination of Sensitivity

The effective sensitivity of a photographic material depends upon the results desired and upon the exact way in which the material is used. In astronomical photography, exposures of minutes and hours are common. Ordinary camera exposures are of the order of fractions of a second, whereas with modern speed lamps and in sound recording exposures are of the order of milliseconds. The relative sensitivity of photographic materials is of course not constant over this very large range of exposure times and intensity levels.

One of the earliest methods used for measuring sensitivity was a determination of the minimum exposure which would produce a just perceptible image after development. This method was used in Warnerke's sensitometer, the Scheiner instrument and the Eder-Hecht sensitometer. The difficulty of determining what constitutes a just-perceptible image led to a modification of this system in which sensitivity was measured in terms of the exposure necessary to produce a given density. The DIN system adopted by the German Standards Association in 1931 derived speed from the exposure required to give a density of 0.1 above the fog level.

Hurter and Driffield employed a value of speed obtained as $34/i$, where i is the inertia value. The adoption of inertia speed by them was based upon the assumption that, for the correct reproduction of tones in the negative, the scale of luminances in the object must be represented by exposures on the straight portion of the characteristic curve. It has been shown recently that this assumption is unwarranted. Nevertheless, the concept of inertia speed has been found to be useful and is frequently used at the present time. Inertia speed in general is given by the equation

$$\text{Speed} = \frac{N}{i} \tag{11.2}$$

where N is an arbitrary constant, and i is the inertia value. It should be noted that the inertia value is obtained from characteristic curves which have been drawn after the values of density have been corrected for *fog*.

As long as all the extensions of the straight portions of a family of characteristic curves for a given material pass through a common point on the log E axis, inertia, and hence inertia speed, are independent of development. Unfortunately, with many photographic materials the common intersection of the extensions of the straight portions of their characteristic curves does not lie on the log E axis (see Chapter 7 and Fig. 7.3), and the inertia value consequently depends upon the extent of development γ. Inertia speeds may in fact vary as much as 500 per cent with increasing γ. In addition to this complication in the use of inertia speed, materials exist for which there is no single point of intersection for the extrapolated straight portions of the characteristic curves, and others exist for which there is no well-defined straight portion of the characteristic curve. These many complications have made it difficult to obtain a general expression for a practical speed number in terms of the inertia value.

The normal function of a photographic material is to reproduce as density differences the luminance differences in the object being photographed. The minimum useful exposure, therefore, is that required to reproduce the luminance differences in the shadows of the object by some minimum density difference. For exact proportional rendering in the *negative* of the various object luminances, the minimum exposure would be that which would place the exposures representing the shadow regions of the object just at the beginning of the straight portion of the characteristic curve. On the other hand, it should be noted that the density differences in the *print* and not those in the negative are of practical importance. Consequently it is necessary to consider the properties of the printing medium as well as those of the negative.

Since the minimum useful exposure is that which will reproduce detail in the shadows with some minimum contrast in the print, it seemed logical to assume that satisfactory prints might be obtained from *negatives* exposed in such a manner that shadow detail was recorded by some minimum gradient in the toe of the characteristic curve. This idea was first discussed by Luther and was further expanded by Jones and Russell. Although experiments have shown that these assumptions are valid, they have also shown that it is difficult to determine the value to be taken as representing the minimum useful gradient.

L. A. Jones [1] proposed that negative film speeds be evaluated in terms of the minimum exposure required to give a negative from which a print of excellent quality can be made. He conducted a statistical examination of prints made from a series of negatives in which the exposure was increased progressively from very low to very high values. This investigation indicated that the "first excellent prints" were obtained from negatives so exposed that the deepest shadows were reproduced at a point on the toe of the *D*-log *E* curve where the minimum gradient was about 0.3 of the average gradient over a log exposure range of 1.5. A series of "excellent" prints is shown in Fig. 11·2 (*a, b, c*). The characteristic curve for the negative material is shown in Fig. 11·2 (*d*) together with the exposure range covered by each negative. Figure 11·2 (*a*) represents the "first excellent print" and corresponds to section *A* of the characteristic curve.

The American Standards Association [2] has adopted a method for determining the speed of black-and-white negative materials. This method is based upon the minimum exposure which must be incident upon the negative material from an element of the scene in the deepest shadows, in order that a print of excellent quality can be made from the negative. According to this method, the photographic speed of a material is given by the equation

$$\text{Speed} = \frac{1}{E} \qquad (11\cdot3)$$

where *E* is the exposure value at the fractional gradient point. The method of obtaining the value of *E* is illustrated in Fig. 11·3. *E* is the exposure value on the toe where the gradient is 0.3 of the average gradient over a log exposure range of 1.5. A log exposure

FIG. 11·2 (*a, b, c*) Prints made from negatives in which the exposure was increased progressively.

range of 1.5, represented in Fig. 11·3 by the distance AB, is moved along the axis of abscissa until the tangent of the angle a is 0.30 of the tangent of the angle b. Point C at the low end of the log exposure range AB is the exposure value E from which the speed of the material is to be derived.

When the ASA speed values obtained as above are divided by 4, the resulting numbers correspond to those commonly used with

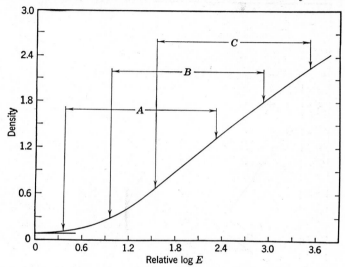

FIG. 11·2 (*d*) Characteristic curve for the negative material, together with the exposure range covered by the negatives used in making the prints shown in Figs. 11·2 (*a*, *b*, *c*).

exposure meters, exposure tables, and exposure computers. The number obtained as the quotient of the ASA speed and 4 is called the *exposure index*. It should be noted that ASA speed relates to the *minimum* exposure which will yield a negative from which an excellent print can be made. Except under the most favorable conditions, an exposure somewhat greater than this should be used for normal photographic work to take care of possible variations in equipment and in the handling of the photographic material. Consequently it is desirable to recommend a somewhat greater exposure than that on which the speed value is based. Exposure meters, tables, and computers for use with exposure indexes are so calibrated that, when the correct exposure index value is used, a safety factor in exposure of 2.5 for continuous-tone black-and-white negative materials is normally realized.

It appears that after further investigations speed values based upon a fractional gradient criterion for the determination of the minimum useful exposure will be employed for an ever wider range of photographic materials. However, there are special applica-

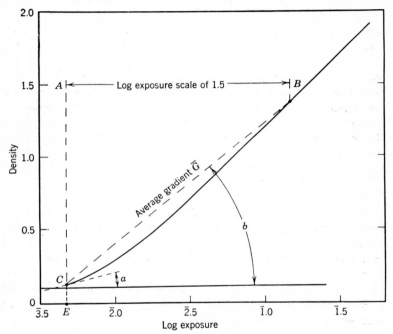

FIG. 11·3   Determination of film speed.

tions of the photographic process, such as in spectroscopy, astronomy, and photoengraving processes, where special methods of measuring speed appear to be desirable. In many applications of photography to spectroscopy and astronomy the photographic material is employed to determine the position and magnitude of the light in an optical image. According to Dunham,[3] adequate detection and measurement of weak absorption lines require both sufficient contrast and a minimum density of about 0.6. On the basis of Dunham's criterion, the speed of spectroscopic and astronomical materials is frequently expressed in terms of the reciprocal of the exposure, expressed in meter-candle-seconds, which will produce a density of 0.6 when developed to a given gamma. Speed values determined in this manner depend upon the order of the exposure times for which they are computed. The speed of a material when used with spectroscopic exposures of the order of 1 second may be as much as ten times as great as that when it is used with astronomical exposures of the order of hours.

In making line and halftone negatives for photoengraving, the ideal process negative consists of clear glass alternating with opaque deposits. There is no graduated scale of density in the ideal negative since the gradations are rendered by various dot sizes and not by various densities. The highest speed material is therefore that which will produce the necessary opacity with the minimum exposure. For example, if two materials have the same inertia speed, but if one can be developed to a higher gamma than the other, the material with the highest gamma will be the faster for photoengraving processes because it will produce a given opacity with less exposure.

Development Constants

The rate of development of a photographic material has been discussed in Chapter 7. In practice, the development character- istics of a photographic material are determined from a family of characteristic curves obtained by developing the material for various times. A typical family of such curves is shown in Fig. 11·4. The time-gamma curve shown in Fig. 11·5 is then obtained from these sensitometric data. This curve may be represented approximately by the exponential equation

$$\gamma = \gamma_\infty(1 - e^{-kt}) \qquad (11\cdot4)$$

where γ_∞ is the value which γ approaches as a maximum on pro- longed development, fog excluded, and k is the velocity constant of development. The values of γ_∞ and k can be determined by solving the simultaneous equations obtained when the values of gamma for times t and $2t$ are substituted in equation 11·4. How- ever, equation 11·4 rarely represents the actual time-gamma curve with sufficient accuracy to be employed in sensitometric calcula- tions (see Chapter 7).

For practical purposes the sensitometric data concerning the rate of development can usually best be obtained from curves simi-

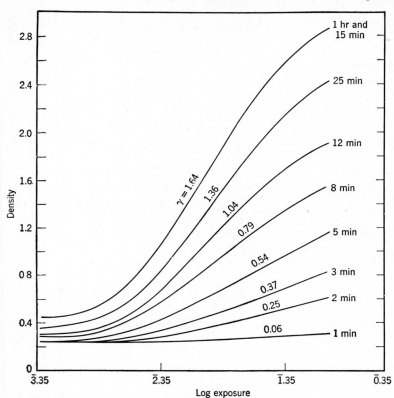

FIG. 11·4 Family of characteristic curves for a negative material.

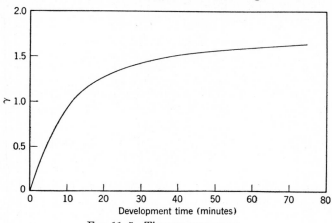

FIG. 11·5 Time-gamma curve.

lar to those shown in Figs. 11·4 and 11·5. To obtain a negative of a given gamma, it is only necessary to refer to the time-gamma curve (Fig. 11·5) for the required time of development.

Sensitometric Constants of Photographic Printing Paper

The sensitometric properties of photographic printing papers are described by a series of numerical constants which are derived

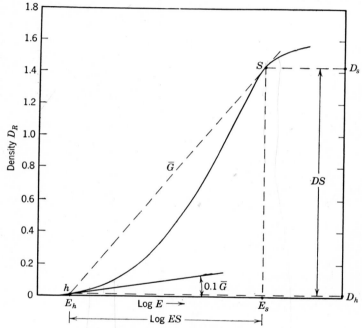

FIG. 11·6   Characteristic curve for a paper.

from the characteristic curves for the papers. The characteristic curve is obtained by plotting reflection density against the logarithm of exposure.

A typical characteristic curve for a photographic paper is shown in Fig. 11·6. The limiting exposure E_s in the high-density region corresponds to the point S on the shoulder of this curve where the gradient is equal to the average gradient $\bar{G}$, and the limiting exposure E_h in the low-density region corresponds to the point h on the toe at which the gradient is equal to $0.1\bar{G}$, where $\bar{G}$ is the average gradient of the curve between these two limiting exposures (see Fig. 11·6). The difference between the limiting exposures E_s and E_h is the *exposure scale ES* of the paper. Therefore

$$\log ES = \log E_s - \log E_h \qquad (11\cdot5)$$

The *density scale DS* is the difference between the ordinate values corresponding to the limiting exposures, and the *useful maximum density* is the ordinate value corresponding to the limiting exposure E_s. The speed of the photographic paper is given by the expression

$$\text{Paper speed} = \frac{10^4}{E_s} \qquad (11\cdot6)$$

Although this speed value is based on a fractional gradient criterion, as is the speed value for negatives, it should be noted that the speed point is now taken in the shoulder region rather than in the toe region as for negative materials. The constants for printing papers as defined above are in agreement with those adopted by the American Standards Association.[4]

In addition to those constants set up by the American Standards Association, it has been common practice to refer to the *contrast of the printing paper*. Contrast is a very complex matter involving both psychological and physical quantities. It has been expressed [5] as

$$\Omega = \frac{(DS)\cdot\overline{G}(D)}{(l\Delta D)^2} \qquad (11\cdot7)$$

where DS is the density scale, $\overline{G}(D)$ is the average gradient computed in terms of equal density increments, and $l\Delta D$ is the smallest density difference which can be distinguished by the eye. Since the denominator is a constant it can be neglected in the calculation of relative contrast. In the computation of $\overline{G}(D)$ the characteristic curve is divided into segments of equal density increment. The gradient of the curve is measured at each division point. The average of these gradient values is $\overline{G}(D)$. When the characteristic curve has a long straight portion the average gradient is approximately equal to the gamma to which the paper is developed. It should be noted that when the contrast of papers with essentially equal density scales are compared, the relative contrasts are equal to the relative average gradients. Contrast may be referred to as the product between a *rate* or *gradient* factor and the *extent* or *density scale* factor.

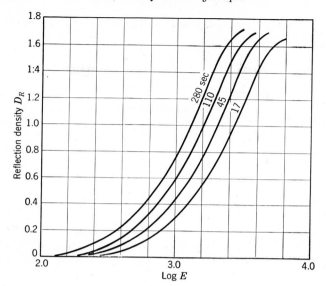

FIG. 11·7   Family of characteristic curves for a chloride paper.

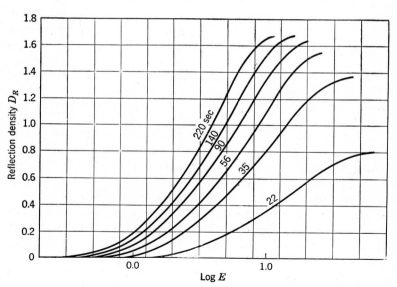

FIG. 11·8   Family of characteristic curves for a bromide paper.

Effect of Development on the Sensitometric Characteristics of Photographic Paper

The velocity of development of chloride and chlorobromide paper is very high, gamma infinity is reached very rapidly, and the only effect of prolonged development, after the initial stages, is an increase in the speed of the paper, as shown in Fig. 11·7. With bromide papers, on the other hand, prolonged development increases the average gradient and the speed simultaneously as shown in Fig. 11·8.

Spectral Sensitivity

In using photographic materials it is important to know the way in which the sensitivity is distributed throughout the spectrum, in both the ultraviolet and the infrared as well as in the visible. All methods of measuring spectral sensitivity involve the isolation of sections of the spectrum and the observation of the response produced when the materials are exposed to these spectral bands and then developed. A wide variety of devices, monochromatic sensitometers, spectrographs, tricolor tablets, color charts, and filter assemblies, have been used in connection with making these exposures. The more refined methods, which involve the dispersion of the radiation with prisms or diffraction gratings, may be divided into two general classes: first, the spectrographs in which the material is exposed to the entire spectrum at the same time; and, second, the monochromatic sensitometers in which the material is exposed to a single narrow band of practically homogeneous radiation.

Monochromatic Sensitometers

Monochromatic sensitometers for the ultraviolet regions of the spectrum have been made which consist of two quartz monochromatic illuminators. The radiation emerging from the exit slit of the first illuminator passes into the second. In this manner most of the stray radiation is eliminated, and the radiation emerging from the second illuminator is of high purity. For longer wave lengths it is desirable to disperse the radiation by means of diffraction gratings because of the low dispersion of the quartz illuminators. A prime requisite for this work is high spectral purity in the isolated band. High spectral purity is particularly necessary for those regions where the relative amount of energy from the light source or the sensitivity of the material is low compared to that in other spectral regions. The samples are exposed to the homogeneous radiation, and the time of exposure is modulated by any of the methods discussed previously (see Chapter 9).

Exposure is normally expressed in terms of visual meter-candle-seconds. However, in monochromatic sensitometry, exposure must be expressed in terms of suitable energy units such as ergs per unit area. One of the most difficult steps in monochromatic sensitometry is the determination of these energy values with sufficient precision. A common procedure is to use a thermopile-galvanometer combination of high sensitivity.

Spectral sensitivity can be expressed in many ways, and the particular method employed must be chosen to fit the problem in hand. For theoretical purposes, it is often desirable to express spectral sensitivity in terms of the reciprocal of the energy required to give a density of unity when development for each wave length is carried to a gamma of unity. On the other hand, for practical purposes spectral sensitivity is often expressed in terms of the reciprocal of the energy required to produce a density of unity for a fixed time of development. The time of development is usually that which, for a white light exposure, will give a gamma approximately equal to that used with the material in practice. The spectral sensitivity curves obtained by the above methods are modified somewhat if a different value of density is chosen for these measurements. Spectral sensitivity can also be expressed in terms of reciprocal inertia values (equation 11·2).

The relative values of spectral sensitivity for various wave lengths depend markedly upon the method employed for expressing spectral sensitivity. The curves for a panchromatic film as measured by several methods are shown in Fig. 11·9. In curve *A* the reciprocal inertia value is plotted against wave length. In curve *B* the reciprocal of the energy required to give a density of unity when development for each wave length is carried to a gamma of unity is plotted against wave length. In curve *C* the reciprocal of the energy required to produce a density of unity for a fixed development time is plotted against wave length, the development time being that required to give a gamma of unity for white light exposures.

Spectral sensitivity curves such as those shown in Fig. 11·9 represent the characteristic of the photographic material itself

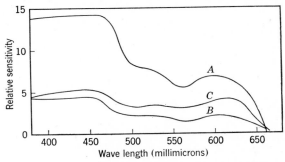

F IG. 11·9 Spectral sensitivity curves for a panchromatic film as expressed by different methods: (*A*) reciprocal inertia, (*B*) reciprocal energy for density of unity and gamma of unity, (*C*) reciprocal energy for density of unity and fixed development time.

and do not take into consideration the energy distribution of the light sources with which they are commonly exposed. These

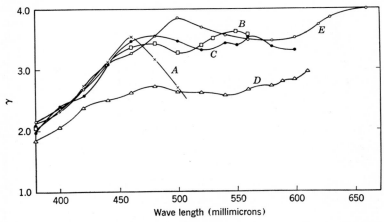

F IG. 11·10   Variation of gamma with wave length for an emulsion (*A*) unsensitized, (*B*) sensitized with a pseudocyanine, (*C*) sensitized with a merocyanine, (*D*) sensitized with a thiacarbocyanine, and (*E*) sensitized with a dibenzothiacarbocyanine.

curves show the relative response of the material only when it is used with a light source which is emitting equal amounts of energy at all wave lengths. The light sources ordinarily used for photography depart greatly from this condition of equal energy radiation. The spectral response curve of a material to any light source can be obtained by multiplying, wave length by wave length, the ordinates of the sensitivity curve of the material on an equal energy basis by the ordinates of the energy distribution curve for the light source (see page 153 and Fig. 9·3).

The relation of gamma to wave length follows no general rule. However, gamma often increases as the wave length of the light employed to expose the material increases. The variation of gamma with wave length depends upon the emulsion and is complicated by reciprocity law failure, particularly in optically sensitized emulsions. Typical curves for the variation of gamma with wave length are shown in Fig. 11·10.

Spectographs

In a spectrograph, the radiation from the source is dispersed by means of a prism or a diffraction grating, and the sample is exposed to the entire spectrum at the same time. When a neutral gray wedge is placed directly over the slit in such a manner as to modu-

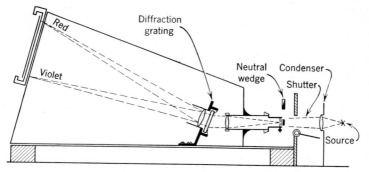

Fig. 11·11   Schematic diagram of a wedge spectrograph.

late the light along a spectrum line of a given wave length, the spectrograph may be made to give directly a graphic representation of the effective spectral response curve of a photographic material and light source combination. Such an instrument is usually referred to as a wedge spectrograph, and the photographic record is called a *wedge spectrogram*. The schematic diagram of a typical wedge spectrograph is shown in Fig. 11·11, and three wedge spectrograms of the type obtained with this instrument are shown in Fig. 11·12. An inspection of wedge spectrograms may yield considerable information about the distribution of sensitivity and some qualitative information concerning the variation of

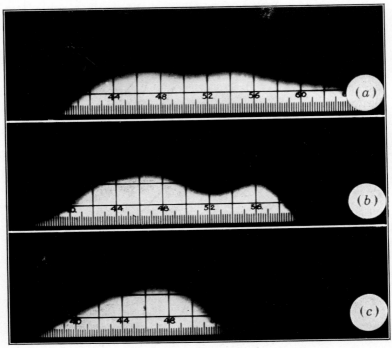

FIG. 11·12 Wedge spectrograms of (*a*) panchromatic, (*b*) orthochromatic, and (*c*) unsensitized materials.

gamma with wave length. The wedge spectrograph has the advantage of simplicity and rapidity. However, it cannot be considered to be as satisfactory for precise determinations as the monochromatic sensitometer.

Specifications of Color Sensitivity

It is often desirable to obtain a simple specification of color sensitivity in terms of a few numerical constants; such a system has been adopted by the American Standards Association.[6] The method consists in dividing the spectrum into three parts and determining the relative response of the photographic material in each of these regions. These regions are blue, green, and red.

Since it is difficult to obtain sharp-cutting filters which will isolate each of these spectral regions individually, the relative responses are determined by exposing the material with no filter, through a yellow filter, such as Wratten No. 12, and through a red filter, such as Wratten No. 25. The yellow filter transmits in the green and red regions of the spectrum but is opaque in the blue. The response to blue light is therefore obtained as the difference between the responses to exposure without a filter and to exposure through the yellow filter. The response to green light is obtained as the difference between the responses to exposure through the yellow filter and through the red filter. The response to red light is determined merely by the exposure through the red filter. The percentage contribution of each of these regions to the total response is taken as the *spectral sensitivity index*. In practice the degree of differentiation given by these index values is frequently greater than that required for many purposes, such as computing exposures. Photographic materials with similar properties of spectral response are therefore classified into groups in terms of *spectral group numbers*. Materials in a given group show similar color responses in photographing colored objects and require similar filter factors when used with the common filters. The spectral group numbers are based upon the relative responses of the material when exposed through a yellow filter such as the Wratten No. 12 and a red filter such as the Wratten No. 25. The two parameters of the grouping system are the sum of the red and green percentage contributions, and the ratio of the red and green percentage contributions. The spectral group number is determined from an appropriate table such as that adopted by the American Standards Association.[6]

REFERENCES

General

Mees, *The Theory of the Photographic Process*, Macmillan, New York, 1942, Chapters 18, 19.

Jones, *Photographic Sensitometry*, Eastman Kodak Co., 1935.

Specific

1. Jones, *J. Franklin Inst.*, **227**, 297, 497 (1939).
2. American Standard Z38.2.1–1947.
3. Dunham, *Ber. VIII intern. Kongr. Phot.*, *Dresden*, 287 (1931).
4. American Standard Z38.2.3–1947.
5. Jones, *J. Franklin Inst.*, **203**, 111 (1927).
6. American Standard Z38.2.4–1947.

The Theory of Tone Reproduction

One of the basic relations in photographic theory is that which exists between the *luminance* * and *luminance differences* in the original scene and the *density* and *density differences* in the photographic reproduction of the scene. The fundamental work on this relationship by Hurter and Driffield, Renwick, Jones, and others has established a series of principles known as *the theory of tone reproduction.*

Introduction

The tone reproduction problem has two major aspects: the objective and the subjective or psychological. In a study of the objective phase, the *luminance* and *luminance differences* in the object being photographed may be considered the starting point. A lens forms an image of the object on the light-sensitive material. When this image has been allowed to act for a sufficient time, a latent image is formed which is then converted into a real image by development and fixation to produce a negative. An image of this negative is now formed on the positive material by means of an enlarger or contact printer, and after sufficient exposure time a latent image is created that is then developed into a real image, and the positive photographic reproduction is obtained. The *density* and *density differences* of this positive are now compared with the log *luminance* and log *luminance differences* of those in the original object. This comparison provides direct information about the perfection with which the photographic process has met the requirements for exact objective tone reproduction.

* See Table II in the Appendix.

A study of the subjective phase of tone reproduction involves the comparison of the sensations and the mental impressions produced by the luminances in the various areas of the scene with those produced by the same areas in the illuminated reproduction. The magnitude attribute of the visual sensation produced by light is termed *brightness.*† These subjective comparisons are difficult to evaluate in precise terms since brightness, being a sensation, cannot be measured directly and recourse must be made to indirect methods. In making these comparisons, it is important to consider the illumination on both the positive and the original scene and the nature of the surrounding areas. The white border on a print, for example, affects its appearance because it reduces the ability of the visual system to see brightness differences and makes the shadow detail in the print more difficult to see. In addition there are the adaptations which take place in the eye or brain. Psychologists refer to these phenomena as brightness constancy and simultaneous contrast.

The foregoing discussion of the tone reproduction problem is entirely qualitative. The quantitative solution of this problem will be discussed in detail in the following sections.

A Graphic Solution of the Objective Phase of Tone Reproduction

The faithfulness of the objective tone reproduction obtained in a negative-positive photographic process depends upon the following factors:

1. Luminance scale of the scene.
2. Optical and physical characteristics of the camera.
3. Negative material and its treatment.
   a. Exposure.
   b. Spectral sensitivity.
   c. Development.
   d. Shape of the D-log E curve.
4. Characteristics of printing system.
5. Positive material and its treatment.
   a. Exposure.
   b. Development.
   c. Shape of the D-log E curve.
6. Method of measuring the densities in the photographic reproduction.

† See Table II in the Appendix.

Luminance Scale of Scenes

The *luminance scale* of a scene is defined as the ratio of the maximum to the minimum luminance in the scene. Since the best reflectors reflect only about 98 per cent of the incident light, whereas the best absorbers reflect as much as 1 or 2 per cent, the maximum luminance scale that can be realized, if all objects are illuminated uniformly, is in the order of 90 to 95 per cent. On the other hand, all the objects in a scene seldom receive the same illumination. Thus, objects in the shadows receive much less illumination than those in direct sunlight, and the luminance scale may be much higher than that for uniform illumination.

For many years it was thought that the luminance scale of an average outdoor scene was approximately 30. This is a log luminance scale of 1.5. Since the density scale of photographic papers is often 1.5 or more, the luminance range in such a scene should be reproducible on photographic paper. However, in 1940 Jones and Condit [1] published data for 126 exterior scenes showing that the average log luminance scale for these scenes was 2.2, the shortest being 1.45 and the longest 2.8. In terms of arithmetic units this corresponds to a scale of 160:1 for an average scene, with 27:1 and 760:1 as the scales of the scenes having the shortest and longest scales, respectively. Later measurements showed that some scenes have scales in excess of 1000. Obviously, a faithful reproduction of the latter scenes would require a positive material having a density scale of more than 3.0. Such a scale can be obtained in a transparency but, if a reflection print is desired, some compression of the tonal scale must be accepted. The photographer usually has his choice of taking the compression uniformly throughout the tonal scale, all in the shadows, all in the highlights, or part in the shadows and part in the highlights. Much of the research in tone reproduction deals with determining which of the possible reproductions are the most pleasing and seeking rules for obtaining such reproductions by control methods.

The measurements of Jones and Condit were made with a portable luminance photometer of the telescopic type in which precautions were taken to reduce flare light to a minimum. A reproduction of one of the scenes in which the luminance distribution was analyzed is shown in Fig. 12·1. The small lettered circles indicate the points at which luminance measurements were made,

FIG. 12·1 Scene for which the luminance measurements in Table 12·1 were made.

and in Table 12·1 are shown the luminance values expressed in foot-lamberts corresponding to these points. The maximum luminance in this scene was 4990 ft-l and the minimum 10.7 ft-l, the luminance scale being 466.

TABLE 12·1

LUMINANCE VALUES OF SEVERAL AREAS IN AN EXTERIOR SCENE

Area	Foot-Lamberts
a	4990
b	1500
c	890
d	475
e	165
f	10.7

The Optical and Physical Characteristics of the Camera

The camera image is not an exact luminous reproduction of the scene being photographed. The illuminance on the photographic material consists of two parts: one, the image-forming light, and the other, the non-image-forming or flare light. If I_i is the total image illuminance, if I_{io} is the illuminance resulting from the image-forming light, and if I_{if} is the illuminance resulting from flare light alone,

$$I_i = I_{io} + I_{if} \tag{12·1}$$

The non-image-forming flare light I_{if} arises from several sources. Light is scattered or reflected by the glass-air surfaces of the lens system, by flaws in the glass, and by dust or fingerprints on the surfaces. Additional flare light may be introduced by reflections from the lens mount, the diaphragm, and the shutter blades.

One of the most important sources of flare light is the multiple reflections from the glass-air surfaces of the lens system. Part of the light passing through the lens is reflected back toward the object at the first surface and therefore need not be considered further. However, part of the light reflected at the second surface is returned toward the image plane by reflection from the first surface. These reflected beams form an image for each reflection at a glass-air surface as shown for a simple meniscus lens system in Fig. 12·2. The image at a, which is produced by a single reflection, can be neglected, but the image at b, which is produced by double reflection, represents a serious source of flare light. Every pair of glass-air surfaces in a lens represents a system which is sending flare light in the direction of the image plane. The number of flare-producing images formed by a lens system equals $N(N-1)/2$, where N represents the number of glass-air surfaces. The light reflected from a cemented surface is small and can be neglected. These images are usually formed near the lens, and the flare light on reaching the photographic material is spread out over the entire film or plate. Frequently, however, this light falling on the plate is not spread uniformly over the surface, and a flare spot or ghost is produced.

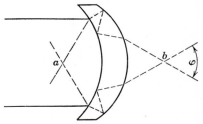

Flare light introduced by reflections from the glass-air surfaces can be reduced by applying one or more layers of the proper transparent material to the surface of the glass. Usually only a single

Fig. 12·2 Flare in a simple lens. (Goldberg.)

layer is used, and it should have an index of refraction equal to the square root of the index of refraction of the glass; its optical thickness should be equal to one-quarter the wave length of green light. Such a layer will reduce the reflectivity for green light falling normal to the surface to nearly zero and will reduce the average reflectivity for all colors to about ½ per cent. Coating a four-element lens should increase its total transmittance by about 50 per cent. This large an increase in transmittance is not realized in practice, and the flare light is not reduced by the theoretical amount because of the flare introduced by the other elements of the camera, such as the bellows and the diaphragm blades.

Flare light compresses the tonal scale considerably because it has a much greater effect on the shadow tones than it has on the highlights. For example, the addition of 1 unit of flare light to 100 units of image-forming light in the highlight region increases the illuminance only 1 per cent, whereas the addition of 1 unit of flare light to 1 unit of image-forming light in the shadows increases the illuminance 100 per cent.

Jones and Condit [1] found that the magnitude of flare depended not only on the type of camera and lens but also upon the type of

scene.   They defined *flare factor* as the ratio of the luminance scale
of the scene to the illuminance scale of the camera image.   Using a
camera with appreciably less flare than an average camera they
found that for 126 different scenes the flare factor varied from
1.15 to 9.50.   The average flare factor with this camera was 2.35.
The flare factor for a typical amateur camera and an average
scene is in the order of 3 to 5.   Since most high-quality negative
emulsions have an exposure scale of several hundred, it is clear
that the flare factor reduces the luminance scale of most scenes to
a camera image illuminance scale which can easily be accommo-
dated by the negative material.

The Flare Curve

The method employed in the graphic solution of the complete
tone reproduction problem as described in this and the following
sections was first suggested by L. A. Jones.[2]   The first step in the

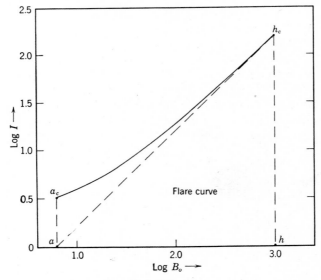

Fig. 12·3   Flare curve.

solution of the objective phase of the problem is to determine the
flare curve as shown in Fig. 12·3.   The log luminance of different
points in the scene, log B_o, is plotted against the log luminance of

the corresponding points in the camera image, log I. If the image were an exact luminance reproduction of the scene, the data in this graph would fit a straight line having a slope of unity. In practice flare light usually has little effect on the gradients in the highlight region. On the other hand, flare light frequently lowers the gradient in the middle tones to 0.7 and those in the shadows to as low as 0.3.

In determining the gradient characteristics of the camera image it is also necessary to consider the optical properties of the lens since the image-forming component I_{io} of the total image-forming light from a uniformly luminous object is not distributed uniformly over the image. If the luminance, B_o, of an object area is known, the value of I_{io} for a corresponding point in the image formed on the photographic material can be computed by the formula

$$I_{io} = B_o \frac{f^2}{4V^2F^2} \quad \cos^4 \theta \cdot H \cdot T_g \qquad (12 \cdot 2)$$

where I_{io} = image illuminance (foot-candles)
   B_o = object luminance (foot-lamberts)
   f = focal length
   V = image distance
   d = diameter of stop
   F = f/d, aperture ratio
   θ = angle of image point off axis
   T_g = transmission factor due to reflection and absorption by glass
   H = transmission factor at points off axis due to vignetting by the lens barrel,

If the object lies on the axis of the lens, the $\cos^4 \theta$ and H terms in this equation may be ignored, and if the object is at infinity the equation simplifies to

$$I_{io} = B_o \frac{1}{4F^2} T_g \qquad (12 \cdot 3)$$

On the average, however, objects are not at infinity, and a correction should be made for the difference in the relationship between I_{io} and B_o as given by equations 12·2 and 12·3.

In a practical formula, account should also be taken of the loss due to vignetting and the optical loss from the angle subtended by off-axis objects. The weighted average displacement from the optical axis of important objects may be taken as 15°. The loss from vignetting by the barrel of the lens depends upon the design of the lens and the aperture, but for a point 15° off axis this loss may be represented by an average of 25 per cent. Light is lost by reflection at the glass-air surfaces of the lens and by absorption within the glass. On the average, modern lenses, which frequently have six or eight glass-air surfaces, do not transmit more than 70 per cent of the incident light. These various factors, which must be considered in the determination of a probable average value of the relation between I_{io} and B_o, may therefore be taken as

$$\theta = 15°$$

$$\cos^4 \theta = 0.866$$

$$T_g = 0.70$$

$$H = 0.75$$

and for a finite object distance,

$$\frac{f^2}{V^2} = 0.90$$

When these four values are inserted in formula $12 \cdot 2$ the result becomes

$$I_{io} = B_o \frac{0.409}{4F^2} \qquad (12 \cdot 4)$$

In the solution of the tone reproduction problem the gradient curve for the camera image (Fig. $12 \cdot 3$) is usually determined for points near the axis. It should be noted that this curve applies *only* to objects near the axis and that a different camera image curve would apply to objects at some distance from the axis. However, if the focal length of the lens is equal to or greater than the diagonal of the negative in the camera, errors introduced in the calculations by disregarding the non-uniformity of the image-forming light I_{io} are small and are usually disregarded.

The Negative Material

The shape of the D-log E characteristic curve of negative materials and their available exposure and density scales is of particular importance in the solution of tone reproduction problems. Since densities represented by the shoulder of the characteristic curve are seldom used in practice, the important characteristics of the material are the lengths of the toe and the straight portions of the characteristic curve. Some materials show long sweeping toes covering a relatively long exposure range; in their curve the straight portion does not begin until fairly high density values are reached. On the other hand, materials of the short-toe type give straight lines beginning at relatively low density values, and the exposure scale covered by the toe regions is quite short.

For many years it was believed that the negative exposure should always be such that the scene was reproduced entirely on the straight portion of the characteristic curve. Recent work has shown, however, that a considerable portion of the toe can be, and frequently is, used with some gain in print quality. The American Standard criterion of negative film speed is, in fact, based on the measurement of a *minimum useful gradient* on the toe as discussed in Chapter 11. The gradient or gamma of the straight portion is usually kept within the limits of 0.7 and 0.9 by controlling the extent of development. If these gamma limits are not exceeded, satisfactory tone reproduction in the final print can ordinarily be achieved even when the negative exposure varies widely.

On the other hand, negative materials are sometimes developed to give a gamma of 0.9 to 1.2 when used in specialized fields such as press photography. Such negatives must be given a carefully controlled camera exposure because the high gamma decreases the camera exposure latitude. Any exposure which is great enough to place the scene on the straight portion of a high gamma curve produces so contrasty a negative that it cannot be printed successfully even on the softest available printing paper. The resulting tone reproduction is poor, and the print is displeasing. The exposures must then be limited to the toe of the negative where the contrast or gradient is sufficiently low for satisfactory printing. This difficulty is avoided when gamma values of 0.7 to 0.9 are used.

For correct objective tone reproduction of the colored objects in the scene, the spectral sensitivity of the negative material should be equal to that of the human eye. Generally, this factor is not critical, although distinctly better tone reproduction is obtained with panchromatic and orthochromatic negative materials than with materials which are sensitive only to blue light.

The second step in the graphic analysis of the tone reproduction cycle combines the flare curve, Fig. 12·3, with the characteristic curve for the negative material. The two curves are combined as shown in Fig. 12·4, where the log I scale of the flare curve has been transferred to the log E axis of the characteristic curve

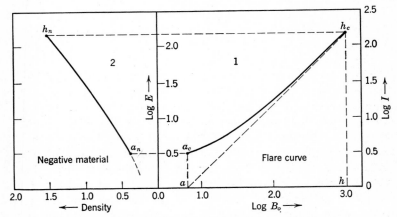

Fig. 12·4   Combined flare and negative characteristic curve.

for the negative material. From these combined curves it is now possible to determine the density produced in the negative by an exposure to any part of the scene having a known luminance value. The characteristic curve employed in this analysis must be obtained by employing a light source, a time of exposure, and development conditions which are in agreement with those used in obtaining the negative.

Characteristics of Printing System

When a negative is printed onto a positive material, either in a contact or a projection printer, the effective densities in the negative depend upon the geometric distribution or degree of diffusion of the light falling on the negative and the fraction of the transmitted light which is collected by the positive. The type of density which is effective when using a given printer must be determined experimentally; it may be diffuse, doubly diffuse, specular, or some intermediate type. This experimentally determined effective density must be the type employed in determining the sensitometric properties of the negative material for the graphic analysis of tone reproduction (Fig. 12·4).

If the negative is stained by development or is spectrally selective for any reason, the spectral quality of the light used in printing and the spectral sensitivity of the positive material should be taken into account; that is, the effective negative densities should be determined for the particular spectral conditions involved (see Chapter 10).

Projection printers also contribute flare light to the projected image. This flare light has the same origin as flare in camera systems but, in general, the amount in projection printers is very much less than that in the negative-making operation. As a rule, the only illuminated area presented to the objective of the projection printer is the negative itself, the surrounding areas being dark. However, particularly for negatives having large density scales, the amount of flare light may be sufficient to produce a very definite distortion in the distribution of illumination on the positive material. If the amount of flare light is sufficient, the effective enlarger illumination must be determined in the manner employed to determine the flare curve (Fig. 12·3). For a given level of illumination on the negative, each density corresponds to a value of log luminance, and this value of log luminance is plotted against the log illuminance of the corresponding point in the enlarger image.

Positive Material

Modern printing papers fall into three general categories: chloride, bromide, and chlorobromide. The first group is characterized by high development rates; in a few seconds the curve shape has attained equilibrium. With extended development, the curve merely moves parallel to itself along the log exposure axis. Bromide papers develop somewhat more slowly and therefore afford a greater control of gradient. The chlorobromide group lies intermediate between the first two but resembles the chloride papers more closely.

In practice, the development of negatives is carried to a fixed extent; therefore, if the scenes vary appreciably in luminance scale, the resultant negatives have a rather wide variation in density scale. To print these various negatives satisfactorily, different grades of printing paper must be used. In Fig. 12·5 are shown the characteristic curves for six grades of a developing-out paper. It is seen that they have approximately the same value of maximum density. The available exposure scale, however, varies from approximately 1.5 in log E units for the No. 0 grade to approximately 0.5 for the No. 5 grade. These materials, as well as practically all commercially available developing-out papers of the chloride type, are characterized by long sweeping toes, straight

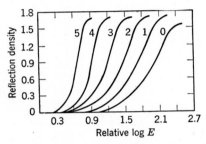

Fɪɢ. 12·5   Characteristic curves for six grades of printing paper.

portions which, if existent, are very short (with respect to exposure scale), and shoulders which break sharply at relatively high densities and become parallel to the log E axis.

The maximum densities obtainable on printing papers depend upon their surface characteristics. With high-gloss surfaces the maximum density obtainable is about 1.7, whereas for semi-matte surfaces it is about 1.55, and for dead-matte surfaces it is about 1.3. It is obvious that there are many luminance scales of natural scenes which cannot be reproduced by an exact objective tone reproduction since the average log luminance scale of the exterior scenes discussed previously is 2.2. This limitation can only be overcome by the use of positive materials having a higher maximum density, such as transparencies which have maximum densities of 3 or 4.

The third step in the graphic analysis of the objective phase of the tone reproduction problem is the combination of the characteristic curve for the positive material with the characteristic curve for the negative material. These curves are combined as shown in Fig. 12·6 where the density scale of the negative has been plotted as the log E scale for the positive. The exact value of log E depends upon the level of illumination of the negative. As pointed out previously, the type of density measured in the negative must

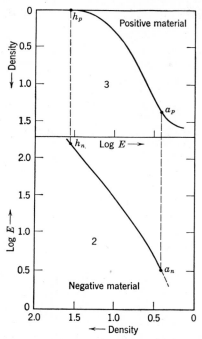

FIG. 12·6 Combined negative and positive characteristic curves.

be that which applies under the printing conditions employed and, if necessary, a curve similar to Fig. 12·3 must be introduced to correct for flare in the printing system.

Viewing Conditions

In the graphic analysis of tone reproduction, it is important that the measured densities of the positive actually represent the relative log luminances in the areas of the photograph as viewed by the observer. As pointed out previously (Chapter 10), the values of reflection density depend very markedly upon the manner in which they are measured. It is clear that the measurement of the reflection densities used in any tone reproduction analysis must be made consistent with the viewing conditions. On the other hand, if the positive is a transparency and is viewed by projection, the flare light and the specularity of the projector must be considered part of the viewing conditions. These effects are particularly important in the projection of motion-picture positives because, in addition to the above factors, the degradation of the image contrast by general illumination in the room or theater must be taken into consideration. These corrections are made by performing a graphical analysis similar to that discussed in connection with the flare curve shown in Fig. 12·3.

The Objective Tone Reproduction Curve

The complete graphic solution of the objective phase of the tone reproduction curve is obtained by combining the separate curves for flare, the negative material, and the positive material

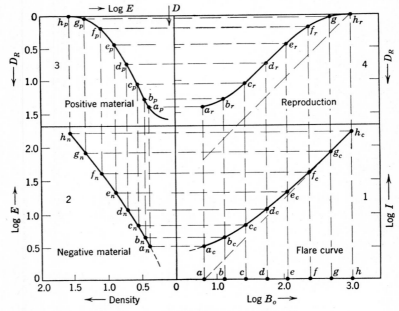

Fig. 12·7   Complete objective tone reproduction curve.

to give the objective tone reproduction curve as shown in the fourth quadrant of Fig. 12·7. The abscissa of the reproduction curve is the log luminance scale of the original scene, and the ordinate scale is the density scale of the positive photographic reproduction. The reproduction curve is obtained by first constructing perpendicular lines from selected object luminances a to h on the abscissa scale of the flare curve. The intersections of these lines with the camera image curve locates points a_c to h_c. Horizontal lines through these points locate points a_n to h_n on the negative characteristic curve. Vertical lines through these points establish points a_p to h_p on the positive characteristic curve, and horizontal lines through these points determine the densities with which luminances a to h in the original object are reproduced in the reproduction. The vertical lines through a to h intersect the horizontal lines through a_p to h_p at points a_r to h_r, and the curve through these points is the desired objective tone reproduction curve because it affords a graphic comparison between the log luminances in the original scene and the densities by which they are reproduced in the photographic reproduction.

For exact objective tone reproduction, the reproduction curve must be a straight line at an angle of 45° to the horizontal axis, and it must pass through the origin. If the gradients at any point a to h on the four curves 1, 2, 3, and 4 in the tone reproduction diagram, Fig. 12·7, are designated G_c, G_n, G_p, and G_r, respectively, these four gradients satisfy the condition that

$$G_r = G_c G_n G_p \qquad (12·5)$$

That is, the gradient of the reproduction curve G_r at any point is equal to the product of the gradients at the corresponding points on the other curves, G_c, G_n, and G_p. For perfect objective tone reproduction, therefore, the product of these three gradients must equal unity. If two of the three gradients are known, the value of the third can be computed. It is often stated that for the straight portion of the characteristic and flare curves this relationship becomes

$$\gamma_r = \gamma_c \gamma_n \gamma_p \qquad (12·6)$$

However, this condition is seldom met in practice because the corresponding points would have to be on the straight portion of every curve; points a to h in Fig. 12·7, for example, would all have to be on the straight portion of each curve. Points G_c and G_n are on the straight portions of their respective curves, but point G_p definitely is not. Perfect objective tone reproduction must therefore satisfy equation 12·5, but it need not satisfy equation 12·6.

A tone reproduction diagram of the type shown in Fig. 12·7 can be used to illustrate some interesting relationships concerning the required shapes for the negative and the positive characteristic curves which are required for correct tone reproduction.

The negative characteristic curve shown in the second quadrant of Fig. 12·4 is combined with the flare curve shown in the first quadrant to obtain the curve shown by A in Fig. 12·8. The curve

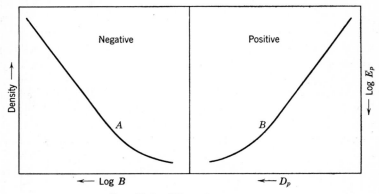

FIG. 12·8 Mirror image curves.

obtained by this combination represents the relation between the log brightness of the scene, log B, and the densities by which these brightnesses are represented on the negative. If this composite curve has the shape shown by A in Fig. 12·8, then for perfect objective tone reproduction the positive characteristic curve must have the shape shown by B. It is evident that these curves are mirror images of each other. This relation is commonly referred to as the *mirror image law*. It should be noted that curve B includes the effect of any flare light in the printing system. If this flare light is appreciable, the required positive characteristic curve as determined sensitometrically is obtained by combining curve B with the flare curve for the printer. The negative and the positive characteristic curves as obtained by sensitometric procedures remain the important properties of these photographic materials irrespective of the flare conditions in the camera or printer, but these curves must be adjusted to take flare into consideration when such operations as the mirror image law are applied. In the general solution of the objective tone reproduction problem as shown in Fig. 12·7, the correction for camera flare is introduced automatically by the operation shown in Fig. 12·4.

For a given negative material, the effect of variations in the

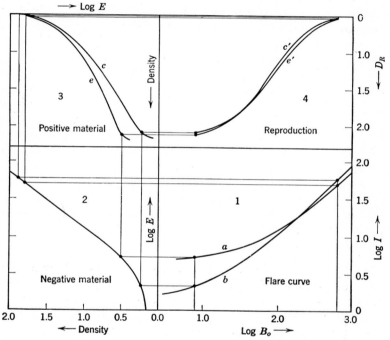

FIG. 12·9 Compensation for flare with different printing materials.

camera flare curve can frequently be compensated for by using positive materials having different characteristic curves. A practical example of this compensation is shown in Fig. 12·9. The flare curves for two different flare conditions, such as different lenses, on a single scene are shown at *a* and *b* in the first quadrant, and the reproduction curves obtained when a single negative material but two different positive materials are used are shown at *c′* and *e′* in the fourth quadrant. By the use of positive materials having the characteristics shown at *c* and at *e*, respectively, in the third quadrant it was possible to obtain these very similar reproduction curves.

The Subjective Phase of Tone Reproduction

If the photograph is a perfect tone reproduction of the original scene from a subjective standpoint, the impression given by the print when viewed must be identical with that received when the original scene was observed. The graphic solution of the tone reproduction problem by the method illustrated in Fig. 12·7 refers to the objective phase. This objective solution is identical with the subjective solution only when the type of scene and the viewing conditions for both the original and the reproduction are such that equal log luminance differences in the original scene and in the reproduction produce equal sensations of brightness differences on the consciousness of the observer.

For the solution of the subjective phase of tone reproduction, it is important to understand the relationships which specify the sensitivity of the human eye to luminance differences. Weber was one of the first to establish a relation between the brightness characteristics of sensation and the stimulus. He found that just noticeable brightness differences at different levels were produced by a fixed ratio between the values of luminance. Fechner expanded this into the so-called Weber-Fechner law, which is represented by the equation

$$\Delta S = K \frac{\Delta B}{B} \tag{12·7}$$

Here ΔS indicates a just noticeable change in the brightness attribute of the sensation, and ΔB is a luminance increment which must be added to the luminance B of the field for $B + \Delta B$ to appear noticeably different from B.

Since the enunciation of the Weber-Fechner law almost a century ago there has been considerable controversy over its validity. It is now agreed among most workers that the use of the word law is inappropriate and that the term *psychophysical relationship* would be more suitable. This particular psychophysical relationship is actually a representation of the sensitivity of the human visual mechanism. In common with all such relationships, it is valid *only* under the conditions used for determining it. The evidence is conclusive that this relationship does not hold over the

entire range of luminance values. However, for values of luminance lying between the approximate limits of 1 to 5000 or 10,000
ft-l, and under certain specified conditions of adaptation, it is
sufficiently valid for practical purposes. The experimental results

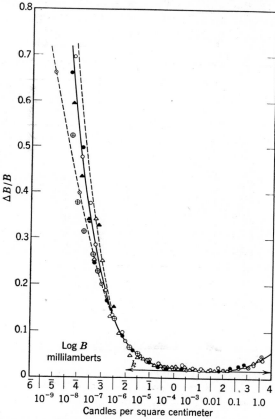

FIG. 12·10   Relation of retinal sensitivity to luminance.

obtained by several different workers who have examined this relationship are shown in Fig. 12·10. It should be noted that
although the integration of equation 12·7 would lead to the result
that the response is directly proportional to the logarithm of the
stimulus, $S = k \log B$, there is a serious question whether this
integration is valid even for the range of values over which the
relationship holds.

In the graphic solution of the subjective phase of the tone reproduction problem, the objective tone reproduction curve (Fig. 12·7) is combined with two response curves for the eye, the first being the curve for the eye when the scene is viewed and the second being the curve for the eye when the print is viewed. In general, the adaptation of the eye is different for these two conditions. These curves are combined as shown in Fig. 12·11. The

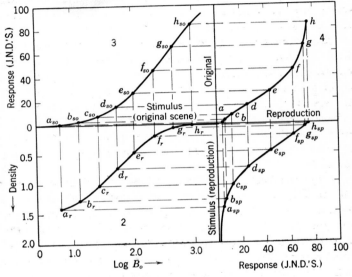

FIG. 12·11　Subjective tone reproduction curve.

density scale of the objective reproduction curve, which is plotted in the second quadrant, is transferred to the log luminance scale of the subjective response curve in the first quadrant. This response curve applies to the eye when viewing the print since at any given level of illumination the density scale of the print becomes the log luminance scale for the eye. The exact shape of the curve is of course determined by the level of illumination under which the print is viewed. The log luminance scale of the reproduction curve is transferred to the log luminance scale of the response curve in the third quadrant. This response curve applies to the eye when viewing the original scene since the log luminance scale of the reproduction curve is the log luminance scale of the original scene (see Fig. 12·7). The particular subjective response curve used in any graphical solution depends upon the level of illumination on the original scene. The response curves used for Fig. 12·11 apply to hypothetical viewing conditions where the level of illuminance on the reproduction is 12 ft-c and the average luminance of the scene is 400 ft-l.

Points a_r to h_r on the objective tone reproduction curve are projected horizontally onto the subjective response curve in the first quadrant at points a_{sp} to h_{sp}. Points a_r to h_r are also projected vertically onto the response curve in the third quadrant at points a_{so} to h_{so}. Points a_{so} to h_{so} are then projected horizontally into the fourth quadrant, and the subjective tone reproduction curve is given by the intersection of these lines with the vertical projections of points a_{sp} to h_{sp} from the first quadrant. This subjective tone reproduction curve shows graphically the subjective relation between the same areas in the original scene and in the photographic reproduction. For perfect subjective tone reproduction, this curve should be a straight line intersecting the axis at an angle of 45°.

It is evident that the subjective tone reproduction curve depends directly upon the objective tone reproduction curve. The assumption is sometimes made that in pictorial photography exact objective tone reproduction is undesirable. This generalization is unwise since research has shown that neglect of the factors which provide the best possible objective tone reproduction is, usually, detrimental to the appearance of the positives.

If data on the sensitivity of the eye are to be used to construct the response curves showing the subjective relationship between brightness and luminance, it is necessary to know what value of field luminance determines the sensitivity. Although it has usually been assumed that the sensitivity of the eye is controlled by the average field luminance, data by Lowry [3] and the work reported by Pitt [4] indicate that this assumption is not strictly correct. They report that when the scene is one in which the luminance varies over an appreciable range, the sensitivity of the eye varies with the portion of the scene being viewed. This effect can be explained, at least in part, by reference to Fig. 12·10. The ordinates are inversely proportional to the sensitivity of the eye, and the abscissas represent the luminance of the sensitizing field. If the sensitivity of the eye is controlled by a small field element, such as one subtending 2° at the eye, then the sensitivity of the eye will vary with the luminance of the portion in the scene which is being viewed. For the range of luminance indicated by K in Fig. 12·10 the sensitivity of the eye *as measured in this specific manner* will not vary with the luminance of the sensitizing field, but for all other ranges the sensitivity will be expected to change as reported by Lowry and Pitt. The range of illuminance indicated by K is realized in practice only if the print is examined under relatively high values of illuminance, in the order of 100 ft-c. Even for the range of illuminance indicated by K, it is not certain that sensitivity remains constant; the eye moves constantly, and hence it is continually subjected to different levels of illuminance rather than to any single general level B, as it is in obtaining the data for Fig. 12·10. It should also be noted that if both the scene and the print are examined at the same level of illuminance, the changes in sensitivity with the area being viewed will tend to be the same except for differences in the angles subtended by the same areas in the scene and in the print.

In those instances where the sensitivity of the eye to luminance changes is a constant or when it varies in the same manner while viewing both the scene and the print, the subjective tone reproduction curve is identical with the objective tone reproduction curve. On the other hand, in general these conditions are not satisfied in practice because the prints are not viewed at a sufficiently high level of illuminance to duplicate the original viewing conditions or to give a constant value of sensitivity to the eye. Moreover, the areas surrounding the print and the scene are often quite different in their brightness characteristics and in their effect on the adaptation of the eye. In most instances, it may be impossible to use a single curve to represent the relationship between the brightness attribute of the sensation and luminance differences for the reasons given by Lowry and Pitt. To obtain an exact solution of the subjective phase of the tone reproduction problem it will often be necessary to use several different curves to represent the relationships that should be plotted in the first and third quadrants of the subjective tone reproduction cycle (Fig. 12·11). Each curve will apply to a different area in the print.

In addition to the possible necessity for using different subjective response curves for different areas in the graphic solution of the subjective phase of the tone reproduction problem, it is also necessary to consider errors introduced by the phenomenon of simultaneous contrast and brightness constancy. The relation of these phenomena to tone reproduction has been examined in detail by Evans,[5] who points out that, in general, perfect objective tone reproduction does not give a positive assurance that the process will lead to the correct appearance in the resulting print when the illuminance of the scene is non-uniform. If a scene is uniformly illuminated, brightness will correlate with apparent reflectance. However, in an unevenly illuminated scene, such as one having part of a wall in direct sunlight and part in a shadow, the average observer will perceive that the part in the light and the part in the shadow have the same reflectance even though they differ in luminance. It is only through the knowledge that this is a shadow that the observer can reach this conclusion. When viewing the print, therefore, the observer must also be aware of the existence of the uneven illumination or he will mistakenly interpret the lower density of the region in the shadow as a result of a difference in reflectance rather than of a difference in illumination. The magnitude of these effects is governed by such factors as whether the print is surrounded by a light border or a dark border. Although the effect on tone reproduction introduced by these phenomena may be very large, in general they cannot be compensated for by distortion of the objective tone reproduction cycle. The most successful method of minimizing these effects lies in controlling the lighting of the subject. It is often helpful to increase the illuminance of the shadow areas by means of reflectors or auxiliary lights. This additional illuminance reduces the subjective tone reproduction errors introduced by the phenomenon of simultaneous contrast and brightness constancy. It also has the beneficial effect of decreasing the luminance scale of the scene, thereby making it easier for the photographic process to give exact objective tone reproduction over the entire tonal range of the scene.

Another method of obtaining useful data on the subjective phase of the tone reproduction problem is to plot the objective reproduction curves for various prints made from the same negatives and then to examine the reproduction curves for those prints which were found to be the most pleasing in the opinion of competent judges. Two prints from the same negative but on different grades of paper are shown, together with their objective reproduction curves, in Fig. 12·12. The print shown in (b) was judged the

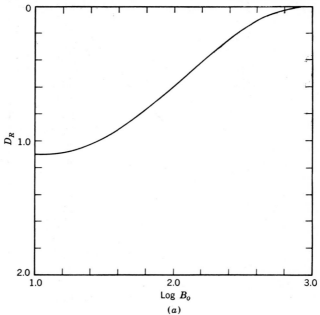

(a)

Fig. 12·12 Prints from the same negative on two grades of

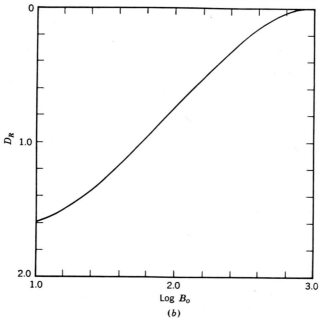

(b)

paper together with the objective tone reproduction curves.

best print which could be obtained from this negative, and the print shown in (*a*) was judged definitely inferior to the first choice print. It has been found that in general the most pleasing prints are those whose objective tone reproduction curves have a relatively straight portion making an angle of 45° with the axis. Investigations of this nature have enabled manufacturers to improve the characteristics of the negative and positive materials in a manner that leads to improved subjective tone reproduction.

Tone Reproduction as Applied to Photographic Printing

Experimental studies in tone reproduction have led to useful rules and procedures for obtaining high-quality photographic prints. Since the properties of the negative and the positive materials have been controlled by the manufacturer to yield the highest number of first-quality prints under normal conditions, research on photographic printing is directed toward the choice of the optimum grade of paper and printing exposure.

Trial-and-error methods are commonly used in making prints. The operator examines the negative visually and estimates the grade of paper and the exposure which in his opinion will give a pleasing print. If the contrast of the print is too high or too low, or if the exposure was incorrect, he makes another print, using a different grade of paper or a different exposure. This process of trial and error is repeated until a satisfactory print is obtained. This method can yield results of very high quality and, if the operator has experience and skill, the time and materials consumed are not excessive. Some skilled operators will make a high percentage of good prints on the first trial.

There has long been both a need and a desire for methods of making prints automatically or by instrumental control based upon physical measurements made on the negatives and the printing papers. The investigations of Tuttle showed that the integrated density of the negative as a whole could be used successfully as a criterion of printing exposure for any given grade of paper. Accordingly, he designed an automatic printer based on this principle. He used a medium grade of paper and found that the majority of negatives were properly printed with respect to both the grade of paper and the exposure. Tuttle discovered that the minimum density of the negative could also be used as a criterion of printing exposure. However, the minimum density criterion of exposure was not used in an automatic printer because of the difficulties involved in measuring this property of a negative automatically as compared with its integrated density. Tuttle reported that the maximum density of the negative was a poor criterion of printing exposure.

Jones and Nelson [6] and their coworkers made a very comprehensive investigation of the control of photographic printing by measuring the characteristics of the negative. They found, like Tuttle, that the minimum density of the negative when used as a criterion of printing exposure gave a very high percentage of properly exposed prints. Furthermore, they found that the difference between the maximum and the minimum densities in the negative, that is, the *density scale* of the negative, could be used satisfactorily as a criterion for choosing the grade of paper. The following sections describe the research of Jones and Nelson in greater detail.

Selecting the Grade of Paper from the Density Scale of the Negative

One method of approaching the problem would have been to assume that exact tone reproduction was desired in the final print and then to work out the theoretical relations between the properties of the negatives and the positives which would give this assumed tone reproduction. However, such a solution would be based on the assumption that exact tone reproduction, either subjective or objective, would give the most pleasing prints. As pointed out previously, it is very difficult, if not impossible, to obtain the exact solution of the subjective phase of the tone reproduction problem. In addition, because of the limited density scale of photographic papers it is sometimes impossible to obtain an exact objective tone reproduction of the entire tonal scale of natural scenes. To solve the problem by theoretical considerations, it would therefore be necessary to make assumptions concerning the necessary compromises in the tone reproduction solutions which would be least detrimental to the print quality. There is no way of determining in advance the compromises which would furnish the optimum quality prints.

Consequently, the problem was approached by the more laborious method of making a number of prints which differed in tone reproduction and then judging the prints to determine which ones were the most pleasing to most people. The negatives represented about 165 different exterior scenes and a few interior scenes. Five prints, differing progressively in exposure, were made from each negative on each of three, and sometimes four, different grades of paper. Each set of prints was judged by a number of people to determine which print they considered best. The judges did not have an intimate knowledge of the technical details involved, and each judge worked separately to avoid being influenced by other judgments.

Density measurements were made on the negatives and on the selected prints, and a correlation was sought between the density scales of the negatives and the log exposure scales of the papers. A correlation was found to exist, but it was far from perfect. The minimum or shadow densities in the negatives were found to print at very nearly a fixed point on the shoulder of the D-log E curve of the paper, but the maximum or highlight densities of the negatives were found to print at widely different points of the D-log E curve of the paper, depending upon the type of scene. In fact, the extreme highlights in many of the best prints were completely off the toe of the paper curve, that is, at zero reflection density and zero gradient. One set of such data are shown graphically in Fig. 12·13. Each horizontal line represents a first choice print. The extremities of these lines represent the minimum and the maximum densities in each print, and the small circles on the lines represent the average density of the print.

The relation between the density scale of the negative and the sensitometric log exposure scale of the paper was found to be a complex one. For soft grades of paper, the density scale of the negative usually *exceeded* the log exposure scale of the paper. For the hard grades, the density scale of the negative usually was *less than* the log exposure scale of the paper.

The sensitometric *log exposure scale* of each paper was determined by taking the difference between the log exposure corresponding to a point on the shoulder of the curve where the gradient was equal to $1.0\overline{G}$ and the log exposure corresponding to a point on the toe of the curve where the gradient was equal to $0.1\overline{G}$, $\overline{G}$ being the average gradient between the two points on the curve. This fractional gradient method was chosen because it gave values of the log exposure scale which were in closest agreement with the average of the density scales of the negatives which gave first choice prints on each paper. No sensitometric criterion for log exposure scale was found which would give perfect agreement. The discrepancies were not due to experimental errors but appeared to be related to variations in the distribution of luminance in different types of scenes.

From the experimental data, Jones and Nelson worked out an empirical conversion chart relating the sensitometric log exposure

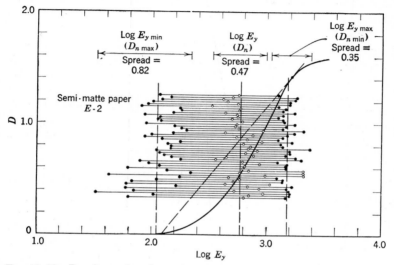

Fig. 12·13   Density scales of negatives from which "first choice prints" were obtained together with the characteristic curve for the positive material on which the prints were made.

scales of papers, ES_y, to the density scales of negatives, DS_n. The construction of the conversion chart as shown in Fig. 12·14 is described by the authors [6] as follows: "Assume a set of four photographic papers differing in contrast grade whose log exposure scales have been found to be 0.60, 1.00, 1.20, and 1.50, respectively. These are then plotted as the points 1, 2, 3, 4, on the horizontal log ES_y scale. The DS_n scale is numerically equal to the log ES_y, but is displaced downward by a convenient distance d. From the 1.2 point on the log E_y scale a vertical line is erected having a height equal to $4d$. The point P at the top of this line serves as a pivot for a straight edge which is made to pass through P and the midpoint between any two adjacent papers on the log ES_y scales.

The straight edge (lines PA, PB, or PC) intersects the DS_n scale at the proper points A, B, C between the papers. The shaded triangles are then constructed using the points 1, 2, 3, 4, and A, B, C. The base of each shaded triangle embraces the negatives which

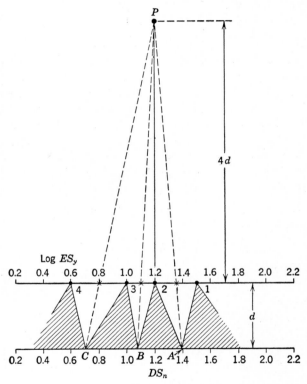

FIG. 12·14 Conversion chart relating sensitometric log exposure scales of papers to density scales of negatives.

should be printed on the paper found at the apex of the triangle. It can be readily seen that these triangles are not all isosceles and that they lean toward the center of the diagram. This is a graphic representation of the fact that for contrasty negatives the density scale of the negative tends to exceed the log exposure scale of the paper and for flat negatives the density scale of the negative tends to be less than the log exposure scale of the paper." It should be noted that the authors point out that this method does not always give the best possible print, but rather that, on the average, a higher percentage of best quality prints will be obtained by this procedure than by using any other known method of predicting the contrast grade of printing paper to be used in printing a given negative. These results were found to apply to enlarging as well as to contact printing.

Determining the Printing Exposure

In the research described in the previous section, a record was kept of the illuminance on the negatives and the exposure times used in making all prints. Thus, the printing exposures were known for the prints which were found to be the most pleasing to the majority of observers, and an excellent correlation was found between the optimum printing exposure and the minimum density in the negative. Although the integrated density of the negative as a whole was a good guide to printing exposure, as reported by Tuttle, it was found to be inferior to the minimum density criterion as given by the formula

Log printing exposure

$$= \text{minimum density of negative} - \log \frac{\text{speed of paper}}{K}$$

where K is an arbitrary constant used in expressing the speed of the paper as discussed in Chapter 10.

REFERENCES

General

Mees, *The Theory of the Photographic Process*, Macmillan, New York, 1942, Chapter 20.

Specific

1. Jones and Condit, *J. Optical Soc. Am.*, **31,** 651 (1941).
2. Jones, *J. Franklin Inst.*, **190,** 39 (1920).
3. Lowry, *J. Optical Soc. Am.*, **18,** 29 (1929).
4. Pitt, *Proc. Physical Soc.*, **51,** 817 (1939).
5. Evans, *J. Optical Soc. Am.*, **33,** 579 (1943); **34,** 533 (1944).
6. Jones and Nelson, *J. Optical Soc. Am.*, **32,** 558 (1942).

13.

The Structure of the Developed Photographic Image

The process by which the exposed silver halide grains are transformed into silver has been discussed in Chapter 5. In examining the structure of the resulting image, it is necessary first to understand the relation between the silver grains in the image and the silver halide grains from which the image was formed.

The Structure and Distribution of the Silver Grains

Photomicrographs of developed and undeveloped grains are shown in Fig. 1·1. The developed silver grains shown in this photomicrograph occupy *approximately* the same positions as the undeveloped silver halide grains. In general, however, the shape and position of the developed grains are only roughly related to the shape and position of the silver halide grains. Whereas the undeveloped grains have definite geometrical shapes, the developed grains are generally quite irregular in shape and tend to form clumps. Although it is generally assumed that developability is not transferred from one grain to another, there is conclusive evidence that this assumption is not always valid (see Chapter 5).

With the advent of the electron microscope, it has been possible to examine the developed silver image in greater detail. From electron micrographs such as those shown in Figs. 5·2 and 5·3 it is seen that at least some of the silver exists in the form of filaments. The filamentary structure is very apparent in silver grains obtained by the development of silver halide grains which had first been removed from the emulsion, and thus were not subjected to the confining action of the gelatin during reduction. Grains which have been fully developed in their normal surrounding of the emulsion show evidence of a filamentary structure around the edges, but in the center they usually appear opaque to the electron beam.

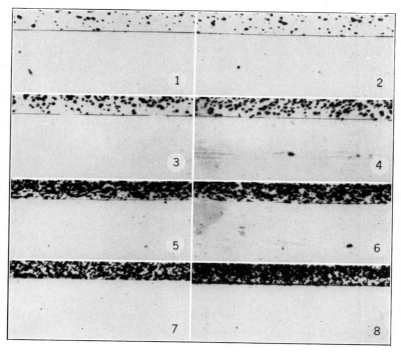

FIG. 13·1 Cross sections showing growth of image with exposure. (Hodgson.)

If the centers of these grains have a filamentary structure, as they probably have, the electron microscope does not resolve this structure.

The distribution of the image in the depth of the emulsion is shown in Fig. 13·1. Each photomicrograph shows a cross section of a different density, the difference in density being obtained by constant development and variable exposure. Although a small part of the increase in density is produced by a higher concentration of developed grains near the surface, the larger part of the increase in density results from an increase in the concentration of the grains throughout the emulsion. On the other hand, when an increase in density is obtained by increasing the development and holding the exposure constant, there is a steady growth of the image toward the bottom of the emulsion. The extent of this effect varies appreciably with the nature of the developer. As

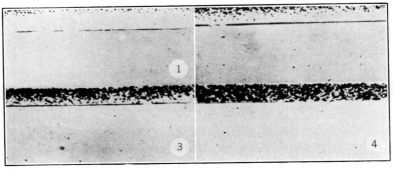

FIG. 13·2   Cross sections showing growth of image with development.
(Hodgson.)

shown by the photomicrographs in Fig. 13·2, the image starts at the surface and penetrates downward as development increases. The depth of the image also depends very markedly upon the wave length of the radiation to which the material is exposed because of the absorption of the radiation by the emulsion. With ultraviolet light, the image is confined to the surface, whereas with x-rays the image is distributed almost evenly throughout the emulsion.

Graininess and Granularity

Most photographic images appear to be homogeneous when viewed without magnification. When magnified, however, these images are seen to be inhomogeneous arrangements of silver grains in gelatin. It should be noted that this structure is the result not only of the distribution of the individual grains and clumps of grains in a plane parallel to the surface, but also of the patterns produced by the overlapping of the grains in a plane perpendicular to the surface as shown in Fig. 13·3.

One of the important aspects of this inhomogeneous structure of the image is that which is apparent when the enlarged image is examined visually. The impression or sensation of non-uniformity

in the image, produced on the consciousness of the observer when
such an image is viewed, is termed graininess. The term granularity is used to designate the objective aspect of these inhomo-
geneities in terms of spatial variations in the transmitting or
reflecting properties of the developed photographic image. In the
literature the term graininess has frequently been used for both

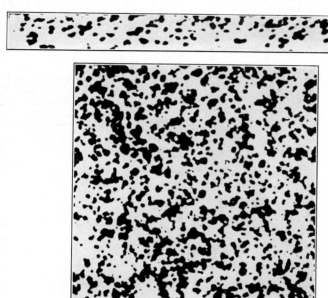

Fig. 13·3   Photomicrographs of a cross section (top) and horizontal plan
(bottom) of a photographic image.

graininess and granularity. Both of these properties of the photographic image are important but they are not identical, and the
two terms should not be used interchangeably.

The graininess of different materials can be compared by
examining them side by side at a constant magnification. It
should be noted that this method is purely subjective because it
does not measure but rather compares the graininess of the materials. One method of assigning a value of graininess to photographic materials would be to make a series of enlargements at
different magnifications and then to observe them from a constant
distance to determine the maximum magnification at which graini-

ness is not objectionable. Although this procedure is a reasonable one, it is very difficult to employ in practice because of the difficulty encountered in making the several enlargements identical from the standpoint of tone reproduction.

One of the first methods of measuring graininess is that proposed by Jones and Deisch.[1] With this method an enlarged image of a uniformly exposed and developed photographic material is moved away from the observer until it appears homogeneous. A schematic diagram of the Jones-Deisch instrument is shown in Fig. 13·4. Light from the lamp S_1 passes through the condenser C_1

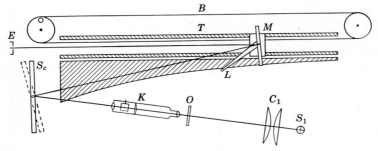

FIG. 13·4   Schematic diagram of Jones-Deisch graininess instrument.

and the sample O. The microscope K forms an enlarged image of the sample on the magnesium carbonate screen S_c. The observer sees this image on the screen by means of the traveling mirror M. This mirror moves along the track T and is so oriented by the template L that the observer on looking through the artificial pupil E always sees the image of the sample on the screen. Graininess measurements are made by reading the blending distance on the tape B after the mirror has been moved back until the image of the sample appears homogeneous. In order to compensate for differences in visual acuity between observers and changes in visual acuity for a single observer, the blending distance for a 500-line halftone screen is measured before and after each set of observations. The graininess value is computed by the formula

$$\text{Graininess} = \frac{508x}{d} \qquad (13\cdot1)$$

in which x is the merging distance for the sample and d is the merging distance for the halftone screen. The constant 508 is the quotient of 100,000 and the number of lines per millimeter for the halftone screen (508 = 100,000/197). The exact values of graininess as computed by this formula depend upon the magnification employed in the instrument.

Several other methods of measuring graininess have been proposed. Two of these methods, those employed by Crabtree and by Lowry, were similar to that of Jones and Deisch in that they measured graininess in terms of a blending distance. Crabtree measured the graininess of motion-picture films by determining the minimum distance from the projection screen at which the image appeared homogeneous. Lowry designed an instrument by which the observer viewed an aerial image of the photographic deposit. The magnification of this virtual image was varied until the deposit appeared homogeneous. The relative magnifications required to give homogeneous images were used as the measure of graininess.

Conklin studied graininess with a comparison microscope by which the samples were magnified and compared under the same viewing conditions. The granular structure of each sample was visible at all times, and the relative magnifications of the two samples were adjusted until the samples appeared to be equally inhomogeneous. These relative values of magnification were taken as a measure of graininess. However, there is evidence that granular structures which appear to be equally inhomogeneous at relatively high magnifications are not always equal in graininess as determined by practical picture tests.

The various methods of measuring graininess as described above must be evaluated in terms of their ability to give values which are in agreement with practical picture tests. On this basis the merging distance method appears to be the most satisfactory. It should be noted that all these methods are psychophysical in that they evaluate a purely physical stimulus (the spatial inhomogeneity of the developed silver image) in terms of the subjective response.

Many methods have been suggested for measuring the objective quantity granularity. Although the granularity of a photographic image is important in many instances, such as sound recording and spectrum analysis, the main purpose of these suggested methods of measuring granularity is to find an objective method which will assign values in agreement with graininess measurements.

Threadgold suggested that granularity, as measured in terms of the Callier coefficient Q (Chapter 10), should be related to graininess. The use of the Q factor was studied by Eggert and Küster who defined granularity by the formula

$$\text{Granularity} = 100 \log Q \qquad (13 \cdot 2)$$

where the value of Q is measured on a deposit having a diffuse density of 0.5. They found a satisfactory agreement between graininess and granularity measured in terms of the Q factor. Although these results were confirmed by Hanson and Keck, Lowry reported a very poor correlation between the Q factor and graininess. A later investigation by Jones and Higgins [2] confirmed Lowry's result. Eggert and Küster [3] pointed out that "only the grains actually in the layer cause scattering of the light. Grain images printed from a negative onto a positive do not affect the light-scattering properties of that positive. If, for example, a negative having a Callier quotient of 2.0 is printed upon a grainless positive, the Callier quotient of that positive will still be 1.0, because there is no substantial graininess in the positive material. If, however, the print is examined, images of the negative grain will be seen." This means that the positive described by Eggert and Küster would appear non-homogeneous, or would have graininess, when viewed by an observer, even though the granularity value as given by equation 13·2 would be zero.

Dunham made the suggestion that the granularity of a photographic material might be measured by the variations in a microphotometer trace made on the sample. van Kreveld,[4] Goetz and Gould,[5] and Selwyn [6] designed granularity instruments which were essentially special types of microphotometers.

van Kreveld and his coworkers measured granularity by splitting into two parts the image of the sample formed by a microscopic projection system and measuring an average difference in transmittance between these two adjacent areas on the film. This average difference in transmittance was taken as the value of granularity.

Goetz and Gould defined a granularity coefficient by the distribution function

$$y = \frac{2}{G'\sqrt{\pi}} \int_0^x \exp\left[-\left(\frac{x}{G'}\right)^2 \right] dx \qquad (13 \cdot 3)$$

for the relative transmittance fluctuations in a photographic deposit. The granularity coefficient G is equal to $1000G'$, where G' as given by equation 13·3 is the standard deviation of the relative transmittance fluctuations from the mean transmittance multiplied by the square root of two ($G' = \sigma\sqrt{2}$). The relative transmittance fluctuation, designated by x in equation 13·3, is equal to $\Delta T/T_m$, where ΔT is the value of the individual fluctuation from the mean transmittance T_m.

The value of granularity G, as measured by the Goetz-Gould method, is therefore given by the formula

$$G = 1000\sigma \frac{\Delta T}{T_m} \sqrt{2} \quad (13\cdot4)$$

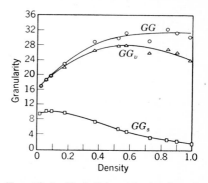

These workers measured the relative transmittance fluctuations in order to approximate the logarithmic relation which they said existed between the stimulus and the sensation of graininess. They stated that since this logarithmic relationship held only within certain ranges of illumination, the

Fig. 13·5 Variation with density of the three types of granularity defined by Goetz and Gould: GG, relative transmittance fluctuations; GG_v, granularity GG corrected for change in contrast sensitivity of the eye; and GG_s, absolute transmittance fluctuations.

measurements in terms of relative transmittance fluctuations must be corrected by the function for the change in contrast sensitivity of the eye. Goetz and Gould also suggested that the absolute variations in transmittance ΔT were of importance in many instances, such as sound recording, and pointed out that the granularity values obtained in terms of $\Delta T/T_m$ could be converted to absolute values by multiplying by the mean transmittance T_m. The variation with density of the three types of granularity defined by Goetz and Gould is shown in Fig. 13·5.

Selwyn's method of measuring granularity is based on the standard deviation of the density fluctuations from the mean as measured on a large number of small but equal areas on the photographic image. The granularity coefficient is defined by the distribution function

$$y = \left(\frac{a}{G^2\pi}\right)^{\frac{1}{2}} \int_{-\infty}^{x} \exp\left(\frac{-x^2 a}{G^2}\right) dx \qquad (13 \cdot 5)$$

where x is the deviation of density from the mean, a is the scanning area, and G is the granularity coefficient. The granularity coefficient as defined by this equation is equal to the standard deviation of density from the mean multiplied by the square root

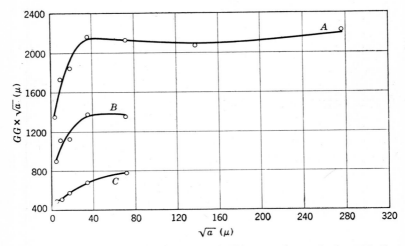

Fig. 13·6   The variation of the Goetz-Gould type of granularity with the square root of the scanning area.

of twice the scanning area $G = \sigma d \sqrt{2a}$. Selwyn suggests that the values of granularity be given in density microns.

The van Kreveld, Goetz-Gould, and Selwyn methods of measuring granularity are all based on the assumptions that the distribution of transmittance or density fluctuations is essentially Gaussian and that the standard deviation of these fluctuations is inversely proportional to the square root of the scanning area. Jones and Higgins[7] investigated the distribution of density and transmittance fluctuations as measured with small circular scanning apertures varying in diameter from 5 to 157 μ. The distribution of the fluctuations as measured with the larger apertures (diameters of 40μ and larger) were essentially Gaussian, but the distribution for the measurements with the smaller apertures departed widely from a Gaussian distribution. The product of the standard deviations of the density or transmittance fluctuations and the square root of the scanning area were not inversely proportional to the square root of the area employed in making the measurements. The variation of this product with the square root of the scanning area for granularity measured in terms of transmittance fluctuations is shown in Fig. 13·6 and for density fluctuations in Fig. 13·7.

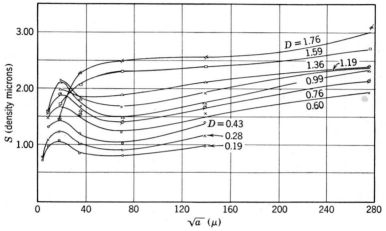

FIG. 13·7   The variation of Selwyn granularity with the square root of the scanning area.

Romer and Selwyn [8] designed an essentially new type of instrument to measure granularity in terms of the ability of a photographic deposit to obscure fine detail. An enlarged image of the sample being examined was projected on a test chart consisting of 26 circular patterns each containing 10 pairs of lines. The patterns decreased in size logarithmically and were numbered consecutively. The spacing between the parallel lines in that test pattern for which half of the pairs of lines could be resolved was found to be proportional to the value of granularity as measured in terms of the standard deviation of density. All measurements by this method are made as a comparison with a standard. It should be noted that this method is not entirely objective because the decision concerning which pattern has half the pair of lines resolved is made by an observer.

Selwyn [9] proposed that, for pictorial purposes, the graininess of a negative should be taken as the quotient of the granularity and the slope of the characteristic curve at a point one log exposure unit above the Jones $0.3\bar{G}$ point. Although this may be an excellent suggestion, there does not seem to be sufficient information available on the relation between the granularity of a negative and the graininess of a print made from that negative to determine whether the proposal is valid.

Jones and Higgins [2] investigated the relation between graininess as measured with the Jones-Deisch instrument and granularity as measured by the methods described in the preceding sections. These measurements were made on a group of materials differing widely in grain size and sensitivity. No method of measuring granularity gives the same functional relation between granularity and density as that existing between graininess and density. A typical set of curves for the relation between granularity or graininess and density is shown in Fig. 13·8. The graininess of the deposit increases rapidly with density for low densities, goes through a maximum, and then decreases for high densities. The maximum value of graininess usually occurs at a density between 0.2 and 0.4. On the other hand, with the exception of measurements by the van Kreveld method, the granularity of the deposit generally increases with density for low densities and then tends to approach a limiting value for high densities. The granularity-density function for measurements by the van Kreveld method and by the Goetz-Gould method in terms of absolute transmittance fluctuations (see Fig. 13·5) goes through a maximum at densities between 0.2 and 0.5. However, the rate of decrease of granularity with density after this maximum has been reached is much greater than the rate at which graininess decreases. This rapid decrease in granularity with increasing density occurs, at least in part, because these measurements are in terms of transmittance fluctuations which would normally be expected to decrease with increasing density.

Although no method of measuring granularity gives a granularity-density function in agreement with the graininess-density function, the values of granularity would still be useful in comparing the graininess of photographic materials if they ranked the materials in the same order as graininess measurements. By arbitrarily choosing a density level to make granularity measurements, it is possible to assign a single number for the granularity of any material. These granularity numbers rank different samples in approximately the same order as graininess measurements, but no method of measuring granularity ranks *all* samples in their exact order of graininess.

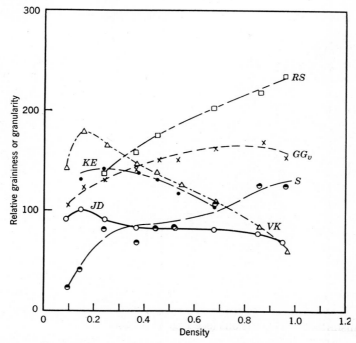

Fig. 13·8 Dependence upon density of the relative graininess or granularity as determined by the methods of van Kreveld (*VK*), Jones and Deisch (*JD*), Eggert and Küster (*KE*), Goetz and Gould (*GG_v*), Romer and Selwyn (*RS*), and Selwyn (*S*).

In relating physical measurements to the visual appearance of photographic materials, it is important to note that there may be a difference between the sizes of the effective scanning spots in the two cases. It seems reasonable to assume that the effective scanning area of the eye is related to the size of the cones in the fovea. Using the value of 17.2 mm for the focal length of the eye and 1.5μ for the distance between the centers of two adjacent cones, Jones and Higgins [7] computed the center distances between the cones when projected back on the samples at the merging distance by the optics of the eye and the graininess instrument. These center distances ranged from about 3μ for very fine-grain materials to about 15μ for very coarse-grain materials. Using these computed values for the center distances between cones,

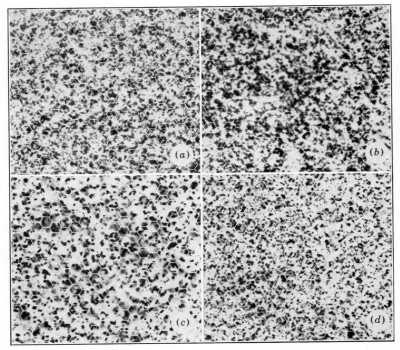

FIG. 13·9 Retinal mosaic projected on sample at merging distance.

Jones and Higgins prepared photomicrographs representing the distribution of illuminance on the retina when an observer is looking at a granular pattern at the blending distance. Four of their photomicrographs are shown in Fig. 13·9. The hexagonal grid of white lines represents a conventionalized retinal mosaic of closely packed hexagonal cones. The magnification of the grain pattern is adjusted for each photomicrograph to that value, computed from the merging distance, which will represent the distribution of illumination on this retinal mosaic. The configuration of the luminous patterns on these mosaics is surprisingly similar for these four materials, despite the wide differences in the coarseness of their granular structure. Although this evidence is not conclusive concerning the size of the effective scanning aperture of the eye, it should be noted that these diameters are those which, when applied to the scanning spots, will give definitely non-Gaussian distributions.

Although none of the proposed methods of measuring granularity gives values which are in complete agreement with graininess measurements, a further investigation of the mode of functioning of the human visual mechanism may lead to a more satisfactory technique for measuring granularity.

Turbidity and Sharpness

When a photographic emulsion is exposed to light while partially shielded by a knife edge in contact with the emulsion, the developed image does not end abruptly at the knife edge, but encroaches into the shielded area. The formation of an image in the area shielded by the knife edge results from the radiant energy reaching this area within the emulsion by reason of refraction, reflection, diffraction, and scattering at the silver halide grains. The property of a material by which light is diffused into the region receiving no direct illumination is called *optical turbidity.*

According to the indications of experiments with filtered light, diffraction and Rayleigh fourth-power scattering should be responsible for most of the diffusion of light in fine-grain emulsions, and reflection and refraction should be the predominant causes of diffusion in coarse-grain emulsions. Microscopic examinations of images on fine-grain emulsions show that diffusion increases from the front to the back of the emulsion as required by diffraction and fourth-power scattering, whereas with coarse-grain emulsions diffusion is almost independent of depth as required by reflection and refraction.

When an emulsion is exposed through a slit bounded by parallel knife edges that are in contact with the emulsion, the image obtained after development rarely has the same width as the slit. The greater the exposure, the wider the image. A set of such images made through an optical wedge which modulates the light logarithmically is shown in Fig. 13·10. This increase in the width of the image depends not only upon the optical turbidity but also upon the opacity of the emulsion. If the opacity of the emulsion is high for actinic light, the light diffused sidewise is rapidly absorbed and the image is kept within narrow bounds. Since the turbidity of an emulsion is normally measured in terms of the diffusion of the *image*, it should be noted that this photographic turbidity may differ appreciably from optical turbidity. Emulsions can be made which have both a high optical turbidity and a high opacity for actinic light. This high opacity limits the diffusion of the image, and therefore the photographic turbidity is low although the optical turbidity is high. In photography, the term turbidity is generally used to mean photographic turbidity.

FIG. 13·10   Photomicrographs (25×) of the image of a slit covered by an optical wedge: (a) microfile, (b) process, and (c) portrait film.

Several investigations have been made to determine the effective absorption laws for the undeveloped silver halide emulsion. If Beer's law held, as it does for homogeneous materials, the density of the silver halide layer would be

$$D = aW^1 \tag{13·6}$$

where a is a constant and W is the concentration of the silver halide. Bloch and Renwick found, however, that for white light the value of the exponent was not unity but 0.64. Calculations from equation 13·6 employing Bloch and Renwick's values of 0.66 for a and 0.64 for the exponent give the curves shown in Fig. 13·11, where lines A to N represent equiluminous surfaces in an emulsion, and the dotted line II' represents the geometrical boundary of the illuminated area. These surfaces, each of which represents an additional 10 per cent absorption, are not equidistant as they would be if the absorption obeyed Beer's law.

One of the first investigations of the turbidity of photographic emulsions was that of Mees, who employed a technique which gave "tadpole" images similar to those shown in Fig. 13·10. Goldberg [10] was one of the earliest to make a quantitative investigation of turbidity. A photographic emulsion was exposed through a diaphragm consisting of three fine holes which were placed in contact with the material. A series of exposures was then given to the material, and turbidity was expressed as the amount of spreading per unit increase in the logarithm of the exposure, $dx/(d \log E)$. Turbidity measured in this way usually increases with increasing exposure. Wildt, however, found a

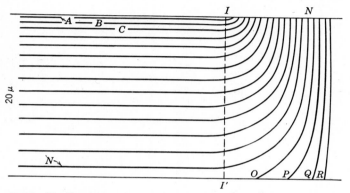

Fig. 13·11   Equiluminous surfaces at the edge of an image on an emulsion.

strictly linear relationship between image diameter and the logarithm of exposure when these exposures were made with monochromatic light. He employed four wave lengths and three diameters of diaphragm. Turbidity was found to be independent of the diameter of the diaphragm for any given wave length, but it was found to increase with wave length for measurements with a single diaphragm. On the other hand, Wildt found that this linear relation between image diameter and the logarithm of exposure no longer held when he made his exposures with a mixture of red and blue light of low intensity.

Various methods have been proposed for expressing turbidity numerically. One of the most convenient of these methods is Ross's quantity Δ, which is the increase in the width of the image when exposure is doubled. This is equal to Goldberg's ratio $dx/(d \log E)$ when $\log E = 0.3$.

Many experimental difficulties are encountered in making turbidity measurements. The first of these is the problem of impressing an image of a small spot or narrow slit on the material. Usually less difficulty is encountered in making the exposures through small holes which are placed in contact with the emulsion. However, it is then very difficult to determine accurately the size of the image obtained after development. The simplest procedure for obtaining narrow line images is to photograph a large single-line test object on a microscopic scale. The objective

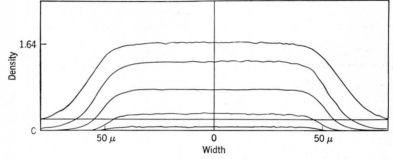

Fig. 13·12   Microdensitometer traces across the image of a slit.

used in making this reduction must be the best available since the sharpness of the edge of the optical image is reduced by lens aberrations and diffraction.

The next experimental difficulty encountered is the problem of measuring the width of the image. The width of a line image can be determined by scanning this image with a microdensitometer whose slit is parallel to the edge of the image. A set of microdensitometer traces showing the variation in density across the image of slit 100 μ wide is shown in Fig. 13·12. Each curve represents a different exposure, the exposure time for each curve being twice that of the one directly below. While the point where the density of the image equals fog density might be considered the edge of the image, it is clear from the traces shown in Fig. 13·12 that it would be a difficult point to determine accurately. It is more convenient to define the edge of the image as that point where density has reached some set fraction of the maximum density. If the edge of the image is taken as the point where the density is equal to one half of the maximum density, the width of the images represented by the traces in Fig. 13·12 can then be

plotted as a function of log E, as shown in Fig. 13·13.   The slope
of this line is Goldberg's ratio $dx/(d \log E)$.

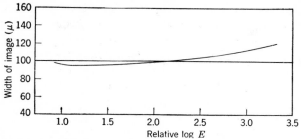

FIG. 13·13   Width of the images in Fig. 13·12 as a function of log E.

The *sharpness* of the image is closely related to turbidity.   As
just pointed out, a photographic image does not end abruptly at
the geometrical boundary be-
tween an exposed and unexposed region on the emulsion.
The rate of change of density
with distance from the edge
of the geometrical boundary,
$-dD/dx$, is used as a measure
of sharpness.

A numerical evaluation of
sharpness can be obtained
from microdensitometer
traces showing the variation
of density across the edge of
an image of a slit or knife
edge.   The slope of these
traces, such as those shown
in Fig. 13·12, is equal to
dD/dx.   Since the slope is
variable, it is convenient to
take the value for the straight
portion of the trace as the
measure of sharpness.   The
slopes of the straight portions

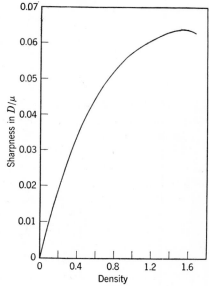

FIG. 13·14   Slopes of the straight portions of curves in Fig. 13·12 as a function
of maximum density.

of the traces in Fig. 13·12 are plotted as a function of maximum
density in Fig. 13·14.   It should be noted that sharpness increases
with density.

The exact relation between turbidity and sharpness is not known. For the straight portion of the characteristic curve

$$\gamma = \frac{dD}{d \log E} \tag{13·7}$$

The product of sharpness and turbidity should therefore be equal to γ since

$$\frac{dD}{dx} \cdot \frac{dx}{d \log E} = \frac{dD}{d \log E} = \gamma \tag{13·8}$$

The validity of this equation has not been verified experimentally. It is doubtful that it should be considered more than a rough

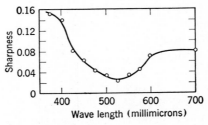

FIG. 13·15   Variation of sharpness with wave length.

approximation because of the effect on sharpness and turbidity of the development phenomena which are discussed in the following section.

The relation between sharpness and turbidity is further complicated by the part the toe of the characteristic curve plays in the sharpness of an image. The relation shown in equation 13·7 applies only to the straight portion of the characteristic curve. Consider two materials having the same turbidity: one with a long sweeping toe and the other with a short toe. The sharpness near the geometrical image on the first of these two materials might be high and yet, because of the long toe, the density would trail off gradually into the shadow. Thus the short-toe material would produce a sharper image than the one having a long toe, although the turbidity of both materials is the same.

The effect of increasing the opacity of the emulsion on the turbidity and sharpness of the images affords an additional indication of the close relationship between these two properties.

Ross found that dyeing a plate yellow, which increased its opacity to blue light but not to red, increased its sharpness for blue light but not for red. Moreover, Sandvik found that the sharpness of an ordinary emulsion varies with wave length as shown in Fig. 13·15. The increase in sharpness for blue light can be explained by the opacity of the emulsion to this radiation.

Development Phenomena and the Interaction between Adjacent Photographic Images

The manifold forms of development phenomena have been instrumental in introducing several names for the same effect. It is customary to use descriptive terms such as Eberhard effects to

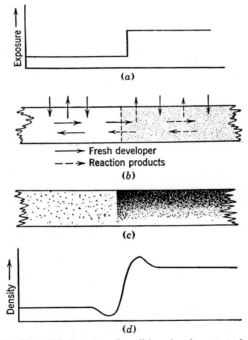

FIG. 13·16   Pictorial diagrams describing development phenomena.

describe the manifestations of these phenomena, and they can all be described by the generic term adjacency effects.

The development phenomena can best be explained by reference to a set of pictorial diagrams such as those shown in Fig. 13·16.

The essential condition for obtaining an adjacency effect is a relatively sharp boundary between two areas having a large difference in density such as would result from an exposure similar to that shown in Fig. 13·16 (*a*). During the process of development the developer has relatively little silver halide to reduce to silver in the lightly exposed region while it is being exhausted by the reduction taking place in the heavily exposed region. As shown in Fig. 13·16 (*b*), the fresh developer and the reaction products

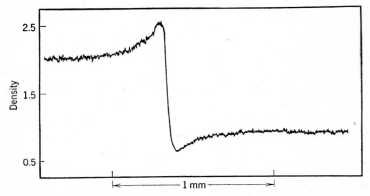

Fig. 13·17   Microdensitometer trace across boundary between exposed and unexposed areas on developed emulsion.

pass back and forth across this boundary between the heavily exposed and lightly exposed areas. The influx of the relatively fresh developer into the heavily exposed region from the lightly exposed area accelerates the growth of density in the heavily exposed region, and thus the image near the boundary of this region is more dense than elsewhere. Likewise, the diffusion of the reaction products, largely bromides, from the heavily exposed region into the lightly exposed area, retards development in this area with the result that density near the boundary is reduced below the level of the surrounding low density. A cross section of the emulsion at the boundary would appear similar to Fig. 13·16 (*c*), and the variation of density across this boundary would be similar to that shown by the curve in Fig. 13·16 (*d*).

The presence of a faint dark line just within the high-density side of a boundary between a lightly exposed and heavily exposed region on a developed emulsion is known as the *border effect*. The presence of the corresponding faint light line just within the low-density side of the margin is referred to as the *fringe effect.* These lines have been called *Mackie lines.* The microdensitometer trace shown in Fig. 13·17 represents the variation in density across the border between a lightly exposed and a heavily exposed area on an emulsion which was developed without agitation. The border effect is shown by the rise in density at the high-density edge of the border, and the fringe effect is shown by the depression in density at the low-density edge of the border. These two effects are commonly called the *edge effect.*

Development phenomena may also produce bromide and developer streaks in the developed image. The *bromide streaks* are light areas which are produced by the flow of reaction products, and the developer streaks are the dark areas which are produced by the flow of fresh developer. The flow of the solutions may be the result of either convection currents or unsatisfactory types of agitation. Streaks are most pronounced when the emulsion is suspended vertically and development is carried out without agitation. Under these conditions the light bromide streaks and the darker development streaks may be as much as an inch or two in length. When the film is developed in a horizontal position, with emulsion side up, the irregular accumulation of the reaction products on the emulsion surface may give rise to a mottled appearance.

When two small areas of unequal size are given equal exposure and development, the density of the smaller area will in general be higher than that of the larger area. This dependency of the density of small areas upon the size of the area is known as the *Eberhard effect.* It is a special form of the border and fringe effects. The microdensitometer traces reproduced in Fig. 13·18 show the variation in density across four small images of unequal size. Each of these images is the result of identical exposure and development. These traces show quite clearly the increase in density which accompanied the decrease in size.

The *Kostinsky effect* is another special form of the border and fringe effects in which an apparent increase in the separation of two small nearby images is produced by a shift in the geometric center of the images. This shift in the geometric center is caused by the increased concentration of the development products between the two images which leads to an asymmetrical growth of the image.

Two other phenomena which are related to development are the *gelatin effect* and the *Ross effect*. The gelatin effect refers to the slight shrinkage of the image and its gelatin support which is produced by the tanning action of the development products on the gelatin. This tanning action introduces unequal rates of dry-

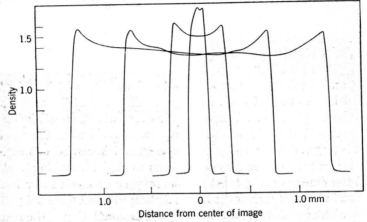

FIG. 13·18 Microdensitometer traces showing Eberhard effect.

ing in the gelatin with a consequent shift in the position of the developed silver grains. It should be noted that this effect is not present in the wet emulsion. The gelatin effect applied to two very small nearby images is known as the Ross effect. The Ross effect is a movement toward each other of two nearby images because of the interacting gelatin effects. These phenomena are of special importance in such fields as astronomy and spectroscopy.

The results of the development phenomena are reduced when development is carried on under conditions which accelerate the removal of the development products, or when development is sufficient to give a gamma approaching γ_∞. It should also be noted that turbidity tends to reduce the magnitude of the adjacency effects because it reduces the slope of the illuminance gradient between the lightly exposed and the heavily exposed areas. Under normal processing conditions these adjacency effects are usually not noticeable in general photography. However, for special types of photographic work, such as photoengraving, it is sometimes desirable to employ techniques which will produce these effects in order to increase the density of the edges of an image such as a halftone dot.

Resolving Power

The ability of a photographic emulsion to record fine detail is its *resolving power*. In order to obtain a numerical value of resolving power, it becomes necessary to adopt some definite criterion

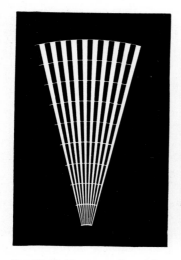

FIG.13·19 Fan type of resolving power test object.

FIG. 13·20   Parallel line type of resolving power test object.

as a measure of detail. Of the many types of test objects which have been used to measure photographic resolving power the fan and the parallel line types have been employed the most extensively. The fan test object, as shown in Fig. 13·19, is relatively easy to make, and it covers a wide range of resolving powers. However, it is very difficult to evaluate. One of the most satisfactory types of test objects is that designed by Sandvik. This parallel line test object consists of several sets of three parallel lines separated by spaces having a width equal to the width of the line as shown in Fig. 13·20. Each set of lines varies from that of its neighbor by 5 or 10 lines per millimeter. As commonly used, this test object consists of clear lines on an opaque ground. The reverse, or negative, consisting of opaque lines on a clear ground, gives a much lower value of resolving power when photographed by projection because of the flare arising from the background.

The test object can be printed either by contact or by projection on the photographic material being examined. If the test object is to be printed by contact, it must have a higher resolution than that of the best material to be measured. This is difficult to attain except when measuring materials of relatively low resolving power. Furthermore, it is difficult to obtain sufficiently good contact between the test object and the sample. It should also be noted that, even when the test object is printed by contact, the distribution of the light in the image of the test object is effected by diffraction.

The more common procedure is to photograph the test object on the sample to a reduced scale. The test object is now less difficult to make because it can be comparatively large. On the other hand, the choice of a lens becomes very important. In the Kodak Research Laboratories, routine resolving power measurements are made with an $f/5.0$ objective of 150 mm focal length. This is a specially designed lens having a very little chromatic aberration. The theoretical resolving power of this lens is 300 lines per millimeter, and experiments confirm this figure. Similar cameras using microscope objectives have been designed. By employing a camera with a microscope objective, it has been possible to measure resolving powers of the order of 1000 lines per millimeter. It is important to note that, even though the resolving power of a lens may be 300 lines per millimeter, the image of the test chart formed on the sample at 50 lines per millimeter, for example, is still not a geometrical image of the test chart. A lens having a resolving power of 100 lines per millimeter may give a value of resolving power for a very coarse-grain material of 35 lines per millimeter, whereas a lens having a resolving power of 300 lines per millimeter may give a resolving power of 40 or 50 lines per millimeter for the same material. The distribution of illuminance for a 50-line test chart as formed with an $f/8.4$ lens is shown in Fig. 13·21. Even for this "perfect" lens where only diffraction is considered, the energy falling in the geometric shadow is 10 per cent of that falling in the highlight region. This figure would also apply to a 100 lines per millimeter image as formed with an $f/4.2$ lens. It has been shown by Selwyn that, if a test chart was used in which illumination varied sinusoidally, the illuminance in the image of resolving power test charts of all degrees of fineness would vary sinusoidally, although differing in amplitude.

The resolving power sample, after exposure and development, is examined in an ordinary microscope. With the Sandvik type

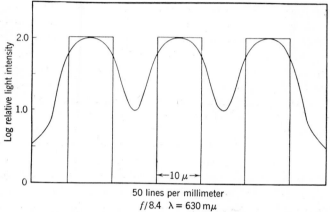

50 lines per millimeter
$f/8.4$ $\lambda = 630\,m\mu$

Fig. 13·21   Distribution of illuminance in image of test object.

of test chart, that set of three parallel lines which has the least spacing but which can still be distinguished as three separate lines, is used to determine the value of resolving power. The numerical value of resolving power is given in terms of the number of lines per millimeter in this test chart as it is imaged on the sample. It should be noted that a line as used here refers to the space between the centers of two adjacent dark bands.

The resolving power of a photographic material depends upon the sharpness, turbidity, and granularity of the emulsion. The exact relation between resolving power and these several properties of the emulsion is not known. However, it is known that resolving power normally increases as turbidity and granularity are lowered and sharpness is increased.

In addition to the inherent properties of the photographic material, the resolving power also depends upon such factors as exposure, development, type of test chart, test object contrast, and the wave length of the light used in making the exposures. The following effects have been studied for a limited number of emulsions.

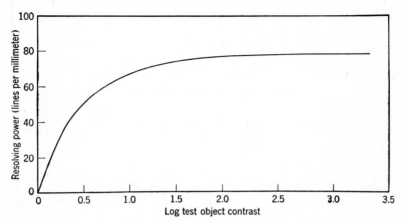

Fig. 13·22 Variation of resolving power with test object contrast.

1. Sandvik showed that a linear relation exists between resolving power and the logarithm of the ratio of the line-to-space width. It is customary to make this ratio equal to unity.

2. The resolving power tends to increase exponentially as the

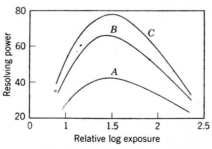

Fig. 13·23 Variation of resolving power with exposure.

test object contrast is increased, as shown in Fig. 13·22. Although it is customary to quote the resolving power of a material as the maximum obtainable, the highest contrast object under the optimum conditions being used, there are some cases, such as aerial photography, where it has been suggested that it might be desirable to use test objects of lower contrast.

3. Although it is well known that the wave length of light affects the resolving power, the exact manner in which this variation takes place is not conclusively known. However, the data indicate that in general, resolving power increases with decreasing wave length in the visible spectrum.

4. While some fine-grain developers improve resolving powers, it is not a universal characteristic of all such developers. The

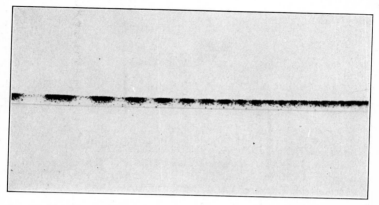

Fig. 13·24 Photomicrograph of cross section of resolving power image.

effect of the composition of the developer on resolving power is not well established.

5. Over the useful range of development times, resolving power is essentially constant.

6. Resolving power goes through a maximum as exposure increases, as shown in Fig. 13·23. The sharpness of this maximum depends largely upon the gamma of the material. The optimum exposure is little affected by long development times, but the optimum density rises slowly.

7. It has been shown that the resolved image resides near the surface of the emulsion and that fine structures on emulsions of high resolving power can be entirely destroyed by a brief treatment in Farmer's reducer without greatly affecting the total density. A cross section of a resolved image is shown in Fig. 13·24.

8. Dyeing an emulsion yellow increases its resolving power very appreciably to blue light, although it is accompanied by a serious loss in sensitivity. The dye apparently reduces the effect of turbidity by increasing the absorption of scattered light and thus confining the image to the surface of the emulsion.

9. In general, resolving power increases with the contrast of the emulsion.

10. Fine-grain and good resolution are usually synonymous, but there are cases where this relationship does not hold. In general, however, materials having small grain size have low turbidity and high resolving power.

REFERENCES

General

Mees, *The Theory of the Photographic Process*, Macmillan, New York, 1942, Chapter 21.

Ross, *Physics of the Developed Photographic Image*, Eastman Kodak Co., 1924.

Specific

1. Jones and Deisch, *J. Franklin Inst.*, **190**, 657 (1920).
2. Jones and Higgins, *J. Optical Soc. Am.*, **35**, 435 (1945).
3. Eggert and Küster, *J. Soc. Motion Picture Engrs.*, **30**, 184 (1938).
4. van Kreveld, *J. Optical Soc. Am.*, **26**, 170 (1936).
5. Goetz and Gould, *J. Soc. Motion Picture Engrs.*, **34**, 279 (1940).
6. Selwyn, *Phot. J.*, **75**, 571 (1935); **79**, 513 (1939).
7. Jones and Higgins, *J. Optical Soc. Am.*, **36**, 203 (1946).
8. Romer and Selwyn, *Phot. J.*, **83**, 17 (1943).
9. Selwyn, *Phot. J.*, **83**, 227 (1943).
10. Goldberg, *Phot. J.*, **36**, 300 (1912).

Sensitizing and Desensitizing

The spectral sensitivity of a photographic material is governed by the spectral distribution of the light which the silver halide can absorb. It is difficult to carry out quantitative measurements of the spectral range of the absorption by photographic emulsions experimentally, but the ones which have been made show good agreement between absorption and sensitivity.

Spectral Absorption of Photographic Materials

The absorption, and hence the inherent sensitivity, of plain silver halide emulsions is confined largely to the ultraviolet, the violet, and the blue regions of the spectrum. Thus, silver chloride is almost colorless and is sensitive only to violet and ultraviolet radiation. Silver bromide is pale yellow and its sensitivity extends into the blue, but the sensitivity ends at about 500 mμ for practical purposes. Silver iodobromide emulsions are sensitive to somewhat longer wave lengths, but their practical sensitivity does not extend beyond 540 mμ. The bromide and iodobromide emulsions are, however, very slightly sensitive to radiation of much longer wave length. For example, Eggert and Biltz found that a developable image could be obtained with an iodobromide emulsion even at 700 mμ, but the exposure energy required was about ten million times that required at 400 mμ.

Silver iodobromide is remarkable in that its spectral sensitivity extends beyond that of the pure iodide itself. The longer wave length absorption of iodobromide containing more than 1 per cent iodide is already greater than that of pure silver iodide, and it increases with increasing iodide content up to about 30 per cent.

The spectral distribution of sensitivity of a silver halide emulsion in the visible region depends somewhat upon the gelatin used and the method of preparation of the emulsion. This is illustrated [1] in Fig. 14·1, where the logarithm of sensitivity is plotted against wave length. A break occurs in the curve at around 500 mμ in

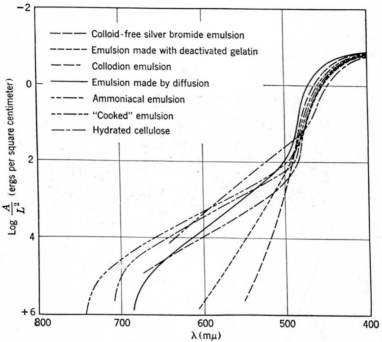

FIG. 14·1 Spectral absorption of photographic emulsions of various types, showing the effect of the dispersing agent (protective colloid) on the long wave length absorption. The curves have been plotted to give equal absorption at 400 mμ. (Eggert and Kleinschrodt.)

every example except that of silver bromide in the absence of gelatin or other protective colloid. When gelatin is present, the extent of the break depends upon the type of gelatin and the emulsion formula. It is very slight for the emulsions prepared with a special inert gelatin (that is, inert with respect to chemical sensitizing of the type discussed in Chapter 2), but it is quite pronounced for the emulsions prepared with normal photographic gelatin. These results are consistent with the hypothesis that sensitivity in the region beyond 500 mμ depends upon impurities in the silver bromide grain. Silver sulfide and probably silver itself produce induced sensitization of this type, but it is quite weak and of little practical importance.

Optical Sensitization by Dyes

A marked extension of spectral sensitivity can be obtained by the use of certain dyes. Many such sensitizing dyes are known, and by a suitable choice of dyes the spectral sensitivity of silver bromide emulsions can be extended throughout the visible region

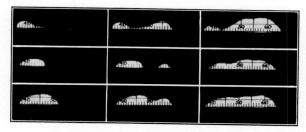

Fig. 14·2   Wedge spectrograms of unsensitized and optically sensitized silver chloride, silver bromide, and silver iodobromide emulsions.

and into the infrared to about 1300 mμ. It is doubtful, however, whether the sensitization can be extended much beyond this point. The strong absorption which water (always present in the gelatin and the atmosphere) shows around 1400 mμ probably will impose a limit for most practical purposes.

The extent of spectral sensitivity can be measured conveniently by means of the wedge spectrograph which was described on page 195. Some spectrograms obtained with this instrument are illustrated in Fig. 14·2. The scale indicates the extent of the measured sensitivity, each division representing 10 mμ. (Thus, the 50 marker signifies 500 mμ.) The three spectrograms at the left of the figure represent the inherent sensitivities of the silver halide emulsions. The top is for silver chloride, the middle for silver bromide, and the bottom for silver iodobromide. The second (center) set of spectrograms represents the corresponding emulsions sensitized by erythrosin. Each spectrogram still shows the initial inherent sensitivity of the emulsion, but an additional sensitive region appears in each. This is the region sensitized by the dye. The third (right-hand) set of spectrograms shows the much more extended region of sensitization obtained with a thia-carbocyanine dye.

Figure $14 \cdot 3$ shows wedge spectrograms of a representative group of sensitizing dyes. With the aid of these dyes, the entire visible spectrum and the infrared spectrum up to 1100 mμ can be covered.

The Sensitizing Dyes

The discovery of dye sensitization resulted from the systematic investigation of an accidental observation. Vogel, in 1873, noticed that some collodion dry plates which he was using showed definite sensitivity in the green, and he traced this unusual sensitivity to the presence of a dye which had been added to prevent halation. In the years that followed, dyes of practically all the known classes were tested as sensitizers. Many were found to be effective to varying extents, but sensitization to longer wave lengths was often accompanied by such a sharp decrease in sensitivity to white light (desensitization) that the dyes were of little practical value.

The great majority of dyes contain a conjugated chain of carbon atoms, that is, a chain linked by alternate single and double bonds. Moreover, this chain contains an *uneven* number of carbon atoms and is terminated by atoms which allow the sequence of linkage in the chain to be readily reversible:

$$-\overset{|}{C}=\overset{|}{C}-\overset{|}{C}=\overset{|}{C}-\overset{|}{C}= \;\leftrightarrow\; =\overset{|}{C}-\overset{|}{C}=\overset{|}{C}-\overset{|}{C}=\overset{|}{C}- \qquad (14\cdot1)$$

This reversible transition can occur easily if the terminal atoms, X and Y, can readily change their covalent linkage to the carbon from one to two, and *vice versa*. The general transition can be represented by

$$X-\overset{|}{C}=(\overset{|}{C}-\overset{|}{C})_n=Y \;\leftrightarrow\; X=\overset{|}{C}-(\overset{|}{C}=\overset{|}{C})_n-Y \qquad (14\cdot2)$$
$$(a) \qquad\qquad\qquad (b)$$

where n is an integer. If the dye is to show an intense color, the two forms (a) and (b) must be of comparable stability.

Very few atoms are capable of fulfilling the requirements for X and Y, the most important being oxygen and nitrogen. When X and Y are both oxygen, the two forms can be represented by

$$\bar{O}-C=(C-C)_n=O \;\leftrightarrow\; O=C-(C=C)_n-\bar{O} \qquad (14\cdot3)$$

3,3′-Diethyl-4,5,4′,5′-dibenzothiacyanine chloride

3,3′-Diethyl-4,5,4′,5′-dibenzothiacarbocyanine bromide

3,3′-Diethylthiacarbocyanine iodide

1,1′-Diethyl-6,6′-dimethyl-2,4′-cyanine bromide (orthochrome T)

1,1′-Diethyl-2,2′-carbocyanine iodide (pinacyanol)

3,3′-Diethylthiatricarbocyanine iodide

12-Acetoxy-3,3′-diethylthiapentacarbocyanine perchlorate

FIG. 14·3   Wedge spectrograms of a chlorobromide emulsion sensitized with various dyes.

This system carries a single negative charge and represents an anion in which the charge is shared between two oxygen atoms. When X and Y are nitrogen atoms, the two forms can be represented by

$$=N—C=(C—C)_n=\overset{+}{N}= \quad \leftrightarrow \quad =\overset{+}{N}=C—(C=C)_n—N= \quad (14\cdot4)$$

where the system is a cation with a positive charge shared between the terminal nitrogens. When X is oxygen and Y is nitrogen, the system can be represented by

$$O=C—(C=C)_n—N= \quad \leftrightarrow \quad \overset{-}{O}—C=(C—C)_n=\overset{+}{N}= \quad (14\cdot5)$$

The molecule here is not ionized.

In each of the preceding cases, the two forms listed are to be considered fictitious extremes. This is not an occurrence of tautomerism. The real dye consists of a single form, a sort of hybrid which lies between the two extremes in structure and possesses a lower potential energy than either. Such a hybrid is termed a resonance hybrid, and its existence is usually represented, for lack of a better method, by giving the two extreme forms and connecting them with a double-headed arrow ($\leftrightarrow$). The resonance hybrid is the actual entity which absorbs the light, and in doing so it is raised to an excited state.

The large majority of the sensitizing dyes belongs to the classes represented by formulas $14\cdot3$, $14\cdot4$, and $14\cdot5$. Representative members of each class will be considered in turn.

Dyes Containing the Carboxyl Ion System ($14\cdot3$)

The phthaleins constitute the most important group of sensitizing dyes containing the carboxyl-ion system. They include the well-known photographic sensitizer erythrosin:

$$(14\cdot6)$$

Formula 14·6 represents only one of the fictitious extreme structures, but the formula of the second is clear from the preceding discussion and need not be represented here. The conjugated chain is indicated by heavy lines. The region of sensitization of this dye has already been indicated (Fig. 14·2).

Dyes Containing the Amidinium Ion System (14·4)

The amidinium ion system occurs in several classes of dyes. These include the cyanines (the most important group of sensitizers), the hemicyanines and styryls (most of which are sensitizers), and other groups such as the triphenyl methanes (most of which are desensitizers or only weak sensitizers).

In the cyanine dyes, both nitrogen atoms are members of heterocyclic ring systems. The conjugated chain joining these nitrogen atoms passes through a part of each heterocyclic ring. (The latter condition excludes from the cyanine class some dyes which meet the initial requirement.) The simple cyanines contain the single carbon linkage, =C—, between the heterocyclic nuclei, as in the formula

$$(14·7)$$

1, 1′-Diethyl-4, 4′-cyanine halide

Dyes containing the three-carbon linkage =C—(C=C)— are termed *carbocyanines;* those containing the five-carbon linkage are termed *dicarbocyanines;* those with the seven-carbon linkage, *tricarbocyanines*, and so on.

The position of attachment of the nuclei to the chain is indicated by the appropriate numbers. Each position in a given nucleus is numbered, starting with the key atom (nitrogen for the dyes thus far considered) of the ring as one. Positions in the second nucleus are indicated by primed numbers. Reference to the following formula will clarify the system:

1,1′-Diethyl-2,4′-cyanine halide (Ethyl Red)

$$(14\cdot8)$$

This dye is a 2,4′-cyanine as distinguished from formula 14·7, which represents a 4,4′-cyanine. The position of any substituent in the ring is likewise indicated by the appropriate number. If the chain is longer than the simple —C=, the appropriate prefix is added in naming the compound: for example, 2,2′-*carbo*cyanine; 4,4′-*dicarbo*cyanine.

The first cyanines used as sensitizers contained only quinoline nuclei, and the terms cyanine, carbocyanine, and the like are still used both for these classes of dyes in general and for the quinoline cyanines in particular. Other heterocyclic nuclei can form cyanines, and some of them are as important as quinoline in practice. Examples are benzothiazole (yielding *thia*cyanine dyes), benzoxazole (*oxa*cyanines), thiazole (*thiazolo*cyanines), thiazoline (*thiazolino*cyanines), benzoselenazole (*selena*cyanines), α-naphthothiazole, and β-naphthothiazole.

The positions of any substitutions made in the carbon chain are indicated by number, just as are substitutions made in the nuclei. The numbering of the carbon atoms continues from the last assigned position in the ring. Thus, the dye represented by the formula

$$(14\cdot9)$$

is 3,3′-dimethyl-9-ethylthiacarbocyanine bromide.

The absorption spectrum of a cyanine dye depends upon both the length of the connecting chain and the nature of the nuclei. An increase in the length of the chain results in a shift in absorption toward longer wave lengths. This is well illustrated by a series of thiacyanine dyes having the general formula

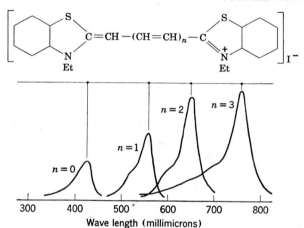

$$\left[\begin{array}{c} \text{S} \\ \text{C=CH—(CH=CH)}_n\text{—C} \\ \text{N} \\ | \\ \text{Et} \end{array} \right] \text{I}^- \quad (14 \cdot 10)$$

The first member of the series ($n = 0$) is pale yellow and will sensitize a chloride emulsion to the blue. The second member, the

thiacarbocyanine, is magenta and will sensitize to the green and red. The thiadicarbocyanine is blue and will sensitize to the deep red, and the thiatricarbocyanine is greenish blue and will sensitize to the infrared. The absorption spectra of the dyes in methanol solution[2] are given in Fig. 14·4. The shift in wave length between the maxima amounts to roughly 100 mμ for each added vinylene group. Similar shifts occur in the spectral sensitization. Comparable changes in the absorption maxima have been observed with cyanine dyes containing nuclei other than benzothiazole.

The cyanine dyes considered thus far have all been symmetrical and both ends of the chain have been terminated by the same kind of nucleus. Many dyes are known, however, in which the two nuclei are different in structure. For example, one end of the chain might be attached to a benzothiazole nucleus and the other to a quinoline nucleus. Obviously, the number of possible combinations is very large.

Substitution of other atoms or of radicals for hydrogen atoms, either in the nuclei or in the chain, also can modify the character of a dye. An alkyl group in the central position of a carbocyanine usually produces a slight shift to the shorter wave lengths in the absorption of the dye in solution, but it may cause much larger changes in the location of the sensitization maxima. No general rule can be given for this, or for substitution in the nuclei, although positive groups in the nuclei, such as alkoxy or dialkylamino, normally shift the sensitization to longer wave lengths.

The Hemicyanines

The hemicyanines form a group of dyes in which only one of the two terminal nitrogen atoms is situated in a heterocyclic ring with the conjugated chain passing through a portion of the ring. An example of a dye of this type is given by the formula

$$(14 \cdot 11)$$

The styryl dyes, of which pinaflavol is an example, are closely related:

$$(14 \cdot 12)$$

Pinaflavol

The Merocyanines $(14 \cdot 5)$

The number of known sensitizers has been considerably augmented in recent years by the discovery [3] of a large new group which can be considered to be derived from formula $14 \cdot 5$. The members of this group are part cyanine (Greek *meros* = part) since the terminal nitrogen atom forms part of a heterocyclic ring and the conjugated chain passes through part of that ring. These dyes can be represented by the following two general formulas:

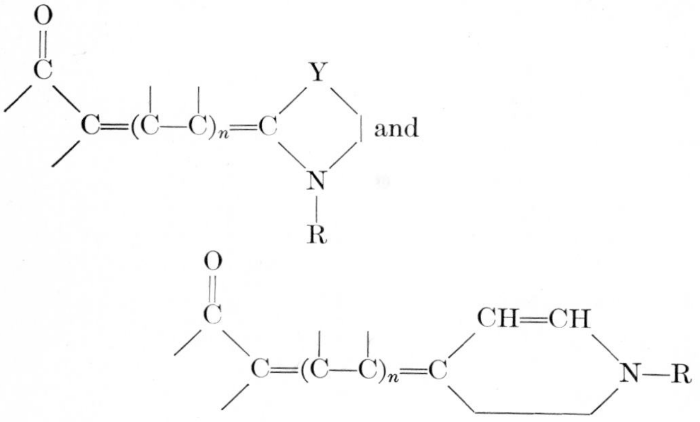

in which Y represents O, S, Se, Me_2C, or —CH=CH—, and R is an alkyl group. The molecule as a whole is neutral, but resonance can occur between the N atom and the oxygen of the carbonyl group.

Certain other sensitizing dyes are known which contain the same amide grouping as the merocyanines but in which the nitrogen atom is not part of a heterocyclic nucleus.

Mechanism of Dye Sensitizing

In spite of a large amount of research on the subject, little is definitely known about the mechanism of dye sensitizing. A few facts are well established, however, and any general theory of the mechanism must account for them.

The sensitizing dyes are strongly adsorbed by the silver halide, and this adsorption is essential to sensitization. The dyes of the cyanine group are strongly ionized, and they are probably held to the surface of the grain by the attraction of the halide ions for the positive dye ions. Merocyanines and dyes containing the carboxyl ion system both tend to form silver compounds and are probably attached via the silver ions.

If a sufficient amount of gelatin-free silver chloride or bromide is added to a dilute solution of a cyanine dye, the latter to all appearances will be completely adsorbed by the silver halide. If more dye is added, practically complete adsorption continues until a point is reached where it stops rather abruptly. This point presumably corresponds to the formation of a complete monolayer of dye. The presence of gelatin, which is itself strongly adsorbed by the silver halide, retards the adsorption of sensitizing dyes but does not prevent it. Just how the gelatin and the dye molecules share the silver halide surface (if they do) is not known.

The amount of a given dye required to cover a unit area depends upon how the dye ions are oriented with respect to the surface: flat, edge-on, or end-on. The adsorption data [4] in general favor an edge-on orientation, but the question has not been settled conclusively.

In concentrated water solution, or in more dilute solution in the presence of salts, some dyes exist as molecular aggregates. Evidence from microscopic observations indicates that the molecules in such aggregates are well oriented, and the absorption spectra show characteristic sharp bands corresponding to the aggregates. Dyes adsorbed to silver halides also may show sharp absorption bands which are considerably displaced from the molecular absorption in solution. This large displacement is best explained on the basis of the assumption that the dye molecules aggregate when they are adsorbed on the grains. When aggregates can be formed in solution (as by the addition of salt to the solution), a good correspondence between their absorption bands and the displaced bands of the dyes adsorbed to the grains is usually observed, although the correspondence is not exact. The evidence indicates that aggregation occurs in more dyes when they are adsorbed to the grain than when they are in solution. Aggregation of a dye on the grain surface is favored by an increase in surface concentration, by digestion of the emulsion with the dye, and by the presence of supersensitizers as described subsequently.

The absorption spectrum of a non-aggregated sensitizing dye in solution does not coincide exactly with that of the non-aggregated adsorbed dye, the spectrum being shifted and usually broadened as a result of the adsorption. The region of photographic sensitization corresponds to the region of light absorption by the *adsorbed* dye. The correspondence between sensitization and the absorption of light by the sensitized emulsion is illustrated [5] in Fig. 14·5. The sensitivity curve follows the absorption curve closely, and the

differences between the sensitivity and the absorption maxima in
the red are within the limits of experimental error. A good correspondence between absorption and sensitivity is noted also in

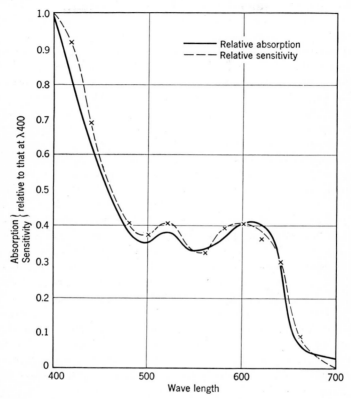

Fig. 14·5 Correspondence between absorption and sensitivity in a panchromatic photographic emulsion. (Leermakers.)

the region of inherent sensitivity of the silver halide (wave lengths
shorter than 500 mμ).

The amount of sensitization produced increases with increasing amounts of adsorbed dye until an optimum value is reached.
Beyond the optimum, the sensitivity decreases with increasing
amounts of added dye. The formation of photolytic silver follows
a roughly parallel course. The observed decrease in sensitizing
beyond the optimum is not limited to the spectral region of sensi-

tizing but applies to the blue region as well. The dye thus is acting as a general desensitizer.

Optical sensitization and desensitization are not, as the term tends to suggest, alternative and mutually exclusive properties. In fact, the evidence [6] obtained by measuring sensitivity in the far violet, where most of the sensitizing dyes do not absorb, indicates that practically no dyes are free from desensitizing action. Usually, this action can be detected well below the optimum concentration for optical sensitization and, therefore, in the region where sensitivity is still increasing with increasing amounts of dye. Desensitization appears to be a chemical effect on the grains of the emulsion, which reduces the response to light of any wave length. The relative extent of sensitizing and desensitizing varies greatly with the structure of the dye; a dye with marked desensitizing properties is useful only in unusual circumstances, for example, sensitizers for the longer infrared where nothing else is available.

The concentration of dye giving maximum sensitization corresponds, in some dyes at least, to a constant degree of coverage of the grain surface. Experiments [7] with three dyes in seven emulsions, representing a range of grain sizes in both neutral and ammoniacal emulsions, have been reported. These experiments showed, for one thiacarbocyanine, optimum sensitization in the range of 8 to 11×10^{-11} moles per square centimeter of surface; for another thiacarbocyanine, an optimum sensitization at 11 to 12×10^{-11}; and for a thiadicarbocyanine, an optimum at 4 to 5×10^{-11}. The figures for these cyanines correspond approximately to monolayer coverage if the molecules lie flat; the figures are smaller if the molecules are edge-on. Evidence obtained from studies of other dyes indicates, however, that the optimum concentration is not independent of the nature of the dye for all dyes.

Although adsorption of the dye by the silver halide grains and absorption of light by the dye or dye-silver halide combination are both necessary for sensitization, they are not sufficient. Precisely what constitutes the sufficient conditions for sensitization is not known. Some dyes have structures not greatly different from powerful sensitizers and are strongly adsorbed by the silver halide, but nevertheless do not sensitize. Moreover, the sensitizing action of a given dye can be greatly influenced by the surroundings or environment of the dye in its adsorbed state. If two or more dyes are used together, the sensitization by each is often affected by the presence of the other. The most common result is a mutual interference. Sometimes, however, the dyes actually reinforce each other, and the sensitization is greater than the sum of the separate sensitizations. Such action is termed supersensitizing. It is of considerable practical importance.

Many 2'-cyanines are supersensitized by certain other types of dyes, including oxathiazolocarbocyanines, styryls, and styryl bases. In these combinations, the spectral absorption of the 2'-cyanine is practically unchanged, although that of the other dye is added to it. The supersensitization takes the form of an increase in efficiency of energy transfer from the dye to the grain; the increase can amount to as much as sixfold. Supersensitization can also involve a change in spectral absorption. The 9-alkyl thia- and selenacarbocyanines are supersensitized by some 2'-cyanines with a change of distribution of sensitivity in the red. This is more clearly evident in the supersensitization of dyes of the same type by certain colorless materials, such as certain aromatic ketones; these compounds favor the formation of a new maximum of sensitivity at longer wave length, which appears to be associated with the formation of an aggregate. In general, dyes which show maxima resulting from aggregation have high susceptibility to supersensitization.

The parallel trends in the spectral distribution of photoconductivity in silver halide crystals and photographic sensitivity of emulsions which had not been optically sensitized was mentioned in Chapter 3. This parallel extends into the sensitized region. Comparisons using actual photographic emulsions for the measurements have been made [8] of the spectral distribution of photoconduction and photographic sensitivity of optically sensitized emulsions. The dyes used included members of the cyanine, carbocyanine, dicarbocyanine, and merocyanine classes. Invariably a parallel between the two phenomena was observed. Moreover, when certain supersensitizers were added the manner in which photoconductance was increased was analogous to that in which the sensitivity was increased.

No general agreement has been reached regarding the mechanism by which the energy absorbed by the sensitizing dye is transferred to the silver halide for the purpose of latent image formation. It is known that some dyes, at least, are not destroyed in the act of sensitizing, and that in such a dye one ion or molecule can sensitize the formation of many silver atoms. Two alternative inner mechanisms of dye sensitization have been suggested.[9] In the first, the adsorbed dye or complex, upon absorbing light, emits an electron at the interface between the dye and the silver halide. This electron subsequently is accepted by a silver ion in the crystal, and a silver atom is produced. The dye regains an electron from a halide ion in a manner not specified and reverts to its original condition. In the second mechanism, the dye passes into an excited state as the result of light absorption. The excited dye or adsorption complex transmits its energy to a halide ion of the crystal, and an electron is emitted into the conductance band as a result of the energy transfer. From that point on, the latent image is formed in the manner postulated in Chapter 3. Thus far, there is no means of deciding between the two mechanisms. It is possible that neither is correct. Even the quantum efficiency of dye sensitization in the infrared is not known accurately. At wave lengths shorter than about 650 mμ, however, the quantum efficiency of photolysis of silver halide sensitized by the best sensitizers is close to that of photolysis of the silver halide in the region of its natural absorption.

Desensitizing

It is sometimes desirable in practice to carry out photographic development under brighter illumination than can be ordinarily used in the darkroom. Lüppo-Cramer [10] in 1920 showed that this could be done if the exposed plate or film were bathed in a dilute solution of phenosafranine prior to development, or even if the dye were added to the developer itself. Phenosafranine desensitizes the silver halide to the normal action of light.

Numerous desensitizers are now known. An ideal desensitizer should destroy the sensitivity of an emulsion without attacking the latent image. Furthermore, it should be stable in solution, should not cause complications in processing, and should be nonstaining. Although no substance that completely fulfills these requirements is known, several have properties near enough to the ideal to be of practical use. Most desensitizers are dyes, but the absorption spectra of the dyes are not connected with the ability to desensitize. Desensitization usually covers the entire spectral range of sensitivity of the silver halide, including the blue. When selective desensitization of an optically sensitized region of the emulsion occurs, an effect on the sensitizing dye itself is involved.

The mechanism of general desensitization is still obscure. Experiments with an azacyanine desensitizer which was almost sufficiently powerful to eliminate normal photographic sensitivity have shown that photoconductance was little impaired by the presence of the dye.[8] Thus, the desensitizer apparently does not inhibit the liberation of photoelectrons; its action is exerted later. The desensitizer may act as alternative traps for photoelectrons and thus reduce the effectiveness of the normal sensitivity centers, or it may attack the latent image after the latter has begun to form. Oxygen plays some rôle in the overall process of desensitization, as normally carried out, since exclusion of oxygen results in a decrease in desensitizing action.[11] The nature of the rôle of oxygen is still a matter for speculation, however.

The activity of many desensitizers appears to be associated with a nitrogen atom which participates in a conjugated chain but which cannot act as a terminal for that chain. This is brought out in a comparison of two isomeric dyes, one of which is a good sensitizer, the other a desensitizer devoid of sensitizing properties. For example, the dye

$$\left[\quad \text{C}=\text{N}-\text{CH}=\text{CH}-\text{C} \quad \right] \text{I}^- \qquad (14 \cdot 14)$$

is a sensitizer belonging to the azacyanine group.* Its isomer,

$$\left[\quad \text{C}=\text{CH}-\text{N}=\text{CH}-\text{C} \quad \right] \text{I}^- \qquad (14 \cdot 15)$$

in which the central nitrogen is separated from the terminal nitrogens by two carbon atoms on each side, is not only devoid of sensitizing properties but is also a strong desensitizer. A significant distinction between the two dyes is that the chain nitrogen

* These dyes are like the cyanines in structure, except that a carbon of the connecting chain has been replaced by nitrogen.

of the former can function as a terminal nitrogen and share a positive charge with the nitrogen atoms of the heterocyclic rings, whereas in the latter dye the nitrogen remains invariably trivalent.

Permanently trivalent nitrogen atoms appear in some of the commonly used desensitizers, such as phenosafranine and pinakryptol green. The latter dye is one of the most useful of all known desensitizers, being superior to phenosafranine chiefly because of a smaller tendency to stain. However, desensitizers are known which do not contain a permanently trivalent nitrogen. For example, some of the triphenylmethane dyes are powerful desensitizers. Likewise, several compounds which have been sold under the name of pinakryptol yellow are good desensitizers. One of these compounds is represented by the formula

$$\left[\text{EtO} \ldots \text{N}^+ \text{—CH=CH—} \ldots \text{NO}_2 \right] \text{Cl}^- \qquad (14\cdot16)$$

The others have similar structures.

If desensitizers are applied to color-sensitized emulsions, the optically sensitized region often is preferentially attacked. This action can be ascribed to a partial replacement of the sensitizer by the desensitizer, which is likewise adsorbed by the silver halide surface. The claim is made in the patent literature that some desensitizers derived from anthraquinone owe their desensitizing properties to their ability to form very insoluble salts with the basic cyanine dyes, thus removing the sensitizer from the silver halide surface. These desensitizers show a definite selective desensitization in the sensitized regions; they are ineffective toward the blue sensitivity and toward sensitization by erythrosin.

REFERENCES

General

Mees, *The Theory of the Photographic Process*, Macmillan, New York, 1942, Chapters 23, 24, 25.

Brooker, "Spectra of Dye Molecules. Absorption and Resonance in Dyes," *Rev. Modern Phys.*, **14**, 275–293 (1942); "Resonance in Organic Chemistry," *Frontiers in Chemistry*, Interscience Publishers, Inc., New York, 1945, Vol. III, pp. 63–136.

Wheland, *The Theory of Resonance and Its Application to Organic Chemistry*, Wiley, New York, 1944.

Specific

1. Eggert and Kleinschrodt, *Z. wiss. Phot.*, **39**, 155 (1940).
2. Brooker, *Rev. Modern Phys.*, **14**, 275 (1942).
3. Kendall, Brit. Pat. 428,222 and 428,360; Brooker, U. S. Pat. 2,089,729.
4. Sheppard, Lambert, and Walker, *J. Chem. Phys.*, **7**, 265 (1939).
5. Leermakers, *J. Chem. Phys.*, **5**, 889 (1937).
6. Spence and Carroll, private communication.
7. Leermakers, Carroll, and Staud, *J. Chem. Phys.*, **5**, 893 (1937).
8. West and Carroll, *J. Chem. Phys.*, **15**, 539 (1947).
9. Sheppard, Lambert, and Walker, *J. Chem. Phys.*, **7**, 426 (1939).
10. Lüppo-Cramer, *Phot. Korr.*, **38**, 421 (1901); **75**, 311 (1920); *Phot. Ind.*, 378, 505 (1920); *Z. angew. Chem.*, **40**, 1225 (1927).
11. Blau and Wambacher, *Nature*, **134**, 538 (1934).

Appendix

Optical Terminology

The optical terminology employed in this book is that recommended by the Colorimetry Committee of the Optical Society of America.[1] The names, such as transmission and reflection, have been reserved as a description of the process, and the terms, such as transmittance and reflectance, are used to indicate the property of an object. These terms are given in Table I.

TABLE I

Process Name	Property
Transmission	Transmittance
Reflection	Reflectance
Illumination	Illuminance
Absorption	Absorptance

The theory of tone reproduction, the measurement of ASA speed, the measurement of graininess, and many other aspects of photographic theory are based on psychophysical measurements. Psychophysics is the science which deals with problems lying between or common to the fields of psychology and physics. The reader who is not familiar with the theory of psychophysical processes is referred to the general references at the end of this Appendix.

Psychophysical quantities are neither physical nor psychological, but a combination of both. In psychophysical theory three categories of quantities must be considered: physical, psychophysical, and psychological. The terms given in Table II are listed under these three headings.

TABLE II

Physical	Psychophysical	Psychological
Radiance	Luminance	Brightness
Reflectance	Luminous reflectance	Lightness

It should be noted that the term luminance is now employed in the sense in which brightness has commonly been used, and that brightness now refers to the quantity which has previously been referred to as brilliance.

REFERENCES

General

L. A. Jones, *J. Optical Soc. Am.*, **34,** 66 (1944).

L. T. Troland, *The Principles of Psychophysiology*, Van Nostrand, New York, 1929.

Colorimetry Committee, Optical Society of America, *J. Optical Soc. Am.*, **34,** 245 (1944).

Specific

1. Colorimetry Committee, Optical Society of America, *J. Optical Soc. Am.*, **33,** 544 (1943).

Index

**RETURN
TO ➤**

CHEMISTRY LIBRARY
100 Hildebrand Hall • 642-3753

LOAN PERIOD 1	2	3
4	5	6

1 MONTH

ALL BOOKS MAY BE RECALLED AFTER 7 DAYS
Renewable by telephone

DUE AS STAMPED BELOW

MAY 27 2000		
MAY 23 '01		
JUN 09 '02		
MAY 12		
JAN 02		

FORM NO. DD5